HERBAL AND AROMATIC PLANTS

Lawsonia inermis

HENNA

HERBAL AND AROMATIC PLANTS

Lawsonia inermis

HENNA

CULTIVATION, PROCESSING UTILIZATIONS AND APPLICATIONS

By

Dr. HIMADRI PANDA

Ph.D., F.I.C., F.I.C.S.
Industrial Consultant
Technical Consultant, Afro-Asian Countries, G.I.D.C.
Fellow of the Essential Association of India
Fellow of Indian Pulp & Paper Technical Association
Fellow of Indian National Science Congress
Fellow of Oil & Colour Chemist's Association (U.K.)
Member of Chinese Academy of Forestry
Former Chemist (R&D), I.T.R. Co. Ltd., Bareilly
Former Chief Chemist (QC & R & D), Tarpina Private Ltd.
Ramnagar, Uttarakhand

DPH

DISCOVERY PUBLISHING HOUSE PVT. LTD.
INDIA

Published by:
Namit Wasan
DISCOVERY PUBLISHING HOUSE PVT. LTD.
4383/4B, Ansari Road, Darya Ganj
New Delhi-110 002 (India)
Phone : +91-11-23279245, 43596064-65
Fax : +91-11-23253475
E-mail : discoverypublishinghouse@gmail.com
namitwasan9@gmail.com
sales@discoverypublishinggroup.com
web : www.discoverypublishinggroup.com

***First Edition:* 2018**

ISBN: 978-93-86841-16-2 (*Lawsonia inermis*)

Printed at:
Infinity Imaging Systems
Delhi

Preface

This fascinating plant is world wide known for the beautiful colouring dye that is used by the Orientals in the colouring their hands and body. The Egyptians are said to have prepared both an oil and an ointment from the flowers for making the limbs supple. Egyptians Royalty were said to dye their hair with Henna leaves. Henna's botanical name is *Lawsonia inermis*, its common is Jamaica Mignonette, Mendee, Egyptian privet, smooth *Lawsonia*. Its Arabic name is henna and the most popular Indian name is Mendhi.

The earliest civilizations that can be proved to have used henna include the Babylonians, Assyrians, Sumerians, Semites, Ugaritics and Canaanites. The leaves of the henna plant are the source of a red-brown dye widely used for body art, known as mendhi in South Asia. First used in the Near East and South Asia, henna art is now popular around the world.

There are numerous artifacts from Iraq, Palestine, Greece, Egypt, Crete and Rome from 1400 BCE to 1AD that show women with henna patterns on their hands. The early center of the use of henna as a woman's adornment seems to have been in the eastern Mediterranean, where it grows wild. It was used by the Canaanite women in pre-biblical times. The Canaanites spread their traditions, including the use of henna, across North Africa between 1700 and 600 BCE, specifically establishing the Berber traditions of henna in Morocco.

Henna was used in Palestine from the earliest historical period, and there are Roman records of henna being used by Jewish people living in Jerusalem during the historical period of the birth of Christ.

When Islam began in the 6-7th centuries AD, henna was incorporated into the customs of Muslims from the western Middle Eastern women's henna traditions that were widespread and long established. As Islam expanded quickly into other countries, the use of henna went with it. All of the countries that were part of the Islamic world have used henna at some time, most frequently as part of wedding celebrations. Most of them continued to celebrate the "Night of the Henna" and regard henna as a beautiful and suitable ornament for women until present day.

Since 1890 it has been widely used in Europe for tinting the hair, usually in the form of a shampoo, many shades being obtainable by mixing with the leaves of other plants, such as indigo. As a dye for the skin or nails the powder may be mixed with lemon juice, made into a paste with hot water, and spread on the part to be dyed, being allowed to remain for one night.

The parts used are the leaves that are dried and then crushed to form a dark green powder. The flowers and also the fruit are also used. Flowers are numerous, small, white or rose coloured and fragrant. The plant lives scarcely in dry decidious forests, widely cultivated as a hedge plant. It is mostly found in Egypt, India, Kurdistan, Iran, Syria.

It is widely cultivated in tropical countries but probably native to North Africa and Asia. It is widely naturalized in the West Indies and Mexico where it is known as "mignonette." Its leaves produce the henna or alhenna of the Arabs (cyprus of the ancients), a yellow die which is used in Egypt and elsewhere by women to color their nails, and by men to die their beards, and for other similar uses including horses manes and tails. It is known in the West Indies as "Egyptian privet", and sometimes as "reseda".

The small, white and yellow, heavy, sweet-smelling flowers are borne on dwarf shrubs 8 to 10 feet high and reaching a height of up to 6 meters, the plant has fragrant white or rose-red flowers.

Henna is planted today primarily as an ornamental hedge, but is probably best known for the dried, ground leaves traditionally used to produce colorfast orange, red, and brown dyes.

The constituents of Henna is found in it in a brown substance of a resinoid fracture, having the chemical properties which characterize the tannins, and therefore named *hennotannic acid*. Dried, powdered leaves of henna contain about 0.5 to 1.5 percent lawsone, the chief constituent responsible for the dyeing properties of the plant. Henna also contains mannite, tannic acid, 2-hydroxy-1:4-naphthoquinone resin mucilage, gallic acid, glucose, mannitol, fat, resin and mucilage are also present. The colouring matter is the quinone and napthaquinone.

USES

Medicinal Action and Uses

As a medicinal plant, henna has been used as an astringent, antihemorrhagic, intestinal antineoplastic, cardio-inhibitory, hypotensive, and a sedative. It has been employed both internally and locally in jaundice, leprosy, smallpox, and affections of the skin. The fruit is thought to have emmenagogue properties.

It has also been used as a folk remedy against amoebiasis, headache, jaundice, ranging from beriberi to burns and bruises ans leprosy.Henna extracts show antibacterial, antifungal, and ultraviolet light screening activity. Henna has exhibited antifertility activity in animals and may induce menstruation.

Henna has been used as medical treatment for wide range of ailments to cure almost anything from headache to leprosy and other skin disorders. It is used to create an instant 'Scab' on large areas & is believed to have antiseptic properties. As a cooling agent it is used for burning of skin. It also has great dandruff fighting ability.

Henna is also used for rheumatic and arthritic pains. Alcoholic extract of the leaves showed mild anti-bacterial activity against Staph aureus and E. coli'. Antibacterial and antifungal activities have been confirmed.The antihaemorrhagic properties are attributed to lawsone. The naphthoquinone has emmenogogue and oxytocic actions.

The dried leaf and petiole of henna are generally recognized as safe when used as a color additive for hair. A distilled water prepared from them is used as a cosmetic, and the powdered leaves have been in use from the most ancient times in Eastern countries for dyeing the hair and the nails a reddish-yellow. Traditionally henna is used to decorate hands and feet during weddings and other ceremonies.

Henna features in the Siddha system of medicine. Siddha physicians consider parts of henna to be astringent, detergent, deodorant, cooling and a sedative. Fresh leaves mixed with vinegar or lime juice are bandaged onto the soles of the feet to treat 'burning feet', a symptom of beriberi. Ground leaves are applied to sore joints to ease rheumatism. The juice of the plant can be applied to the skin for headaches, and the oil is applied to hair to prevent it from going grey.

Its flower oil relieves muscular pains, while its seeds are used as a deodorant and to regulate menstruation. Henna flowers induce sleep, cure headaches and bruises. Leprosy has been treated by henna bark, as well as by an extract of leaves, flowers and shoots. The bark has also been used to treat symptoms of jaundice and enlargement of the liver and spleen. It can be applied to the skin to treat eczema, scabies, fungal infections and burns.

The Ayurvedic system uses the henna leaves to treat vitiligo (pale patches on the skin where pigment is lost), and the seeds are used to cure fever. Fruit oil is a folk remedy used in disorders causing hardening of the liver and diaphragm, and an ointment made from young fruit is used to prevent itching.

These scattered informations and datas are collected and published in the form of a book so that every individual connected may be benifitted from this treasure.

Author

Contents

1 Introduction

Henna (*Lawsonia inermis*) is a flowering plant used since antiquity to dye skin, hair, fingernails, leather and wool. The name is also used for dye preparations derived from the plant, and for the art of temporary tattooing based on those dyes. Additionally, the name is misused for other skin and hair dyes, such as black henna or neutral henna, which do not derive from the plant.

The English name "henna" comes from the Arabic, pronounced or colloquially.

Description

Henna is a tall shrub or small tree, 2–6 m high. It is glabrous, multibranched with spine tipped branchlets. Leaves are opposite, entire, glabrous, sub-sessile, elliptical, and broadly lanceolate (1.5–5.0 cm × 0.5–2 cm), acuminate, having depressed veins on the dorsal surface. Henna flowers have four sepals and a 2 mm calyx tube with 3 mm spread lobes. Petals are obvate, white or red stamens inserted in pairs on the rim of the calyx tube. Ovary is four celled, style up to 5 mm long and erect. Fruits are small, brownish capsules, 4–8 mm in diameter, with 32–49 seeds per fruit, and open irregularly into four splits.

Cultivation

The henna plant is native to tropical and subtropical regions of Africa, southern Asia, and northern Australasia in semi-arid zones. Henna's indigenous zone is the tropical savannah and tropical arid zone, in latitudes between 15° and 25° N and S from Africa to the western Pacific rim, and produces highest dye content in temperatures between 35°C and 45°C. During the onset of precipitation intervals, the plant grows rapidly; putting out new shoots, then growth slows. The leaves gradually yellow and fall during prolonged dry or cool intervals. It does not thrive where minimum temperatures are below 11°C. Temperatures below 5°C will kill the henna plant. Henna is commercially cultivated in UAE, Morocco, Yemen, Tunisia, Libya, Saudi Arabia, Egypt, western India, Iran, Pakistan, Bangladesh, Afghanistan, Somalia and Sudan. Presently the Pali district of Rajasthan is the most heavily cultivated henna production area in India, with over 100 henna processors operating in Sojat City. Its called "Maruthani" in Tamil.

Uses

Henna has been used since the Bronze Age to dye skin (including body art), hair, fingernails, leather, silk and wool. In several parts of the world it is traditionally used in various festivals and celebrations. There is mention of henna as a hair dye in Indian court records around 400 CE, in Rome during the Roman Empire, and in Spain during Convivencia. It was listed in the medical texts of the Ebers Papyrus (16th c BCE Egypt) and by Ibn Qayyim al-Jawziyya (14th c CE (Syria and Egypt) as a medicinal herb. In Morocco, wool is dyed and ornamented with henna, as are drumheads and other leather goods.

Use of henna for body art has enjoyed a recent renaissance due to improvements in cultivation, processing, and the emigration of people from traditional henna-using regions.

For skin dyeing, a paste of ground henna (either prepared from a dried powder or from fresh ground leaves) is placed in contact with the skin from a few hours to overnight. Henna stains can last a few days to a month depending on the quality of the paste, individual skin type, and how long the paste is allowed to stay on the skin.

Henna also acts as an anti-fungal and a preservative for leather and cloth. It was listed in the medical texts of the Ebers Papyrus (16th c BCE Egypt)and by Ibn Qayyim al-Jawziyya (14th c CE (Syria and Egypt) as a medicinal herb.

Henna flowers have been used to create perfume since ancient times, and henna perfume is experiencing a resurgence. Henna repels some insect pests and mildew.

Henna's coloring properties are due to lawsone, a burgundy organic compound that has an affinity for bonding with protein. Lawsone is primarily concentrated in the leaves, especially in the petioles of the leaf. Lawsone content in leaves is negatively correlated with the number of seeds in the fruits.

Preparation and Application

Whole, unbroken henna leaves will not stain the skin. Henna will not stain skin until the lawsone molecules are made available (released) from the henna leaf. Fresh henna leaves will stain the skin if they are smashed with a mildly acidic liquid. The lawsone will gradually migrate from the henna paste into the outer layer of the skin and bind to the proteins in it, creating a fast stain.

Since it is difficult to form intricate patterns from coarse crushed leaves, henna is commonly traded as a powder made by drying, milling and sifting the leaves. The dry powder is mixed with lemon juice, strong tea, or other mildly acidic liquids to make a preparation with toothpaste-like consistency, which can be used to make finely detailed body art. The henna mix must rest for 6 to 12 hours before use, to release the lawsone from the leaf matter. Essential oils with high levels of monoterpene alcohols such as tea tree, eucalyptus, cajeput, or lavender will improve skin stain characteristics.

The paste can be applied with many traditional and innovative tools, including resist, shading, thick-paste, and cellowrap techniques. A satisfactory stain may be achieved within minutes, but the longer the paste is left on the skin, the stronger the stain will be, and it may be left for several hours. To prevent it from drying or falling off the skin, the paste is often sealed down by dabbing a sugar/lemon mix over the dried paste, or simply adding some form of sugar to the paste. This also adds to the colour of the end result, increasing the intensity of the shade. At the end of the procedure, the dry paste is simply brushed or scraped away.

Henna stains are orange soon after applicaion, but darken over the following three days to a reddish brown. Soles and palms have the thickest layer of skin and so take up the most lawsone, and take it to the greatest depth, so that hands and feet will have the darkest and most long-lasting stains. Steaming or warming the henna pattern will darken the stain, either during the time the paste is still on the skin, or after the paste has been removed. Chlorinated water and soaps may spoil the darkening process: alkaline products may hasten the darkening process. After the stain reaches its peak color it will appear to fade, as the stained dead cells exfoliate.

Traditions of Henna as Body Art

The different words for henna in ancient languages imply that it had more than one point of discovery and origin, as well as different pathways of daily and ceremonial use.

Henna has been used to adorn young women's bodies as part of social and holiday celebrations since the late Bronze Age in the eastern Mediterranean. The earliest text mentioning henna in the context of marriage and fertility celebrations comes from the Ugaritic legend of Baal and Anath, which has references to women marking themselves with henna in preparation to meet their husbands, and Anath adorning herself with henna to celebrate a victory over the enemies of Baal. Wall paintings excavated at Akrotiri (dating prior to the eruption of Thera in 1680 BCE) show women with markings consistent with henna on their nails, palms and soles, in a tableau consistent with the henna bridal description from Ugarit. Many statuettes of young women dating between 1500 and 500 BCE along the Mediterranean coastline have raised hands with markings consistent with henna. This early connection between young, fertile women and henna seems to be the origin of the Night of the Henna, which is now celebrated worldwide.

The Night of the Henna was celebrated by most groups in the areas where henna grew naturally: Jews, Muslims, Hindus, Christians and Zoroastrians, among others, all celebrated marriages by adorning the bride, and often the groom, with henna.

Across the henna-growing region, Purim, Eid, Diwali Karva Chauth, Passover, Nowruz, Mawlid, and most saints' days were celebrated with some henna. Favorite horses, donkeys, and salukis had their hooves, paws, and tails hennaed. Battle victories, births, circumcision, birthdays, Zβr, as well as weddings, usually included some henna as part of the celebration. When there was joy, there was henna, as long as henna was available.

Henna was regarded as having "Barakah," blessings, and was applied for luck as well as joy and beauty. Brides typically had the most henna, and the most complex patterns, to support their greatest joy, and wishes for luck. Some bridal traditions were very complex, such as those in Yemen, where the Jewish bridal henna process took four or five days to complete, with multiple applications and resist work.

The fashion of "Bridal Mehndi" in Pakistan, Northern Libya and in North Indian diasporas is currently growing in complexity and elaboration, with new innovations in glitter, gilding, and fine-line work. Recent technological innovations in grinding, sifting, temperature control, and packaging henna, as well as government encouragement for henna cultivation, have improved dye content and artistic potential for henna.

Though traditional henna artists were Nai caste in India, and barbering castes in other countries (lower social classes), talented contemporary henna artists can command high fees for their work. Women in countries where women are discouraged from working outside the home can find socially acceptable, lucrative work doing henna. Morocco, Mauritania, Yemen, Libya, Somalia, Sudan, as well as India and many other countries have thriving women's henna businesses. These businesses are often open all night for Eids, Diwali and Karva Chauth, and many women may work as a team for a large wedding where hundreds of guests will be hennaed as well as the bride and groom.

Health Effects

Though user accounts cite few, if any, negative effects of natural henna paste, pre-mixed henna body art pastes may have ingredients added to darken stain, or to alter stain color. The health risks involved in pre-mixed paste can be significant. The United States Food and Drug Administration (FDA) considers these to be adulterants and therefore illegal for use on skin.Some pastes have been found to include: silver nitrate, carmine, pyrogallol, disperse orange dye, and chromium. These have been found to cause allergic reactions, chronic inflammatory reactions, or late-onset allergic reactions to hairdressing products and textile dyes.

"Neutral Henna" and "Black Henna"

Natural henna stains only a rich red brown. Products sold as "black henna" or "neutral henna" do not contain henna, but are instead made from other plants, or from other substances altogether.

"Neutral Henna"

So-called "neutral henna" does not change the color of hair. This is not henna powder; it is usually the powder of the plant *Senna italica* also known as Cassia obovata or a closely related *Cassia* species.

"Black Henna"

So-called "black henna" powder may be derived from indigo (from the plant Indigofera tinctoria). It may also contain unlisted dyes and chemicals.] "Black henna" may contain p-phenylenediamine (PPD), which can stain skin black quickly, but can cause severe allergic reactions and permanent scarring. The FDA specifically forbids PPD to be used for that purpose, and may prosecute those who produce "black henna'. Artists who injure clients with "Black Henna" in the USA may be sued for damages.

"Black Henna" is a misnomer arising from imports of plant-based hair dyes into the West in the late 19th century. Partly fermented, dried indigo was called "black henna" because it could be used in combination with henna to dye hair black. This gave rise to the belief that there was such a thing as "black henna" which could dye skin black. Indigo will not dye skin black. Pictures of indigenous people with black body art (either alkalized henna or from some other source) also fed the belief that there was such a thing as "black henna."

In the 1990s, henna artists in Africa, India, Bali, the Arabian Peninsula and the West began to experiment with para-phenylenediamine (PPD) based black hair dye, applying it as a thick paste as they would apply henna, in an effort to find something that would quickly make jet black temporary body art. PPD can cause severe allergic reactions, with blistering, intense itching, permanent scarring, and permanent chemical sensitivities. Estimates of allergic reactions range between 3% and 15%. Henna does not cause these injuries. "Black henna" made with PPD can cause lifelong health damage. "Black henna" made with gasoline, kerosene, lighter fluid, paint thinner, and benzene has been linked to adult leukemia.

The most frequent serious health consequence of having a "black henna temporary tattoo" is sensitization to hair dye and related chemicals. If a person has had a "black henna tattoo", and later dyes their hair with chemical hair dye, the allergic reaction may be life threatening and require hospitalization. Because of the epidemic of para-phenylenediamine allergic reactions, chemical hair dye products now post warnings on the labels: "Temporary "black henna" tattoos may increase your risk of allergy. Do not colour your hair if:... - you have experienced a reaction to a temporary "black henna" tattoo in the past."

Para-phenylenediamine is illegal for use on skin in western countries, though enforcement is difficult. Physicians have urged governments to legislate against "black henna" because of the frequency and severity of injuries, especially to children. To assist prosecution of vendors, government agencies encourage citizens to report injuries and illegal use of "PPD black henna. When used in hair dye, the PPD amount must be below 6%, and application instructions warn that the dye not touch the scalp and the dye must be quickly rinsed away. "Black henna" pastes have PPD percentages from 10% to 80%, and are left on the skin for half an hour.

Para-phenylenediamine "black henna" use is widespread, particularly in tourist areas. Because the blistering reaction appears 3 to 12 days after the application, most

Henna is a small tree or large shrub, growing to six meters high. It has lateral branches with leaves that grow in pairs, two to four centimeters long.

- ❖ Henna Flowers
- ❖ Growing Henna in the House
- ❖ Germinating Henna Seeds
- ❖ Milling Henna Leaves
- ❖ Use Fresh Henna Leaves
- ❖ Henna in the Bible
- ❖ Health and Henna

- ❖ Henna is Lawsonia Inermis, family Lythraceae
- ❖ Lawsone
- ❖ The Henna Plant Closeup
- ❖ Henna: A Geographical Approach
- ❖ Where Can Henna Grow?
- ❖ Commercial Henna Growing
- ❖ Henna Farming in India
- ❖ Henna Farming in Pakistan

Henna is a juvenile plant for the first two years. The leaves do not have high lawsone content, and the branches do not have thorns. In mature plants, thorns develop at the leaf buds during dormant phases. When hungry animals come to nibble the new leaves, they prick their tongues on the thorns and go look for another plant to eat.

Henna leaves have a red-orange dye, lawsone, and the highest dye concentration is in the petiole (the central vein). Young leaves have the highest petiole dye content. Older leaves have lower dye content. In the picture below, you can see the higher concentration of Lawsone in the petiole (the central vein) of the smaller, younger leaves. All leaves were taken from a 3 year old potted plant in a growth surge during a period of 95 fahrenheit (35 celsius) weather with 2 cm per week precipitation.

High lawsone in petiole of younger leaves at left

Actual size of largest leaf 4 cm

Henna will only grow where minimum temperatures stay above 50 degrees fahrenheit or 11 celsius. It will tolerate extreme heat and long droughts. It grows wild near desert oasis, and in semi-aid regions. It thrives in alluvial soils, where there is annual precipitation of 0.2 to 4.2 meters and a soil pH of 4.3 to 8.0 (4.1-31). Its growth range is detailed in the map at "The Geography of Henna". In ideal conditions, such as detailed in "Henna Farming in Pakistan", and "Where is henna grown, processed and exported in India?", the plant is cultivated for body art quality henna. In slightly less than ideal conditions, it is cultivated for hair quality henna. In cooler, more moist conditions, it is cultivated as a flowering hedgerow shrub. It can be grown as a houseplant in cooler climates.

The flowers are fragrant, and may be white, red, pink or yellow. The four-petaled flowers grow in a branching clusters like a cluster of lilac blossoms. For more information on henna flowers, go HERE or click on the image below:

In the southern and western Mediterranean countries, henna flowers bloom in April and May. The henna fruits ripen at the end of the summer. In each henna fruit there is an average of 40 - 45 seeds.

Henna seeds are very small and polygonal.

Henna Seeds: actual size of seed is 1 - 2 mm

The plant can be propagated by rooting the cuttings, or sewing seeds.

Henna Blossoms are so fragrant, they've been used in perfumes since 1500 BCE. They were the Prophet Mohammed's favorite scent. Would you like to smell them? The Henna Page send you a sample each of three kinds of Henna Blossom Attar. These samples are a few drops of each attar oil on a cotton ball, just enough for you to experience the wonderful fragrances! Henna flower attars are called *Gulhina Attar* and are produced commercially in Uttar Pradesh, India.

Scientifically referred to as *Lawsonia inermis,* henna in the West is most commonly used to dye hair. But with the new popularity of tattoos, henna and the art of Mehndi is considered a safe, painless and non-permanent alternative form of body ornamentation. Although henna is traditionally drawn only on the hands and feet, feel free to create your designs on arms, legs, around the belly button, and even may be behind the neck.

Lawasonia inermis molecule

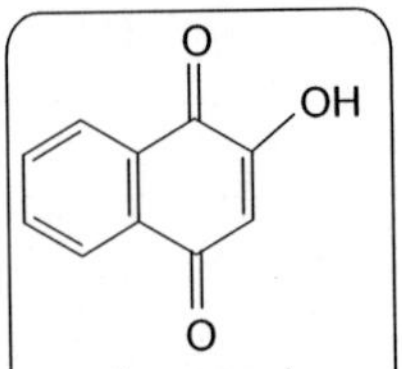

Lawasonia

Scientific Analysis on Henna Family: Lythraceae, (*Lawsonia inermis* L.).

A perennial shrub native to North Africa, Asia and Australia, is naturalized and cultivated in the tropics of America, Egypt, India, and parts of the Middle East. Also known as El-Henna, Egyptian priest, and mignonette tree, the species is sometimes classified as Lawsonia alba Lam. or Lawsonia ruba. Reaching a height of up to 6 meters, the plant has fragrant white or rose-red flowers.

The reported life zone of henna is 19 to 27 degrees centigrade with an annual precipitation of 0.2 to 4.2 meters and a soil pH of 4.3 to 8.0. Henna is planted today primarily as an ornament hedge, but is probably best known for its dried, ground leaves (called henna) traditionally used to produce colorfast orange, red, and brown dyes. Dried, powdered leaves of henna contain about 0.5 to 1.5 percent lawsone, the chief constituent responsible for the dyeing properties of the plant. Henna also contains mannite, tannic acid, mucilage, gallic acid, and naphtaquinone. The leaves of henna have been used in Asia since antiquity as a hair, nail, and skin dye.

In the West and the Middle East, henna is used in hair shampoos, dyes, conditioners, and rinses. Henna dye products are mixed with indigo or other plant material to obtain a greater color range. Extracts of henna are also used to stain wood and to dye fabric and textiles.

As a medicinal plant, henna has been used for astringent, antihemorrhagic, intestinal antineoplastic, cardio-inhibitory, hypotensive, and sedative effects. It has also been used as a folk remedy against amoebiasis, headache, jaundice, and leprosy.

Henna extracts show antibacterial, antifungal, and ultraviolet light screening activity. The flowers possess a pleaseant aroma and crude perfumes are produced in some major growing areas by preparing a suspension of comminuted flowers in vegetable oil.

Henna in the West is most commonly used to dye hair. But with the popularity of tattoos, henna and the art of Mehndi is considered a safe, painless and non-permanent alternative form of body ornamentation.

Although henna is traditionally drawn only on hands and feet, feel free to create your designs on arms, legs, around the belly button, and even may be behind the neck.

How To Germinate Seeds

Henna, *Lawsonia inermis*, produces a red-orange dye molecule, lawsone. This molecule has an affinity for bonding with protein, and thus has been used to dye skin, hair, fingernails, leather, silk and wool.

The dye molecule, lawsone, is primarily concentrated in the leaves, and is in the highest levels in the petioles of the leaf. Products sold as "black henna" or "neutral henna" are not made from henna, but may be derived from indigo (in the plant Indigofera tinctoria) or Cassia obovata, and may contain unlisted dyes and chemicals.

Henna has many traditional and commercial uses, the most common being as a dye for hair, skin and fingernails, as a dye and preservative for leather and cloth, and as an anti-fungal. Henna flowers have been used to create perfume since ancient times, and henna perfume is experiencing a resurgence on the internet.

Henna body art is made by applying henna paste to the skin: the lawsone in the paste migrates into the outermost layer of the skin and makes a red-brown stain. Dried ground, sifted henna leaves are easily worked into a paste that can be used to make intricate body art. Commercially available henna powder is made by drying the henna leaves and milling them to powder, then the powder is sifted. This powder is mixed with lemon juice, strong tea, or other mildly acidic liquids. Essential oils with high levels of "terps", monoterpene alcohols such as tea tree, eucalyptus, cajeput, or lavender will improve skin stain characteristics. The henna mix must rest for 6 to 12 hours so the leaf cellulose is dissolved, making the lawsone available to stain the skin. This is mixed to a toothpaste consistency and applied with a one of many traditional tools. Once applied to the skin, lawsone molecules gradually migrate from the henna paste into the outer layer of the skin. Though henna's lawsone will stain the skin within minutes, the longer the paste is left on the skin, the more lawsone will migrate. Henna paste will yield as much dye as the skin can easily absorb in less than eight hours. Henna tends to crack and fall off the skin during these hours, so it is often sealed down by dabbing a sugar/lemon mix over the dried paste, or simply adding some form of sugar to the paste. This also adds to the colour of the end result, increasing the intensity of the shade.

When the paste has fallen off the skin or been removed by scraping, the stain will be orange, but should darken over the following three days to a reddish brown. Soles and palms have the thickest layer of skin and so take up the most lawsone, and take it to the greatest depth, so that hands and feet will have the darkest and most long-lasting stains. Steaming or warming the henna pattern will darken the stain, either during the time the paste is still on the skin, or after the paste has been removed. Chlorinated water and soaps may spoil the darkening process: alkaline may hasten the darkening process. After the stain reaches its peak color it will appear to fade. The henna stain is not actually fading, the skin is exfoliating: the lower, less stained cells, rise to the surface, until all stained cells are shed.

2 A Phytopharmacological Review

Medicinal plants are part and parcel of human society to combat diseases, from the dawn of civilization. There exits a plethora of knowledge, information and benefits of herbal drugs in our ancient literature of Ayurvedic (Traditional Indian Medicine), Siddha, Unani and Chinese medicine. According to the World Health Organization, 2003 about 80 % of the population of developing countries being unable to afford pharmaceutical drugs rely on traditional medicines, mainly plant based, to sustain their primary health care needs. Herbal medicines are in great demand in the developed as well as developing countries for primary healthcare because of their wide biological and medicinal activities, higher safety margins and lesser cost.

The present attempt is to review and compile updated information on various aspects of *L. inermis* Linn. a plant used all over the world. This plant is commonly known as Henna or Mhendi and abundantly available in tropical and subtropical areas. Ancient history of India describes its diverse uses and also plays appreciable role in Ayurvedic or natural herbal medicines.

Lawsonia inermis Linn.

Genus Lawsonia bears one species, *L. inermis* (*Henna, Mhendi, Shudi, Madurang, Mendi, Manghati, Madayantika* and *Goranti*) till date, having different synonyms as *alba* and *spinosa* belonging to family Lythraceae. It is a biennial dicotyledonous herbaceous shrub. A native of North Africa and South-West Asia, the plant is now widely cultivated through out the tropics as an ornamental and dye plant.

A much branched glabrous shrub or small tree (2 to 6 m in height). Leaves are small, opposite in arrangement along the branches, sub-sessile, about 1.5 to 5 cm long, 0.5 to 2 cm wide, greenish brown to dull green, elliptic to broadly lanceolate with entire margin, petiole short and glabrous and acute or obtuse apex with tapering base. Young branches are green in colour and quadrangular which turn red with age. Bark is greyish brown, unarmed when young but branches of older trees are spine tipped. Inflorescence is a large pyramid shaped cyme. Flowers are small, about 1 cm across,n numerous, fragrant, white or rose coloured with four crumbled petals. Calyx is with a 0.2 cm tube and 0.3 cm spread lobes. Fruit is a small brown coloured round capsule. Fruit opens irregularly and splits into four sections at maturity and is many seeded. Seeds are about 3 mm across, numerous, smooth, pyramidal, hard and thick seed coat with brownish coloration.

Ethnobotanical Uses

Henna has been used cosmetically and medicinally for over 9,000 years. Traditionally in India, mehndi is applied to hands and feet. Henna symbolizes fertility. Its use became popular in India because of its cooling effect in the hot Indian summers. Henna leaves, flowers, seeds, stem bark and roots are used in traditional medicine to treat a variety of ailments as rheumatoid arthritis, headache, ulcers, diarrheoa, leprosy, fever, leucorrhoea, diabetes, cardiac disease, hepatoprotective and colouring.

Henna **leaf** has an orange-red dye and leaf paste or powder is widely used for decorating hands, nails and feet with patterns. It is also used as a hair dye. It is used for alleviating jaundice, skin diseases, venereal diseases, smallpox and spermatorrhoea. **Flowers** are very fragrant and used to extract a perfume, which is used as base for local scents. An infusion of the flowers is a valuable application to bruises. Decoction of the flowers is describes as an emmenagogue. **Seeds** are deodorant. Powered seeds with real ghee (clarified butter) are effective against dysentery. Seeds in powered form are good medicine for liver disorders and associated problems. The **bark** is applied in the form of a decoction to burns and scalds. It is given internally in a variety of affections, such as jaundice, enlargement of the spleen, calculus, as an alternative in leprosy and obstinate skin affections. **Root** is considered as a potent medicine for gonorrhoea and herpes infection. Root is astringent may be pulped and used for sore eyes. Pulped root may also be applied to the heads of children for boils. Cambodians drink a decoction as a diuretic. Decoction of the root generally in combination with prepared indigo as a powerful abortifacient. The root is supposed to be useful in treatment of hysteria and nervous disor.

Chemical Review

The principal colouring matter of henna is lawsone, 2-hydroxy-1:4 napthaquinone ($C_{10}H_6O_3$, m.p. 190° decomp.) besides lawsone other constituents present are gallic acid, glucose, mannitol, fats, resin (2 %), mucilage and traces of an alkaloid. Leaves yield hennatannic acid and an olive oil green resin, soluble in ether and alcohol. Flowers yield an essential oil (0.01-0.02%) with brown or dark brown colour, strong fragrance and consist mainly of α- and β-ionones; a nitrogenous compound and resin. Seeds contain proteins (5.0%), carbohydrates (33.62%), fibers (33.5%), fatty oils (10-11%) composed of behenic acid, arachidic acid, stearic acid, palmitic acid, oleic acid and linoleic acid. The unsaponified matter contains waxes and colouring matter. The root contains a red colouring matter. Phytochemicals reported in *L. inermis* L. are listed in Table 2.1 with their structures.

Biological Review

Although this plant has been widely used in various symptoms and diseases, however few pharmacological studies have been reported.

Antidiabetic activity

Ethanol (70 %) extract of *L. inermis* showed significant hypoglycaemic and hypolipidaemic activities in alloxan induced diabetic mice after oral administration. The feeding of 0.8 g/kg of *L. inermis* extract decreased the concentration of glucose, cholesterol and triglycerides to normal.

Methanol (95 %) extract of leaves of *L. inermis* showed significant *in-vitro* antihyperglycemic effect.

Immunomodulatory effect

Methanol extract of henna leaves at 1 mg/ml concentration had displayed immunostimulant action as indicated by promotion of T-lymphocyte proliferative responses. Seven compounds were isolated adopting the lymphocyte transformation assay (LTA)-guided fractionation of the total methanolic extract of henna leaves. Naphthoquinone fraction obtained from leaves *L. inermis* showed significant immunomodulatory effect.

Hepatoprotective activity

Alcoholic extract of the bark of *L. inermis* showed hepatoprotective effect against the carbon tetrachlorideinduced elevation in serum marker enzymes (GOT and GPT), serum bilirubin, liver lipid peroxidation and reduction in total serum protein, liver glutathione, glutathione peroxidase, glutathione-s-transferase, glycogen, superoxide dismutase and catalase activity. The results suggest hepatoprotective and antioxidant activity of extract of *L. alba* bark. Pretreatment of rats with the extract also inhibited the peroxidation of microsomal lipids in a dose-dependent manner. The hepatoprotective activity of the ethanolic extract of the dried leaves of *L. inermis* and its crude fractions (petroleum ether, ethyl acetate, butanol and butanone fractions) was evaluated against CCl4 induced hepatotoxicity in mice. The ethanolic extract and its fractions reduced the total bilirubin content and SGOT, SGPT and SAL activities, and reduced liver weight compared to LIV.

Antioxidant effect

Modulator effect of 80% ethanol extract of leaves of henna on drug metabolising phase I and phase II enzymes, antioxidant enzymes, lipid peroxidation in the liver of Swiss Albino mice. The hepatic glutathione S-transferase and DTdiaphorase specific activities were elevated above basal level by *L. inermis* extract treatment. With reference to antioxidant enzyme the investigated doses were effective in increasing the hepatic glutathione reductase (GR), superoxide dismutase (SOD) and catalase activities significantly at both the dose levels. Reduced glutathione (GSH) measured as non-protein sulphydryl was found to be significantly elevated in liver. Among the extrahepatic organs examined (forestomach, kidney and lung) glutathione S-transferase and DTdiaphorase level were increased in a dose independent manner Chloroform extract of leaves of *Lawsonia inemris* had shown the highest activity (87.6%) followed by α-tocopherol (62.5%) by using FTC method and based on TBA method significant activity (55.7%) compared to α-tocopherol (44.4%). Total phenolic compound was 2.56 and 1.45 mg tannic per mg of Henna dry matter as extracted with methanol and water respectively. In effect of different concentrations of methanolic extract of henna in comparison with synthetic antioxida 2-hydroxy-1, 4-naphthoquinone (HNQ; lawsone) is the main ingredient of *L. inermis*. During the oxidation of 100μM phenanthridine by guinea pigs aldehyde oxidase formation of superoxide anion (SO_2) and hydrogen peroxide (H_2O_2) at 6-10% and 85-90% resp. HNQ inhibits the production of superoxide anion and substrate oxidation more potently than hydrogen peroxide. The IC50 value of HNQ with phenanthridine oxidation by aldehyde oxidase was 9.3 ±1.1μM, which in excess of 15 fold of maximal plasma concentrations of HNQ, indicating a high degree of safety margin.

Antibacterial activity

Ethanol extracts of 20 plants species used by Yemeni traditional healers to treat infectious diseases were screened for their antibacterial activity against both gram positive and gram negative bacteria. The ethyl acetate extract of *L. inermis* L. was found to be the most active against all the bacteria in the test system Quinonic compounds from henna were studied *in-vitro* for antimicrobial properties. Genotoxic studies on lawsone suggested that it was a weak bacterial mutagen for *Salmonella typhimurium* strain TA98 and was more clearly mutagenic for strain TA2637. Overall, the weight of evidence suggested that henna and hydroxyl napthaquinone possess no genotoxic risk to the consumer Aqueous extract of leaves of *L. inermis* showed the significant antibacterial effect against Aqueous, methanol and chloroform crude extracts of leaf showed the *in-vitro* antimicrobial activity to inhibit the growth of 6 human pathogenic fungi and 4 types of bacteria in dose dependent m.

Antifungal activity

During screening of barks of 30 plant species against *Microsporum gypseum* and *Trichophyton mentagrophytes*, only *L. inermis* L. extract exhibited absolute toxicity. The extract showed broad fungitoxic spectrum when tested against 13 ring worm fungi. Further the fungitoxicity of the extract remained unaltered at high temperature on autoclaving and after long storage. The leaves of *L. inermis* L. were also found to exhibit strong fungi toxicity and non-phytotoxicity. The minimum effective dose against test organism was found to be 1000 ppm. Ethanol, methanol and aqueous extract of leaves of *L. inermis* are involved in defensive mechanism against spore germination of *Drechslera oryzae*. Lawsone isolated from the leaves of *L. inermis* has shown significant antifungal antibiotic effect Aqueous extract of leaves of *L. inermis* was tested for the antifungal potential against eight important species of

Aspergillus which isolated from sorghum, maize and paddy seed samples. *A. flavus* recorded high susceptibility and hence solvent extracts viz., petroleum ether, benzene, chloroform, methanol and ethanol extracts of the plant showed significant antifungal activity Essential oil obtained by hydro-distillation from leaves of *L. inermis* growing in Iran were analysed by GC-MS and showed an antifungal activity Ethanol extract of leaves of *L. inermis* showed significant antifungal effect against phytopathogenic fungi. Ethanol extract could be used as alternative source of antifungal agents for protection of plants or crops against fungal infection.

Antiviral activity

The ethanol soluble fraction of *L. inermis* fruits displayed highly potent activity against Sembiki forest virus (SFV) in swiss mice and chick embryo models exhibiting 100 to 65% activities after 10 to 25 days of virus challenge.

Antitrypanosomal activity

Crude Methanolic extract of leaf of *L. inermis* showed *invitro* activity against *Trypanosoma brucei* at concentration of 8.3 mg/ml of blood in mice but not *in-vivo*. The treatment tends to ameliorate the disease condition, but did not affect the level of parasitaemia and pack cell volum.

Antiparasitic activity

During an ethnopharmacological survey of antiparasitic medicinal plants used in Ivory Coast, 17 plants were identified and collected. Polar, non-polar and alkaloidal extracts of various parts of these species were evaluated *invitro* in an antiparasitic drug screening. Antimalarial, leishmanicidal, trypanocidal, antihelminthiasis and antiscabies activities were determined. Among the selected plants, *L. inermis* L. showed interesting trypanocidal activitie.

Molluscicidal activity

L. inermis showed significant molluscicidal activit.

Antidermatophytic activity

The antidermatophytic activity of ethanol, ethyl acetate and hexane extracts of *L. inermis* were tested on 5 strains each of *Tinea rubrum* and *Tinea mentagrophytes*. All these extracts showed significant antidermatophytic properties *in-vitro*.

Tuberculostatic activity

The tuberculostatic activity of henna was tested *in-vitro* and *in-vivo*. On Lowenstein Jensen medium, the growth of *Tubercle bacilli* from sputum and of *Mycobacterium tuberculosis* H37Rv was inhibited by 6 μg/ml of the herb. *Invivo* studies on guinea pigs and mice showed that the herb at a dose of 5 mg/kg body weight led to a significant resolution of experimental tuberculosis following infection with *Mycobacterium tuberculosis* H37Rv.

Antifertility activity

Ethanol extract prepared from the powdered seeds of *L. inermis* L. failed to show any antifertility activity. However in subsequent studies it was observed that the powdered leaves of when administered as suspension or incorporated into the diet inhibited the fertility of rats. The fertility induced appeared to be permanen.

Analgesic activity

The ethanol extract of 25 plants commonly used in traditional Arab system of medicine for treatment of pain, fever and rheumatism were investigated for their analgesic and antipyretic activities. The extract of leaves of henna showed significant analgesic as well as antipyretic activit The fixed oil obtained from seeds were screened for pharmacological activity both *in-vitro* and *in-vivo.* It was concluded that seed oil is devoid of behavioural and CNS effects and failed to produce any effect on isolated tissue though it possess significant analgesic activit.

Anti-inflammatory activity

Isoplumbagin and lawsaritol, isolated from stem bark and root of *L. inermis* L. showed anti- inflammatory activity against Carrageenan induced paw oedema in rats. The compounds phenylbutazone, isoplumbagin and lawsaritol at the oral dose of 100 mg/kg exhibited 61, 60 and 40 percent inhibition in comparison with controls. Isoplumbagin showed significant anti- inflammatory activity similar to that of phenylbutazone Butanol and chloroform fractions showed more potent anti-inflammatory, analgesic and antipyretic effects than aqueous fraction of crude ethanol extract of *L. inermis* in a dose dependent manner Leaves showed significant anti-inflammatory effect with some active princ.

Cytotoxic activity

Isoplumbagin exhibited up to a 1000 fold range of differential sensitivity, which represents distinct fingerprint of cellular responsiveness. At concentration of 10.5–10.8 M, the compound typically produced LC50 – level responses against a majority of the melanoma and colon cancer cell lines as well as against several of the non- small cell lungs, colon, CNS, and renal cell lines. Isoplumbagin showed an interesting profile of cytotoxic activity. Chloroform extract of leaves of *L. inermis* displayed the cytotoxic effects against liver (HepG2) and Human breast (MCF-7) with IC50 values of 0.3 and 24.85 μg/ml by microculture tetrazolium salt assay (MTT). CAT assay, a zone of inhibition test of bacterial growth and colony-forming efficiency test of transformant *Escherichia coli* strains that express mammalian catalase gene derived from normal catalase mice (Csa) and catalase-deficient mutant mice (Csb), Ames mutagenicity assay and H_2O_2 generation assay are carried out.

Lawsone generated H_2O_2 slightly in phosphate buffer system and was not mutagenic in Ames assay using TA98, TA100 and TA102, both in the absence and presence of metabolic activation. Lawsone exposure inhibited the growth of both Csa and Csb strains in a dose-dependent manner. Oxidative stress probably arises when napthoquinone part in lawsone reduced to a semiquinone by enzymatic systems.

Antisickling activity

Aqueous extract of leaves of *L. inermis* was found to inhibit sickling and to increase the oxygen affinity of HbSS blood.

Abortifacient activity

Methanol extract of roots of *L. inermis* was most effective in inducing abortion in mice, rats and guinea pig. The effect apparently was dosage dependent. The results of the whole animal experiments support the methanol extract effectiveness as an abortant due to its maternal and foetal toxic effects.

Enzymes inhibitory activity

The ethanol extract of *L. inermis* L. leaves and lawsone tested for trypsin inhibitory activity showed an IC50 value of 64.87 and 48.6μg/ml, respectivel.

Memory and behaviour effectiveness

L. inermis showed significant effect on memory and behaviour mediated via monoamine neurotransmitters.

Nematicidal effect

A suppressive effect was obtained by *L. inermis* against *Meloidogyne incognita* development. Henna reduced tomato root gall numbers, number of the egg-laying females and rate of the nematode reproduction, when tomato and henna were grown together. Also, same reduction in the nematode biological processes was found, when tomato plants were grown in soil containing root exudates of henna, but with less amount. When henna was grown alone, root gall index and the rate of nematode production reduced to 75% and 99%, respectively, compared with those of tomato grown alone.

Anticoagulant effect

Lawsone and its oxazine derivatives isolated from leaves of *L. inermis* had proven to be potential anticoagulant agen.

Wound healing effects

Chloroform and aqueous extracts of leaves of the plant were capable of inhibiting the growth of microorganisms that are involved in causing burn wound infecti Ethanol extract of the plant (200 mg/kg/day) was used to evaluate the wound healing activity on rats using excision, incision and dead space wound models. Extract of *L. inermis* when compared with the control and

Table 2.1: Phytochemicals

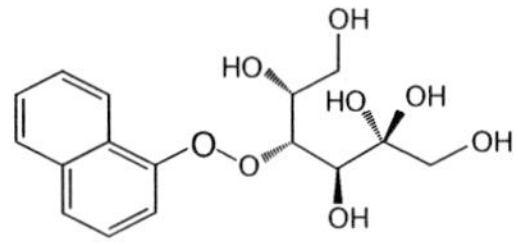

1,2-dihydroxy-4-o-glucosyloxy naphthalene

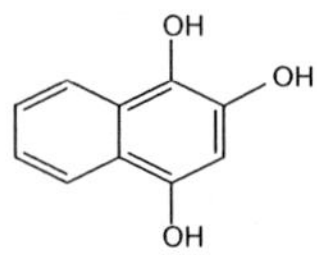

Lawsomaside

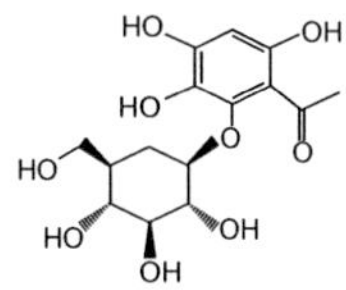

Lahoside

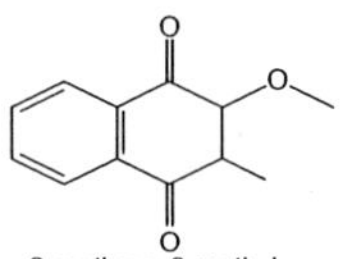

2-methoxy-3-methyl -1-4-Napthoquinone

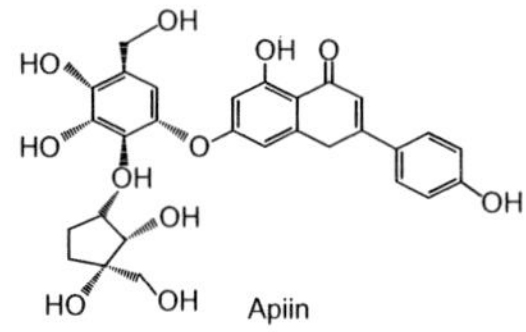

Apiin

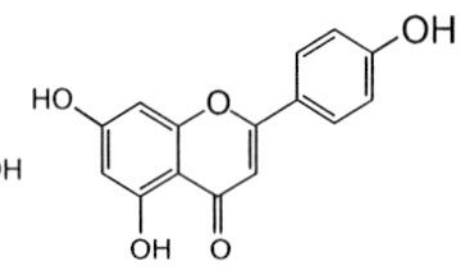

Apigenin

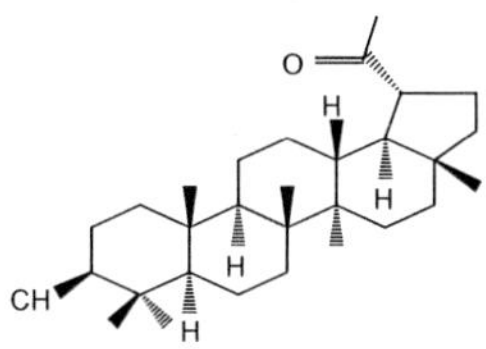

Lupeol

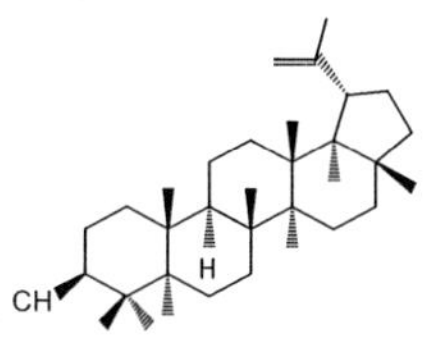

Betulin

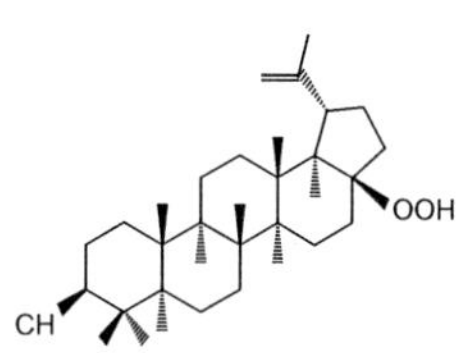

Betulinic acid

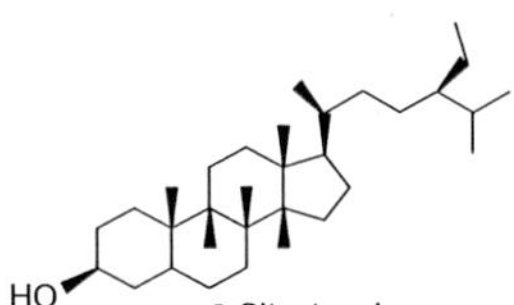

β-Sitostenol

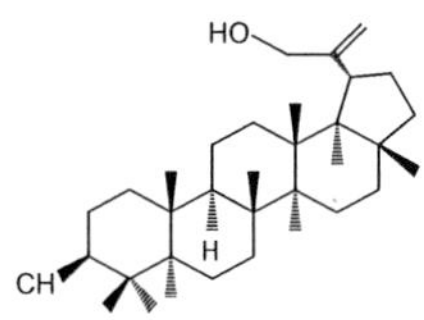

3β, 30-dihydroxylupine -20(29)ene (Hennadiol)

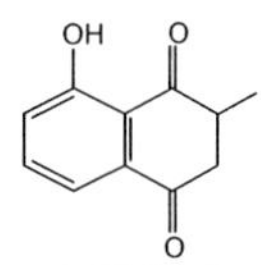

Isoplumbagin

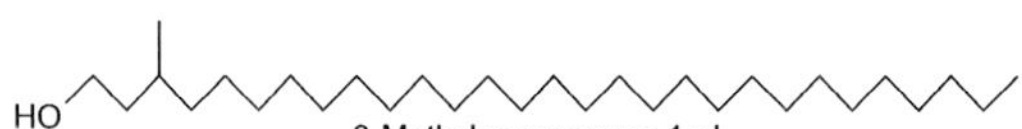

3-Methylnonacosane-1-ol

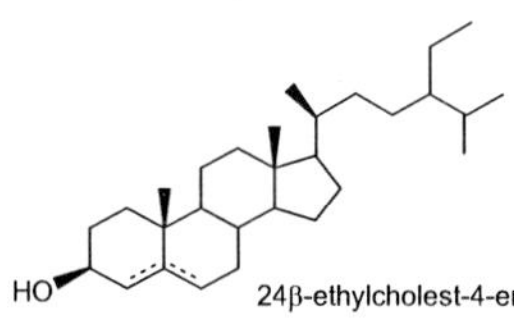

24β-ethylcholest-4-en-3β-ol

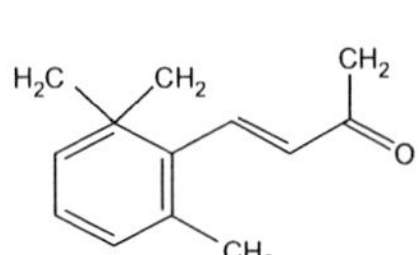

β-Ionone

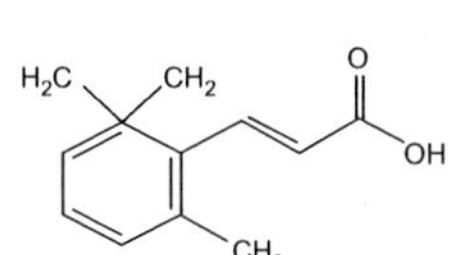

α-Ionone

$CH_3(CH_3)_{20}COOH$
Behenic acid

$CH_3(CH_3)_{15}COOH$
Arachidic acid

$CH_3(CH_2)_{16}COOH$
Stearic acid

$CH_3(CH_3)_{14}COOH$
Palmitic acid

$CH_3(CH_2)4CH{=}CHCH_3CH{=}CH(CH_3)_7COOH$
Linoleic acid

Lawsoshamim (2-acetoxy-3β-hydroxy-olean-12-en-28-oic acid)

Lawsoshamim (3β-hydroxy-24-p-E-coumaroyloxy-olean-12-en 28-oic acid)

3b,28b-dihydroxy-urs-12,20-dien-28-oic acid (Lawnermis acid)

Methyl esters of lawnermis acid

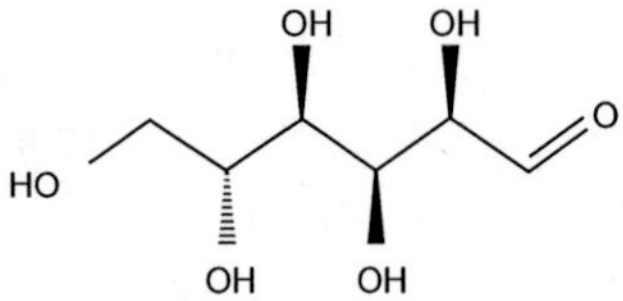

Glucose

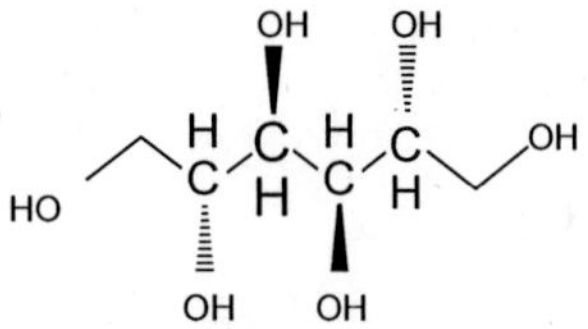

D-mannitol

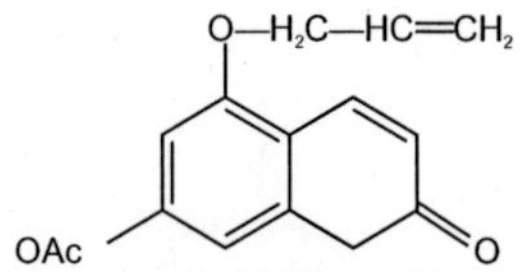

Lacoumanin (5-Allyloxy-7-acetoxy) (coumarin)

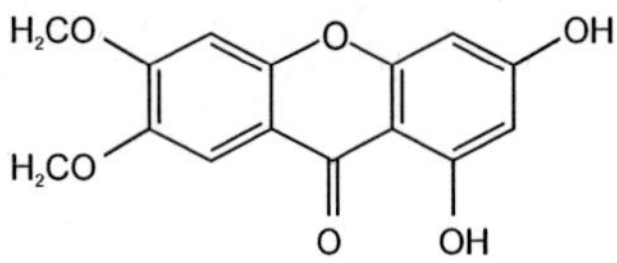

Laxanthone I

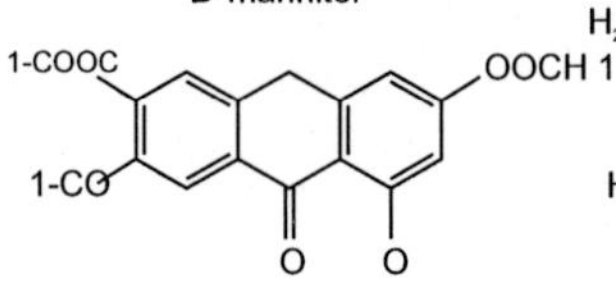

Laxanthone II

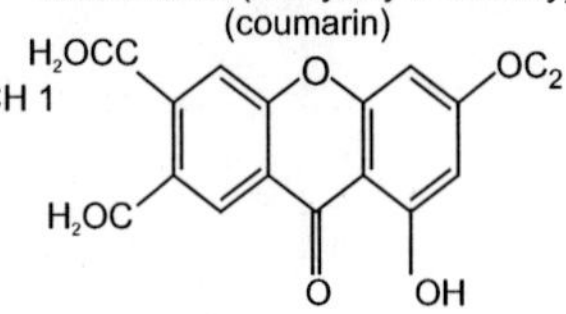

Laxanthone III

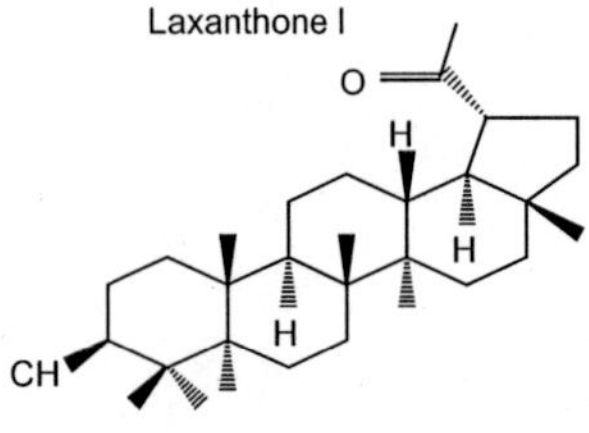

30-Norlupan-3β-ol-20-one

$CH_3(CH_3)_{18}CH_2OH$
n-Tricontyl-n-tridecanoate

$CH_3(CH_3)_{28}OCOCH_3$
n-triacontanol

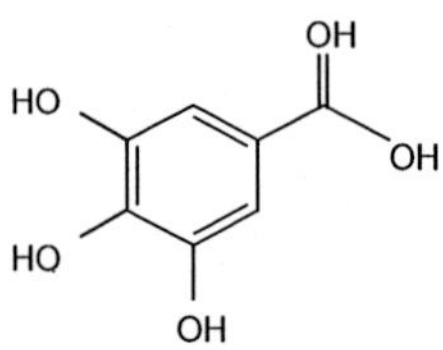

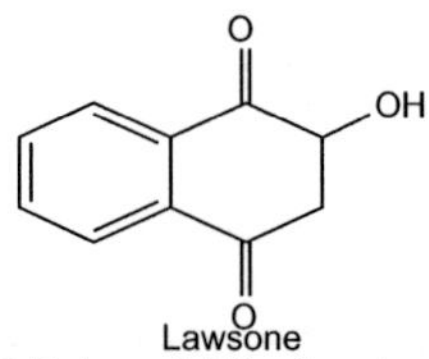

Lawsone
(2-Hydroxy-1,4-Napthoquinone)

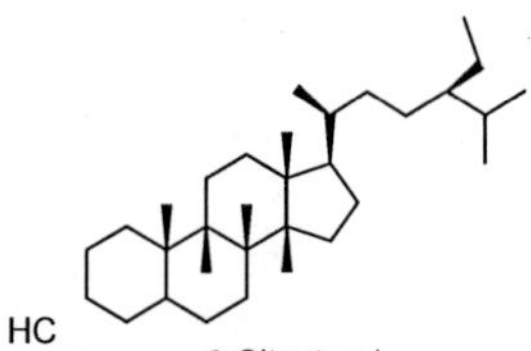

β-Sitosterol

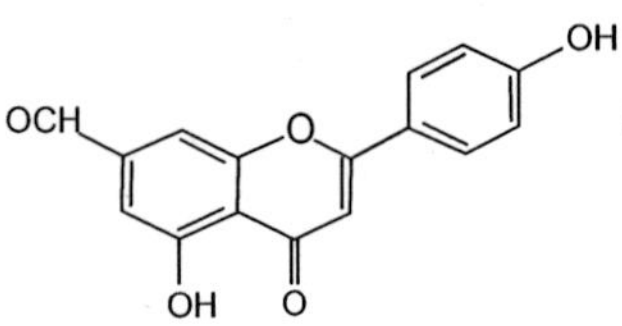

Apigenin-7-glycosidev

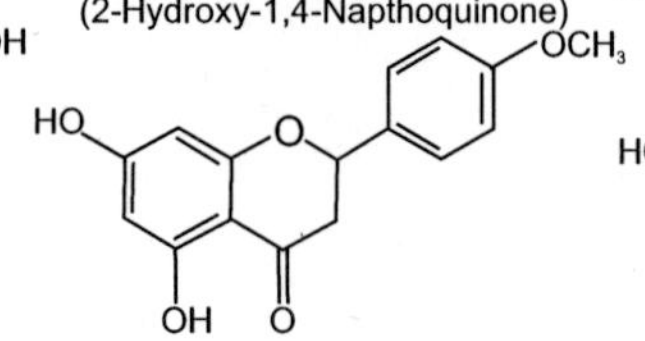

Apigenin-4-glycoside

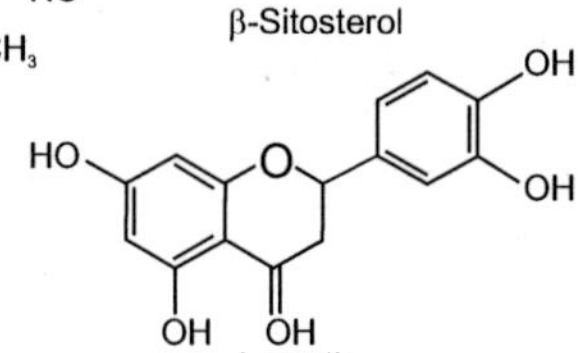

Luteolin

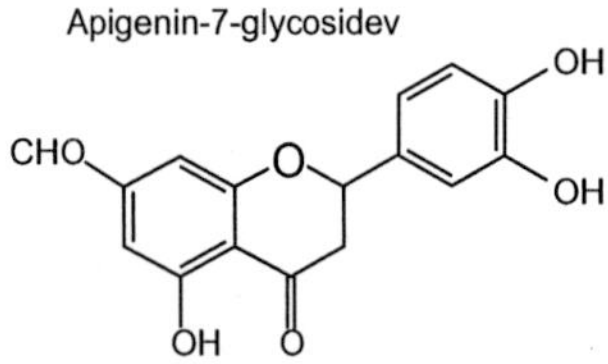

Luteolin-7-glycoside

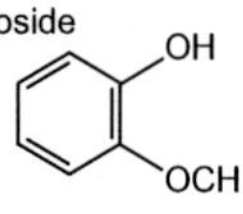

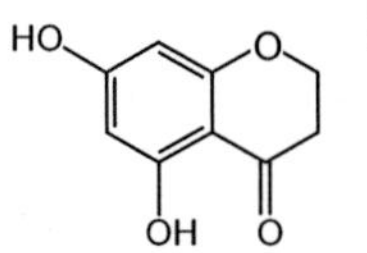

Luteolin-3-glycoside

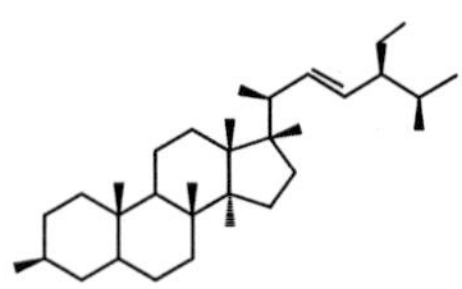

Stigbmesterol

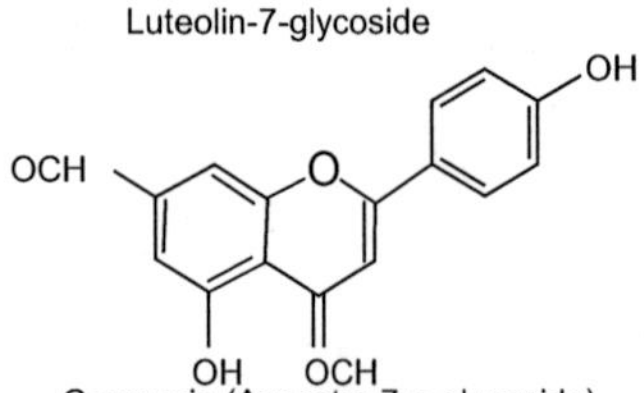

Conmosin (Acacetm-7-o-glucoside)

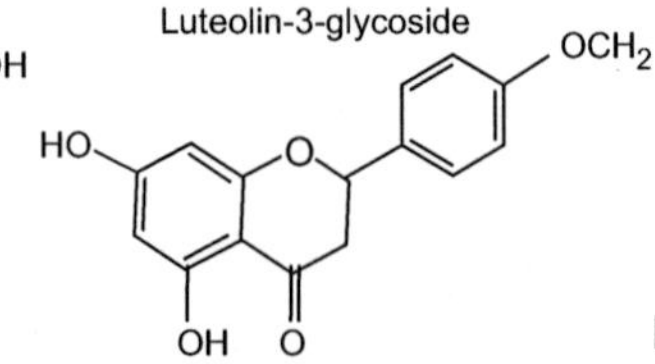

Acacetin

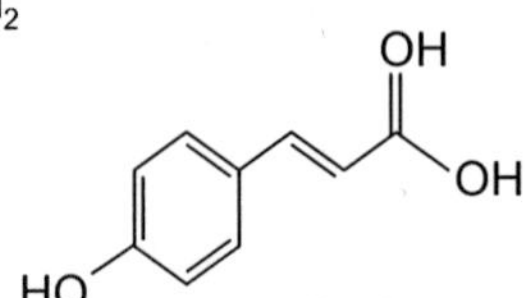

p-coumaric acid

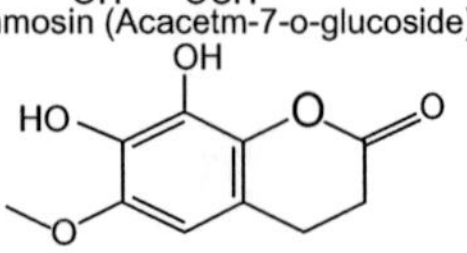

Fraxetin

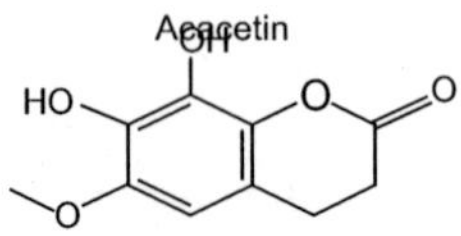

Scopoletin

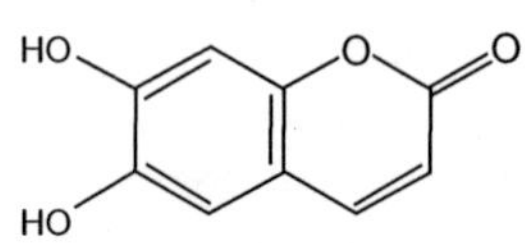

Escyketin

reference standard animals: a high rate of wound contraction, a decrease in the period of epithelialization, high skin breaking strength, a significant increase in the granulation tissue weight and hydroxyproline content. Histological studies of the tissue showed increased well organized bands of collagen, more fibroblasts and few inflammatory cells when compared with the controls which showed inflammatory cells, scanty collagen fibres and fibroblasts.

Protein glycation inhibitory activity

Ethanol extract of the plant tissues was evaluated *in-vitro* for protein glycation inhibitory activity using the model system of bovine serum albumin and glucose. The extract and its components showed significant effect on protein damage induced by a free radical generator in *in-vitro* assay system. It was found that the alcoholic extract, lawsone and gallic acid showed significant inhibition of Advanced Glycated End Products (AGEs) formation and exhibit 77.95%, 79.10% and 66.98 % inhibition at a concentration of 1500 μg/mL, 1000 μg/mL and 1000μM respectively. L. inermis, compounds 1 and 2 were found to be glycation inhibitors with IC50 82.06 ± 0.13μg/mL, 67.42 ± 1.46μM and 401.7 ± 6.23μM respectively.

Safety Evaluation

Most of the toxicological studies report that toxic effects due to the use of herbal medicine are associated with hepatotoxicity. Other toxic effects of the kidney, nervous system, blood and cardiovascular system, as well as mutagenecity and carcinogenicity have also been published in medical journals. Therefore, numerous advance biological experimental techniques have been used as standard safety test prior to the efficacy study. From the literature it has been noted that *L. inermis* L. exhibited significant hepatoprotective, antioxidant, antiinflammatory, antibacterial, analgesic and adaptogenic effects indicating that it is a safe substance to be used as a drug ordinarily.

DISCUSSION

Medicinal plants have provided copious leads to combat diseases, from the dawn of civilization. The extensive survey of literature revealed that *L. inermis* L. is highly regarded as a universal panacea in the herbal medicine with diverse pharmacological activity spectrum. This versatile medicinal plant is the unique source of various types of chemical compounds, which are responsible of the various activities of the plant. Hence extensive investigation is needed to exploit their therapeutic utility to combat diseases. A drug development programme should be undertaken to develop modern drugs with the compounds isolated from henna. Although crude extracts from leaves of plant have medicinal applications from time immemorial, modern drugs can be developed after extensive investigation of its bioactivity, mechanism of action, pharmacotherapeutics and toxicity after proper standardization and clinical trials. As the global scenario is now changing towards the use of non-toxic plant products having traditional medicinal use, development of modern drugs from *L. inermis* should be emphasized for the control of various diseases. Henna imbibing a tremendous potential deserves a special attention of the scientific fraternity to emerge as a milestone for medical science of this millennium due to its various medicinal uses. Further evaluation needs to be carried out on *L. inermis* L. in order to explore the concealed areas and their practical clinical applications, which can be used for the welfare of the mankind.

3

Determination of Lawsone Content in Fresh and Dried Leaves of *Lawsonia inermis*

Lawsonia inermis Linn (Lythraceae), most commonly known as 'henna' invites attention of the investigators worldwide for its pharmacological profile ranging from anti-inflammatory to anti-cancer activities. *L. inermis* is a much branched shrub that grows mainly in middle east of Africa. The leaves of *L.inermis* having the highest yield of lawsone are confined to India, mainly in Punjab and Gujrat and to a small extent in Rajasthan and Madhya Pradesh. The principal colouring substance of henna is a red-orange colored molecule (lawsone, 2-hydroxy-1, 4 napthaquinone) having molecular formula, $C_{10}H_6O_3$ and melting point of 190°C, present in dried leaves in a concentration of 1-1.4% w/w. Lawsone is chiefly responsible for the colorant property of henna leaves. Lawsone is available as yellow to mustard coloured powder which is practically insoluble in water at 0.2%, soluble in 95% ethanol at 0.5%, soluble in methanol at 1%. Lawsone is proposed to be used as a non-oxidising hair colouring agent at a maximum concentration of 1.5% (typical concentration 1.26%) in the finished cosmetic product. The process which is mainly used for the extraction of lawsone from leaves of henna has been patented. *Upadhyay et al* in, confirmed that the quantitative estimation of leaves of *L.inermis* collected in different seasons showed variations in the active ingredient (lawsone). The leaves obtained in march seasoncontain less lawsone content in comparison to october – november season leaves of *L.inermis*.

Henna is not a sacred plant as such, but it is supposed to symbolize prosperity, fertility and happiness. It is widely used in a variety of religious and social ceremonies in India. The leaves of *L.inermis* have bitter bad taste and used in vulnerary, diuretic, headache, hemicranias, lumbago, bronchitis, boils, ophthalmia, syphilitis, sores, amenorrhoea, scabies and spleen diseases and also favours hair growth. In the present study, the content of lawsone in fresh and dried leaves of *L.inermis* was detected and the measurement containing high content of lawsone was proceeded for further investigation by making hydro-alcoholic extract of the chosen plant part since hydroalcoholic extract is known to haul out a variety of chemical constituents (both polar and non-polar). Therefore, it was considered that most of the active components including lawsone has been extracted out in the hydroalcoholic extract. The test extract was further screened for quantitative estimation of lawsone content using high performance thin layer chromatography.

MATERIALS AND METHODS

Synthetic lawsone was purchased from Yucca enterprises, Mumbai, India. All the chemicals used were of analytical grade.

Collection and Authentication of Plant Material

Fresh leaves of *L.inermis* were collected from botanical garden of Maharshi Dayanand University, Rohtak and authenticated by Dr. H. B. Singh, Scientist F & Head, Raw Materials Herbarium & Museum, National Institute of Science Communication and Information Resources (NISCAIR) New Delhi, India (voucher specimen no: NISCAIR/RHMD/Consult/-2011-12/1990/290).

Fig. 3.1: Fresh leaves of *L. Inermis*

Fig. 3.2: Dried leaves of *L. inermis*

Quantitative Estimation of Lawsone in Fresh and Dried Leaves of *L.inermis*

Quantitative estimation of lawsone in fresh and dried leaves was carried out using spectrophotometric method in which 100 mg powdered leaves of *L. inermis* were soaked in 10 ml methanol for 2 h. Thereafter, the mixture was centrifuged at 5000 rpm for 20 min and the clear supernatant was separated out into a test tube. The absorbance of supernatant was read out at 452 nm. A calibration curve was prepared by plotting the concentration versus absorbance at the same wavelength in the concentration range 10-200 µg/ml of pure lawsone. The lawsone content in fresh and dried leaves was then calculated in µg/ml. All the observations were taken in triplicate.

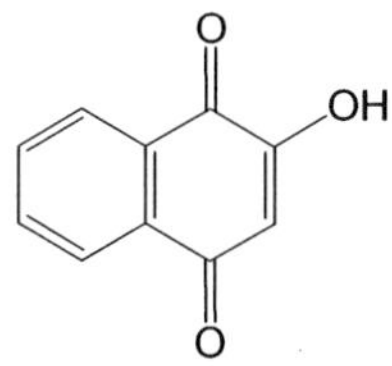

Fig. 3.3: Structure of lawsone

More lawsone as compared to fresh leaves. The absorbance of fresh and dried leaves was found to be 0.549 and 0.688 respectively. From the standard plot of lawsone (Figure 3.3), it was determined that dried leaves of *L.inermis* had more lawsone as compared to the fresh leaves.

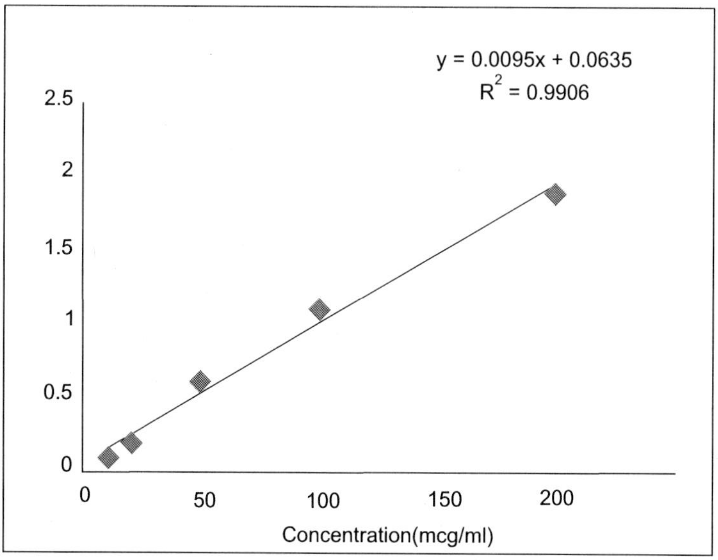

Fig. 3.4: Standard plot of lawsone by UV

The naphthaquinone fraction of hydroalcoholic extract of the leaves of *L. inermis* was characterized using HPTLC. The chromatograms were developed using toluene: ethyl acetate: formic acid (5.5: 4.0: 0.5) as solvent system at 254 nm and 366 nm and were compared with the chromatograms developed by pure lawsone. The chromatogram of hydroalcoholic extract of leaves of *L. inermis* showed the presence of 4.56 mcg/ml lawsone.

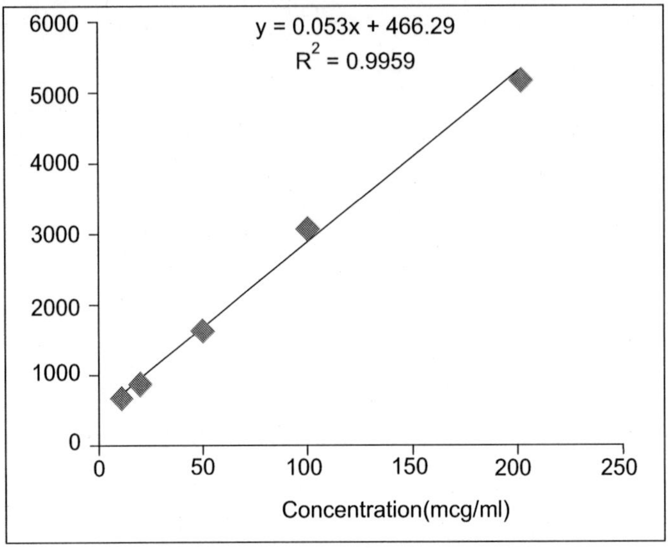

Fig. 3.4: Standard plot of lawsone by HPTLC

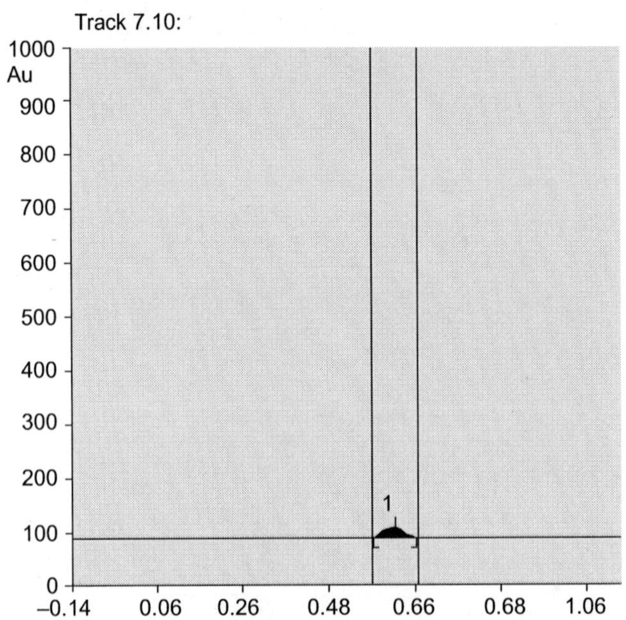

Fig. 3.5(a): Chromatogram of extract of leaves of *L. Inermis* (showing the presence of lawsone)

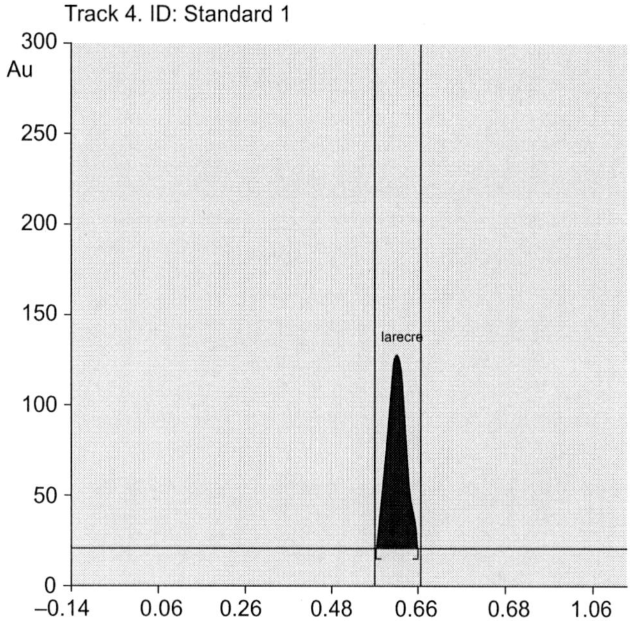

Fig. 3.5(b): Chromatogram of pure lawsone

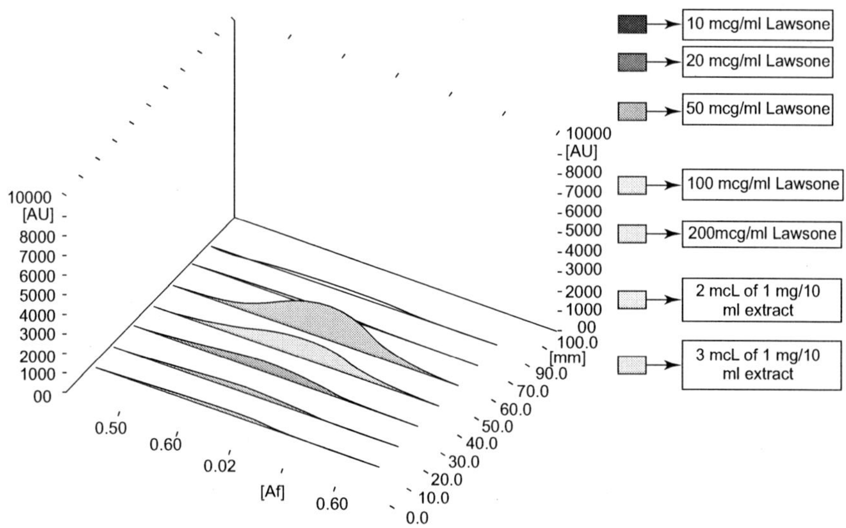

Fig. 3.6: Chromatogram of pure lawsone and hydroalcoholic extract of *L. inermis* at 254 nm.

Lawsone, the main component of *L.inermis,* is not only a colouring agent but also possess diverse assortment of activities. In the present study, quantitative analysis of lawsone was carried out using fresh and dried leaves of *L.inermis.* Before going for the extraction of leaves of *L.inermis,* there was bewilderment whether to use fresh or dried leaves. To some extent, this perplexity can be cleared with the help of spectrophotometric analysis. The value for the concentration of lawsone (in mcg/ml) in fresh and dried leaves was calculated and found to be 5.3 mcg/ml and 6.9 mcg/ml for fresh and dried leaves respectively. On the basis of these findings, the dried leaves had more lawsone content as compared to fresh leaves. Further we also prepared the hydro alcoholic extract of leaves of *L.inermis* and phytochemical investigation of prepared extract showed the presence of carbohydrates, gums and mucilage, tannins and phenolic compounds, flavonoids, steroids and sterols. The hydroalcoholic extract of dried leaves of *L.inermis* was screened for quantitative analysis using HPTLC and its content was found to be 4.56 mcg/ml.

CONCLUSION

Henna finds applications in the treatment of a variety of disorders like vulnerary, diuretic, headache, hemicranias, lumbago, bronchitis, boils, ophthalmia, syphilitis, sores, amenorrhoea, scabies and spleen diseases. The key role behind its therapeutic efficacy is being played by its active constituent, lawsone, which can be further explored by incorporating this compound into novel dosage forms. The studies are further going on to make lawsone an efficient and potent drug molecule by complexing it with suitable legands. Therefore, efforts must be put forward to identify novel, natural and safe legands that may positively interact and synergistically affect the therapeutic efficacy of lawsone.

4 Anthelmintic Activity of *Lawsonia inermis* L.

Helminthiasis or infections with parasitic worms are pathogenic for human beings. Immature forms of the parasites invade human beings via the skin or gastrointestinal tract (GIT) and evolve into well differentiated adult worms that have characteristic tissue distribution. Anthelminthics are the drugs that may act locally to expel worms from the GIT or systemically to eradicate adult helminthes or development forms that invade organs and tissues. Most of the existing anthelminthics produces side effects such as abdominal pain, loss of appetite, nausea, vomiting, head ache and diarrhoea. Chemotherapy is the only treatment and effective tool to cure and control helminth infection, as effective vaccines against helminths have not been developed so far. Indiscriminate use of synthetic anthelmintics can lead to resistance of parasites. Herbal drugs have been in use since ancient times for the treatment of parasitic diseases in human and could be of value in preventing the development of resistance4. *Lawsonia inermis L.commonly* known as Henna or Mehandi and abundantly available in tropical and subtropical areas. Ancient history of India describes its diverse uses and also plays appreciable role in Ayurvedic or natural herbal medicines. The plant has been reported to have analgesic, hypoglycemic, hepatoprotective, immunostimulant, anti-inflammatory, antibacterial, antimicrobial, antifungal, antiviral, antiparasitic, ntitrypanosomal, antidermatophytic, antioxidant, antifertility, tuberculostatic and anticancer properties. It is now considered as a valuable source of unique natural products for development of medicines against various diseases and also for the development of industrial products.

Traditionally, *Lawsonia inermis L.claim* as anthelmintic but scientifically it is not reveled still thus the present study was design to evaluate the in-vitro anthelmintic activity of *petroleum ether extract* of *Lawsonia inermis L.leaves.*

MATERIAL AND METHOD

Plant: The fresh leaves of *Lawsonia inermis L.*were collected in the month of October 2010 from its natural habitat at Hadgaon in Nanded region, Maharashtra, India.

Experimental Animals

All the experiments were carried out in Indian adult earthworms (*Pheretima posthumad*) collected from moist soil and washed with normal saline to remove all fecal matter were used for anthelmintic activity due to its anatomical and physiological resemblance with the intestinal roundworm parasite *Ascaris lumbricoids,* of human beings.Because of easy availability, earthworms have been used widely for the initial evaluation of anthelmintic compounds in *vitro.*

Material: Petroleum ether extracts of *Lawsonia inermis L.* leaves, Piperazine citrate (GSK. Ltd, Mumbai).

Preparation of Extracts of *Lawsonia inermis L.*leaves

The collected leaves of *Lawsonia inermis L.were* dried under shade and undergone crushing in electric blender to form powdered and subjected to extraction by using maceration. The percent yield of *petroleum ether extract* was 20.8% w/w. The extracts were concentrated by evaporation at room temperature and used for pharmacological studies.

Administration of Extract

The suspension of *petroleum ether extract* of *Lawsonia inermis L.* different concentrations (25-75 mg/ml) were prepared by using 0.2% v/v of Tween 20 as a suspending agent and final volume was made to 10 ml for respective concentration of *Lawsonia inermis L.* leaves. Five groups of approximately equal size worms consisting of six earthworms individually in each group were released into 10 ml of desired concentration of drug and extracts.

Administration of Piperazine Citrate

Piperazine citrate (15 mg/ml) was used prepared by using 0.2% v/v of Tween 20 as a suspending agent.

Experimental Design

Indian adult earthworms (*Pheretima posthumad*) collected from moist soil and washed with normal saline to remove all fecal matter were used for anthelmintic activity.

Different concentration (25-75 mg/ml) of *Lawsonis inermis petroleum ether extract* were prepared by using 0.2% v/v of Tween 20 as a suspending agent and final volume was made to 10 ml for respective concentration of *Lawsonis inermis.* A Piperazine citrate (15 mg/ml) was used as standard. The anthelmintic assay was carried out as per the method of with minor modification. The animals were divided into ten y group containing six earthworms each different concentration of extracts and standard drug solution were poured in different Petri dishesh. Observations were made for the time taken for paralysis (Paralysis was said to occur when worm did not revive in normal saline) and death (Time for death of worms was recorded after ascertaining that worms neither moved when shaken vigorously nor when shaken vigorously nor when dipped in warm water (50°C), followed with their body colors fading away).

All the results were expressed as Mean ± S.E.M. of six animals in each group. Statistical analysis were performed by one way analysis of variance (ANOVA) followed by student's t test. At 95% confidence interval, p values < 0.001 were considered significant.

Anthelmintic Effect of *Lawsonia inermis L.leaves* in Indian Adult Earthworms (*Pheretima posthumad*)

For evaluation of anthelmintic activity *Lawsonia inermis L.leaves*, group I and II received normal saline and standard Piperazine citrate while group III, IV and V received different concentration of petroleum *ether extract* of *Lawsonia inermis L.leaves* respectively.

RESULT AND DISCUSSION

From the observation made in the Table 4.1, the *petroleum ether extract* of *Lawsonia inermis L.leaves* was found to show anthelmintic activity when compared to standard drug. *Petroleum ether extract* of *Lawsonia inermis L.* leaves of concentration 25, 50 and 75 mg/ml showed paralysis at 62.57, 54.13 and 30.86 min and death found to 185.20, 143.88 and 124.68 min respectively. *Petroleum ether extract* of *Lawsonia inermis L.*showed paralysis of earthworm at 30.86 min at highest permissible dose (75 mg/ml) which was comparable to standard Piperazine citrate (Table 4.1) From the above result, it is clear that petroleum ether extract of *Lawsonia inermis L.leaves* have significant anthelmintic activity in dose dependent manner when compared with standard anthelmintic drug. It can be concluded that the active constituents responsible for anthelmintic activity present in the *petroleum ether extract* of. *Lawsonia inermis L.leaves*. Further study need to isolate and revealed the active compound contained in the crude extract of *Lawsonia inermis L. and* to establish mechanism(s) of action are required.

CONCLUSION

From the results it conclude that, *petroleum ether extract*s of *Lawsonia inermis L. demonstrate* to possess dose dependant anthelmintic activity when compared to Piperazine citrate. From results, *Lawsonia inermis L.* as an anthelmintic have been confirm as a it displayed activity against the worm used in present study. The potency was found to be inversely proportional to the time taken for paralysis and time of death of the worms. The possible mechanism of the anthelminthics activity of *Lawsonia inermis L.cannot* be explained on the basis of our present results. However, it may be due to its effect on inhibition of glucose uptake in the parasites and depletion of its glycogen synthesis. *Lawsonia inermis L.may* also have activated nicotinic cholinergic receptor in the worms resulting in either persistent depolarization or hyperpolarisation.

The potency was found to be inversely proportional to the time taken for paralysis and time of death of the worms.

Table 4.1: Anthelmintic Potency of *Lawsonia inermis L.leaves*.

Treatment	Group	Concentration (mg/ml)	Time of paralysis (min) (Mean ± S.E.M)	Time of paralysis (min) (Mean ± S.E.M)
Normal Saline (Control)	I	–	–	–
Piperazine citrate	II	15	24.18 ± 0.70	78.21 ± 0.23
Petroleum ether extract of Lawsonia inermis	III	250	62.57 ± 0.63***	185.20 ± 1.41***
	IV	500	54.13 ± 0.63***	143.88 ± 0.68***
	V	750	30.86 ± 0.51***	124.68 ± 1.32***

All values represent Mean ± SEM; n=6 in each group. Values are significantly different from reference standard (Piperazine citrate)

***p<0.001. This activity was Concentration dependent.

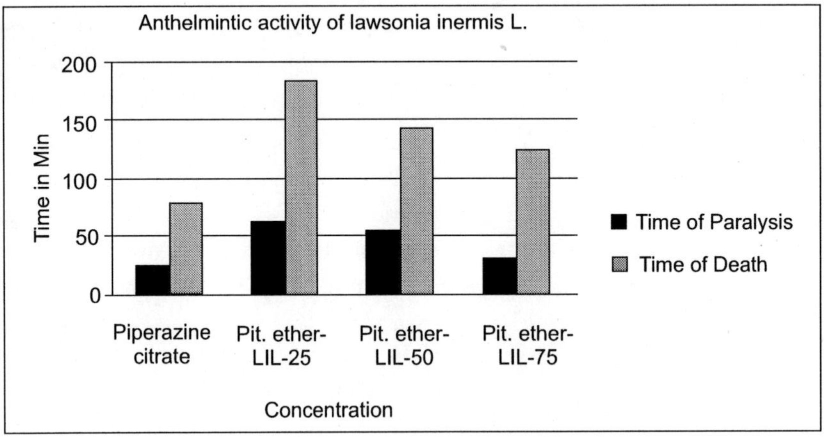

Fig. 4.1: Anthelminthic activity of *Lawsonia inermis*

Pet. ether LIL-Petroleum ether extract of *Lawsonis inermis L.* leaves

5

Antibacterial Activity and Flavonoid Contents of *Lawsonia inermis* (Henna)

Plants are used as medicines since time immemorial. India has a rich heritage of using medicinal plants in traditional medicines such as Ayurveda, Siddha and Unani besides folklore practices. *Lawsonia inermis* syn. *Lawsonia alba* (Henna) is a sole species in the genus in the family Lythraceae. Henna has been found to exhibit Antibacterial, Antifungal and Dermatological properties. It is useful in coloring of skin, scalp and nails etc. Henna has also shown antidiarrhoel, diuretic, emmanagogue and abortifacient prophetically and is found to be practically non-toxic. Alcoholic extract of shade dried leaves of *Lawsonia inermis* intraperitonially injected to rats showed anti-inflammatory activity comparable to that of hydrocortisone. Chloroform extract of leaves exhibit promising antibacterial activity against *Shigella* and *vibrio cholera* Astringent properties. No antifungal activity was detected for henna aqueous solutions]. Out of 24 plant products evaluated their antibacterial activity against six potato pathogenic bacteria, 18 products exhibited antibacterial activity. Gallic acid as found to be the most potent antibacterial agent followed by lawsone. Many plants derived from nature possess antimicrobial and insecticidal activities. The interest in these plants is increasing because of finding safer microbicides in combination with the need of preventing environmental degradation. For centuries preparations containing flavonoids as the principal physiologically active constituents have been used to treat Human Diseases. Increasingly, this class of natural products is becoming the subject of anti-infective research and many groups have isolated and identified the structures of flavonoids possessing antimicrobial and cytotoxic activities.

Henna has been used to treat skin infections such as tinea and it is known to have antibacterial properties which have been attributed to naphthoquinones, including lawsone Reports of activity in the field of antibacterial flavonoid research are widely conflicting, probably owing to their inter and intra assay variation in susceptibility testing. However, several high quality investigations have examined the relationship between flavonoid structure and antibacterial activity and these are in close agreement. Most of the medicinal plants have identified and used for treatment of human diseases are well documented.

MATERIALS AND METHODS

Maintenance of Isolates

A standard MTCC strains belonging to five different species of gram positive cocci and gram negative bacilli were maintained on Brain Heart Infusion Agar (BHA-Himedia).

Preparation of Crude Extract

The powdered plant materials (10 gms) were extracted with 100 ml of methanol for 1 hr on an ultrasonic bath. The extract was filtered the filtrate was evaporated in vacuum at 45°C and then lyophilized. The extracts were prepared according to the polarity.

Preliminary Phytochemical Screening

The preliminary phytochemical screening of *Lawsonia inermis* was carried out for the decotion of various Phyto-constituents using standard procedure. The following solvents were used for the study, petroleum ether, chloroform, ethyl acetate, methanol, ethanol and water. The methanolic extract was found to contain more flavonoids. The preliminary phytochemical screening of methanolic extract reveals the presence of alkaloids, flavonoids, tannins and quinones.

Chemicals

Ampicillin (10 μg/ml) discs, Molten Mueller Hinton (MH) Agar and Nutrient agar medium were obtained from Hi-media laboratories, Mumbai. All other chemicals were of analytical grade and obtained locally.

Test Microorganisms

The bacteria used for antibacterial study were *Staphylococcus aureus* (MTCC 087), *Escherichia coli* (MTCC 729), *Klebsiella pneumoniae* (MTCC 432), *Pseudomonas aeruginosa* (MTCC 1688) & *Proteus mirablis* (MTCC 425).

Total Flavonoids Determination

Aluminum chloride colorimetric method was used for flavonoids determination Each plant extract (0.5 ml of 1:10 g/ml) in methanol were separately mixed with 1.5 ml of methanol, 0.1 ml of 10% Aluminium chloride, 0.1 ml of 1 M potassium acetate and 2.8 ml of distilled water. It remained at room temperature for 30 minutes. The absorbance of the reaction mixture was measured at 415 nm.The calibration curve was prepared by preparing quercetin solutions at concentrations 12.5 to 100 μg/ml in methanol.

Antibacterial Study (Plate Hole Diffusion Method)

The plate hole diffusion assay was used to determine the growth inhibition of bacteria by plant extracts.

Bacteria were maintained at 4°C on nutrient agar plates before us Nutrient agar was prepared and 25 ml of each was poured in to sterile universals. The universals with the broth were inoculated with different species of bacterias and incubated at 37°C overnight. A total of 25 ml of molten Muller Hinton (MH) agar (Himedia) held at 40°C was poured in to sterile universals maintained at 40°C in a water bath Each universal was inoculated with 0.2 ml of different bacterial species mixed well, transferred in to sterile Petri dishes and allows to set. Using a sterile corkborer 6 mm diameter, four holes per plate were made in to the set agar containing the bacterial culture. A total of 0.2 ml of plant extracts were poured in to the wells and one containing distilled water, the plates were kept in incubator overnight and the zone diameter was then recorded if greater than 6 mm.

Screening of Antibacterial Activity (*Lawsonia inermis*)

The methanolic extract of *Lawsonia inermis* leaves for antibacterial screening. The results of the total flavonoid constituent and study was 25.05 ± 0.18 respectively (Table 5.1). The Five bacterias were used for antibacterial screening. Various concentrations of methanolic extract were used (1000 μg/ml, 500 μg/ml, 250 μg/ml, and 62.5 μg/ml) to test the antibacterial activity. From the results of antibacterial screening, 7.2% of methanolic extract were active in the lowest tested concentration of 62.5 μg/ml, 5% active in a concentration of 250 μg/ml, 75.7% active in a concentration of 500 μg/ml, and 92.8% active in a concentration of 1000 μg/ml. Ampicillin (10 μg) was used as standard drug.

Preliminary Phytochemical Screening

The preliminary phytochemical screening reveals the presence of Flavonoids Alkaloids, Tannins and quinones. The results were shown in Table 5.1 and 5.2.

Table 5.1: Flavonoid Contents in Lawsonia Inermis

Plant Name	Flavonoids
Lawsonia inermis	25.05 ± 0.18

Table 5.2: Qualitative Test

	Lawsonia inermis
Alkaloids	+
Quinones	+
Tannins	+
Flavonoids	+

+ Present; – Absent

DISCUSSION

The present study was conducted to study the *in vitro* antibacterial activity of *Lawsonia inermis* used by Indian peoples to show that therapeutic properties. The antibacterial activity was expressed at varying degrees with the activity being both strain and dose dependent.Five bacterias were used for antibacterial studies.

Table 5.3: Antibacterial Study of Methanolic Extract of *Lawsonia inermis*

Bacteria	Zone diameter (mm)*					
	1000 µg/ml	500 µg/ ml	250 µg/ml	125 µg/ml	62.5 µg/ml	Ampicillin 10 µg/ml
Staphylococcus aureus (MTCC 087)	24	18	13	9	9	28
Escherichia coli (MTCC 729)	22	20	12	8	0	24
Klebsiella pneumoniae (MTCC 432)	18	14	9	6	0	24
Pseudomonas aeruginosa (MTCC 1688)	17	14	12	6	0	22
Proteus mirablis (MTCC 425).	23	18	10	6	0	24

Medicinal plants are being used by large proportion of Indian population. The reasons for this include (*a*) True improvement of diseases conditions after herbal treatment, (*b*) Harmful side effects and high cost of the other forms of treatment. In the present study, the results were encouraging, as the *Lawsonia inermis* appeared to contain substances that had antimicrobial properties because of, the methanolic extract of *Lawsonia inermis* leaves were active against five different bacteria's. Five concentrations of the extract were used (1000 µg/ml, 500 µg/ml, 250 µg/ml, 125 µg/ml and 62.5 µg/ml). It is estimated that if an inhibition is obtained by 250 µg/ml-1000 µg/ml) of test solution, the extract can be considered worthy for further investigations. Plants showing significant activity may be due to the presence of alkaloids, flavonoids, tannins and quinones. Among the various microorganisms, the methanolic extract of *Lawsonia inermis* was more active against *Staphylococcus aureus*.

6 Antimicrobial Activity of *Lawsonia inermis* Leaf Extracts

Medicinal plants are potential renewable natural resources and are generally considered to play a beneficial role in human health care. Since the dawn of civilization, medicinal plants are known as nature s best gift to cure a number of diseases of men and animals. There about 121 clinically useful prescription drugs that is worldwide derived from higher plants. About 70 percent of them came to the attention of pharmaceutical houses because of their use in traditional medicine.

In the past, medicinal plants were used intensively in folkloric medicine for treatment of various disorders. Today, it is estimated that about 80 % of people in developing countries rely on traditional medicines for their primary health care. Traditional medicines are becoming popular, due to high toxicity and adverse effects of orthodox medicament. This has led to sudden increase in the number of herbal industries in the drug market. Several plant species are used by various indigenous systems such as Siddha, Ayurveda, Unani and Allopathy for the treatment of different ailments. This review emphasizes the traditional uses and biological properties of *Lawsonia inermis*.

Lawsonia inermis (Lythraceae) is a perennial plant commonly called as henna, having different vernacular names in India viz., Mehndi in Hindi, Mendika, Rakigarbha in Sanskrit, Mailanchi in. It Malayalam, Muruthani in Tamil, Benjati in Oriya, Mayilanchi in kannada and Mehedi in Bengali [is native to North Africa and South East Asia, and often cultivated as an ornamental plant throughout India, Persia, and along the African coast of the Mediterranean sea. Henna grows better in tropical savannah and tropical arid zones, in latitude between 15° and 25° N and S, produces highest dye content in between temperature 35 to 45°C. The optimal soil temperature ranges for germination are 25 to 30°C.

Henna leaves are very popular natural dye to color hand, finger, nails and hair. The dye molecule, Lawson is the chief constituents of the plant; its highest concentration is detected in the petioles (0.5-1.5%). In folk medicines, henna has been used as astringent, antihemorrhagic, intestinal antineoplastic, cardio-inhibitory, hypotensive, sedative and also as therapeutic against amoebiasis, headache, jaundice and leprosy.

India is one of the pioneers in the development and well documented indigenous systems at medicine, namely Ayurveda, Siddha and Unani. For millennia, the India population has depended upon mostly plant based crude drugs for the treatment of variety of human ailments. India has about 18, 000 species of angiosperms, of with about 2,500 species are considered as important source of medicinal and aromatic chemical components. In modern medicine also, plants occupy a very significant place as raw material for some important drugs although synthetic drugs and antibiotics brought about a revolution into controlling different disease. But these synthetic drugs are out of reach to millions of people. Traditional medicines are used by about 60 percent of the world s population. These are not only used for primary health care not just in rural areas in developing countries, but also in developed countries as well as modern medicinal plants, minerals, and organic matter, the herbal drugs are prepared from medicinal plants only.

The main interest in plants because of their medicinally and pharmacologically important active ingredients rapidly. Medicinal plant products have been studied extensively and their role in several useful biological activities, such as antibacterial, antifungal, insecticides and herbicides have been well documented number of plant products with the useful bioactive properties is increasing rapidly as on outcome of several on going research programs on investigation of biological activities of a number of plants. These bioactive compounds have several as lead molecules for the development of many synthetic antibiotics. Hence, the present study was undertaken with the preparation of different solvents extracts of *Lawsonia inermis* and determination of antimicrobial activity of its leaf extracts by disc diffusion and well diffusion method.

MATERIALS AND METHODS

Sample Collection

Wound sample (specimen) was collected with the help of specialist using sterile swabs. The swabs were immediately immersed into normal saline and transported to the laboratory. The specimen should be collected before any antimicrobial agents were administrated. Isolation and identification of pathogens The swabs were immediately inoculated on Mecconkey agar, Mannitol salt agar, Kings B medium which were incubated at 37 °C for 18-24 hrs.

Collection of Plant Material

The plant materials used for this study were collected from the rural area of Mahathevappatanam, Thiruvarur District, Tamil Nadu, South India.

Plant Extract Preparation

The shade dried plant materials were pulverized into coarse powder and extracted in soxhelt apparatus using methanol, ethanol and aqueous extracts were also prepared. The collected methanol, ethanol and aqueous extracts were concentrated under vacuum (500C) dried and weighed for methanol,

ethanol and aqueous extracts taken at different concentration 25%, 50%, 70% and 100% against test pathogens.

ANTIBACTERIAL ACTIVITY

Disc Diffusion Method

Antibacterial activity of the extracts was tested by Disc-diffusion method. 0.2 ml bacterial cultures (4 hrs) were uniformly spread on solidified nutrient agar medium. The filter paper discs prepared with plant extracts were carefully placed over the spreaded cultures by using sterile needle and incubated at 370 C for 24 hrs. After the incubation period, the plates were examined for inhibitory zones (including the diameter of the disc).

Well Diffusion Technique

24 hrs old bacterial cultures were used for well diffusion method. One well of 5 mm size will be made in the help of sterile cork borer under aseptic condition in laminar air flow chamber. The wells were loaded with different concentration such as 25%, 50%, 75%, and 100% of the leaf extracts (5g in 100 ml of solvent). The plates were incubated at 370C for 24 hours. The plates were observed after 24 hrs for clearing zone around the well. The zone of inhibition was calculated by measuring the diameter of the inhibition zone around the well. The reading were taken in all the replicates the average values were tabulated.

Antifungal Activity

Disc Diffusion method Potato-Dextrose Agar medium was prepared and transferred to sterile petri dishes and allowed to solidify. A suspension of identified three fungal spp was added to media and swabs the entire surface of the agar medium separately. The inoculums were equally distributed in surface of the media by rotating the plate. Sterile 5 mm disc in diameter dipped in solutions of the various solvent ethanol, methanol and aqueous plant extracts. The plates were left for 1 hour at room temperature as a period of pre incubation diffusion to minimize the effects of variation in time between the applications of the different solutions. Then the plates were incubated at 240C for 2-3 days and observed for antimicrobial activity. The diameters of the zone of inhibition was calculated and compared with the standards.

Well Diffusion Technique

The fungal culture used for well diffusion method. The Sabouraud agar plates were prepared and the fungal spores were spreaded on the Sabouraud agar plates. One well of 5 mm, size made in the agar plates with the help of sterile cork borer under aseptic condition in laminar air flow chamber. The well were loaded with 0.2 ml of leaf extracts. The plates were incubated at 280C for 48 hrs. The plate was observed after 48 hrs for clearing zone around the well. The zone of inhibition was calculated by measuring the diameter of the inhibition zone around the well.

Statistical Analysis

Random sampling was used for the entire test. The data of all the parameters were statistically analyzed and expressed as

Mean + SD by using the formula given by

$$\text{Mean } (x) = \frac{\Sigma x}{N}$$

Where,

X = Sum of all values of variable

N = Number of observation

$$\text{Standard Deviation} = \frac{\sqrt[2]{\Sigma(x - x)}}{N}$$

Where,

(X-X)2 = The sum of the square of the deviation of each value from the mean.

N = Number of observation.

RESULTS AND DISCUSSION

In the previous studies has been found to be a best solvent for extraction of the active ingredient (asarone) from leaves. Though, solvents such as methnol, ethanol and aqueous used the most of the previous studies studies were also found to be suitable for extracrtion of active ingredients. It is well established that the - asarones found in leaf, roots and rhizomes tissues are responsible for almost all of the antimicrobial activities of the *Lawsonia inermis*.

The ethanol and water extract of the back of *Lawsonia inermis* showed antimicrobial activity against gram positive and gram negative bacteria Diacyl heptenoid and its Fyrosdia crosyenin were identified at the constituent responsible for this activity. In this work, aqueous extracts of *Lawsonia inermis* inhibits the skin pathogens S.aureus, S.mutans and P.aeruginosa potentially at 100% concentration. This extracts control the bacteria and fungal pathogen which cause skin disease.

The antibacterial activity may be attributed to not only a single active principle but to a cocktain of a variety of active principles or alkaloid.

Several recent papers reported that the presences of antibacterial activity are due to flavonoides. Alkaloids are important defence of the plats against pathogenic organisms and herbivores. It also toxin for insects which further modify the alkaloids and incorporate them into their own defense secretion.

The present study has been under taken to find out the effectiveness of the different extracts of *Lawsonia inermis* leaves gainst some human bacterial and fungal pathogens.

Isolation of Organisms

Nutrient agar and PDA plates were prepared. Then the wound samples were inoculated in to the agar plates. The bacterial colonies were identified by gram s staining and biochemical test where as fungi by lactophenol cotton blue mounting technique.

Antimicrobial Activity

The antimicrobial potency of *Lawsonia inermis* leaf extracts were tested against some human pathogenic bacteria and fungi was quantitatively assessed for the presence or absence of zone of inhibition. The results relative to antibacterial activity was observed by measuring the diameter of the zone of inhibition.

Antibacterial Activity of *Lawsonia inermis* by Disc Diffusion Method

The activity of methanol extracts of *Lawsonia inermis* leaves against Staphylococcus aureus showed minimum activity (2.3±2.01 mm) at 25% concentration and maximum activity (9.3±8.9 mm) at 100% level. The activity of methanol extracts of *Lawsonia inermis* against Streptococcus mutans showed minimum activity (2.3±1.516 mm) at 25% followed by 50% (3.6±3.23 mm), 75% (5±5.12 mm) and 100% 17±16.04 mm). The activity of methanol extracts of *Lawsonia inermis* against pseudomonas aeruginosa, showed maximum activity was obtained at 75% (4.6±3.16 mm) followed by 100% (3.3±2.16 mm), 50% (2.8±2.4 mm) and 25% (2.6±2.1 mm). The ethanol extracts of *Lawsonia inermis* leaves against Staphylococcus aureus showed minimum activity (3.1±3.21 mm) at 25% concentration and maximum activity (8.1±6.2 mm) at 100% level. The ethanol extracts of *Lawsonia inermis* leaves Streptococcus mutans showed minimum activity (2.0±4.31 mm) at 25 % concentration maximum activity (9.1±5.1 mm) at 100%. The ethanol extracts of *Lawsonia inermis* leaves against pseudomonas aeruginosa showed minimum activity (9.1±8.61 mm) an 25% concentration and maximum activity (7.6±6.41 mm) at 100%. There was no activity showed by aqueous extracts of *Lawsonia inermis* against Staphylococcus aureus, Streptococcus mutans, and Psseudomonas aeruginosa. The present investigation has been undertaken to find out the effectiveness of the methanol, ethanol and aqueous extracts of *Lawsonia inermis* against some human pathogenic microorganism such as S.aureus, S.mutans, P.aerugenosa, A.niger, A.flavus and Fusarium.

Antifungal Activity of *Lawsonia inermis* By Disc Diffusion Method

The methanol extracts of *Lawsonia inermis* leavesshowed maximum activity at 100% level (2.5±2.3 mm) and minimum activity Value are triplicate and represented as mean ± standard deviation at 25% (0.3±1.1 mm) against A. flavus. The methanol extracts of *Lawsonia inermis* leavesshowed maximum activity at 100% (2.5.0±8.1 mm) minimum activity at 25% (8.3±9.1 mm) against A.niger. For Fusarium also it showed maximum activity of methanol extracts at 100% (4.7±4.4 mm), followed by 25% (1.3±1.8 mm), 50% (2.2±2.1 mm) and

75% (1.3±1.8 mm). The ethanol extracts of *Lawsonia inermis* showed maximum activity at 100% (3.5±1.4 mm) and minimum activity at 25% (2.03±3.03 mm) against A.flavus. Ethanol extracts of *Lawsonia inermis* showed maximum activity at 100% (7.4±6.5 mm) and minimum activity at 50% (3.04±5.5 mm) against A.niger. The ethanol extracts of inermis showed maximum activity at 100% (9.1±8.9 mm) and minimum activity 50% (6.1±9.5 mm) against Fusarium. There was no activity showed by aqueous extracts of *Lawsonia inermis* against Staphylococcus aureus, Streptococcus mutans, and Pseudomonas aeruginosa.

Well Diffusion Method

The same results were obtained by well diffusion method for different against all organisms. Overall results of this study revealed that maximum activity of the leaf extracts of *Lawsonia inermis* was observed at 100% level against both bacteria and fungi. So usage of the extracts at a concentration of 100% might be effective to treat the some human pathogens (Table 6.4). Aspergillus is pathogenic to humans. It causes Aspergillosis. Out of eight species of Aspergillus, Aspergillus niger, fumigates account for most infections.

The antimicrobial activity potency of *Lawsonia inermis* leaves extracts were tested against human pathogenic microorganism and the quantitatively assessed for the presence or absence of zone of inhibition.

The hiumble *Lawsonia inermis* has value in the treatments of acne. The seeds are used, which contain proteins, lecithins, carbohydrates and fats. It is nutritious and anti dermatitis agent. They have been used in cases of acne and on faded, wrinkled skins. In the present study *Lawsonia inermis* leaf extract was studied for their antiseptic and vasodilator activities and antimicrobial activity against skin disease causing pathogens.

In this present study, henna leaves were collected and selected for antimicrobial activity against some human pathogens. Among this study, henna leaves were extracted with methanol, ethanol and aqueous by solvent extraction method. By this study, the pathogens are isolated from soil. The isolated organisms were identified based on cultural, morphological and biochemical characteristics. Hence the isolated bacterial colonies were confirmed as, S.aureus, S.mutans, P.aeruginosa and fungal colonies such as A.niger, A.flaves and Fusarium. By this study, antimicrobial activity was performed by disc diffusion and well diffusion method. The maximum activity was showed in methanol extraction against all isolated human pathogens. In this ethanol extraction, also shows maximum activity (100%). There was no activity in aqueous extract. This result may open important perspectives alternative antimicrobial therapies. In this studies are required to study the effect and toxicity of these compounds in experimental animals (in vivo) and to establish if they could be safety used as antibacterial agent against the pathogens. Thus we concluded that the medicinal plants could be used as drug to treat the infections caused by bacteria and fungi without any side effects.

Table 6.1: Antibacterial Activity of Methanolic Extract of *Lawsonia inermis* (mm)

S.No.	Organisms	Zone of inhibition (mm)			
		25%	50%	75%	100%
1	*S.aureus*	2.3 ± 2.01	2.3 ± 3.0	2.8 ± 2.7	2.5 ± 2.3
2	*S.mutans*	2.3 ± 2.0	2.4 ± 3.1	5.1 ± 4.0	6.6 ± 4.4
3	*P. aeruginosa*	2.6 ± 2.1	2.8 ± 2.4	4.6 ± 3.16	3.3 ± 2.16

Value are triplicate and represented as mean ± standard deviation

Table 6.2: Antibacterial Activity of Ethanol Extracts of *Lawsonia inermis* (mm)

S.No.	Organisms	Zone of inhibition (mm)			
		25%	50%	75%	100%
1	*S.aureus*	3.1 ± 3.21	2.3 ± 3.0	2.8 ± 2.7	8.1 ± 6.2
2	*S.mutans*	2.0 ± 4.31	2.4 ± 3.1	5.1 ± 4.0	9.1 ± 4.1
3	*P. aeruginosa*	2.6 ± 2.1	2.8 ± 2.1	7.6 ± 6.4	9.1 ± 8.61

Table 6.3: Antifungal Activities of Methanolic Extracts of *Lowsonia inermis* (mm)

S.No.	Organisms	Zone of inhibition (mm)			
		25%	50%	75%	100%
1	*A.niger*	0.3 ± 1.1	2.3 ± 3.0	2.8 ± 2.7	2.5 ± 2.3
2	*A.flavus*	8.3 ± 9.1	4.4 ± 3.1	5.1 ± 4.0	2.5 ± 8.1
3	*Fusarium*	2.6 ± 2.1	2.8 ± 2.4	4.6 ± 3.16	4.7 ± 4.4

Values are triplicate and represented as mean ± standard deviation

Table 6.4: Antifungal Activity of Ethanolic Extract of *Lawsonia inermis* (mm)

S.No.	Organisms	Zone of inhibition (mm)			
		25%	50%	75%	100%
1	*A.niger*	3.5 ± 1.4	2.3 ± 3.0	2.8 ± 2.7	2.03 ± 3.03
2	*A.flavus*	8.3 ± 9.1	3.04 ± 5.5	5.1 ± 4.0	7.4 ± 6.5
3	*Fusarium*	2.6 ± 2.1	6.1 ± 9.5	4.6 ± 3.16	9.1 ± 8.9

Values are triplicate and represented as mean ± standard deviation

7

Antioxidant and Immunomodulatory Constituents of Henna Leaves

For centuries, henna leaves were renowned as the most extensively used natural hair dying and tattooing agent in many civilizations and cultures. The word henna which means "to become queen" is indicative of something highly elegant. The plant has got several vernacular names *e.g. Ligusturum egypticum* which is the Latinized English synonym for henna. It arises from the common name for the same plant in England, namely of the Egyptian privet. The plant extract or its purified compounds exhibit a variety of biological activities such as anticomplementary activity, dihydroorotate dehydrogenase inhibitory activity macrophage stimulating activity as a result of stimulation of secretion of GMCSF (granulocyte macrophage colony stimulating factor), antimicrobial activity,anti-sickling activity, hepatoprotective activity, cytotoxic activity, anti-inflammatory, antipyretic, and analgesic activities. In the light of the previous activities, we investigated the compounds responsible for the immunomodulatory effects of henna. In addition, an antioxidant-screening assay was conducted to detect whether a redox mechanism may be involved in the immunomodulatory action of henna.

RESULTS AND DISCUSSION

Seven compounds were isolated adopting the lymphocyte transformation assay (LTA)-guided fractionation of the total methanolic extract of henna (*Lawsonia inermis* L.) leaves. Immunoactive fractions were subjected to further phytochemical investigation. Seven compounds were isolated (Figure 7.1), five from the chloroformic fraction [*p*-coumaric acid (1), lawsone (2), apigenin (3), luteolin (4), and 2-methoxy-3-methyl-1,4- naphthoquinone (5) as well as two compounds from the ethyl acetate fraction [cosmosiin (6) and apiin (7)]. The LTA assay was adapted as a test for cell-mediated immunity. The cell-mediated immune response was determined in the peripheral blood lymphocytes (PBL) in response to mitogenic stimulation using either phytohaemagglutinin (PHA) or concanavalin A (Con A) as mitogens that stimulate human T- and B-cells but T-cells more vigorously. The Lymphocyte transformation (mitogenesis) assay studies a specific immune response *i.e.* it studies the mitogenic effect of the crude drug on T-lymphocyte proliferation. Initiation of T-lymphocyte proliferative responses means immunostimulation, whereas suppression of T-lymphocyte proliferative activities is indicative of immunosuppression. The results of the LTA expressed in terms of the lymphocyte transformation

Fig. 7.1: Compounds Isolated Through Bioassay-guided Fractionation of Henna (*Lawsoniainermis* L.) Leaves; *p*-coumaric Acid

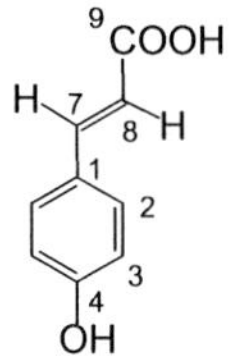

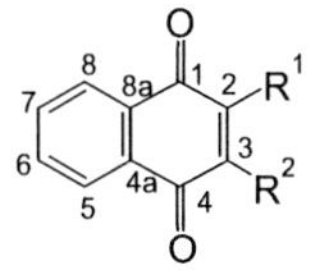

	R^1	R^2
2	OH	H
5	OCH_3	CH_3

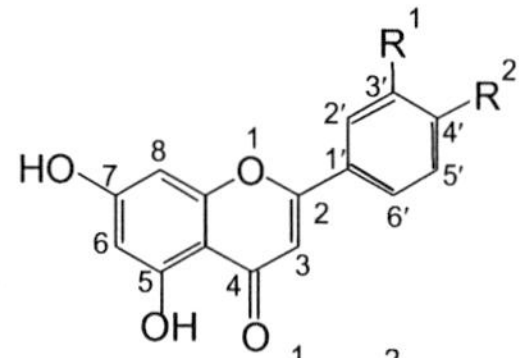

	R^1	R^2
3	H	OH
	OH	OH

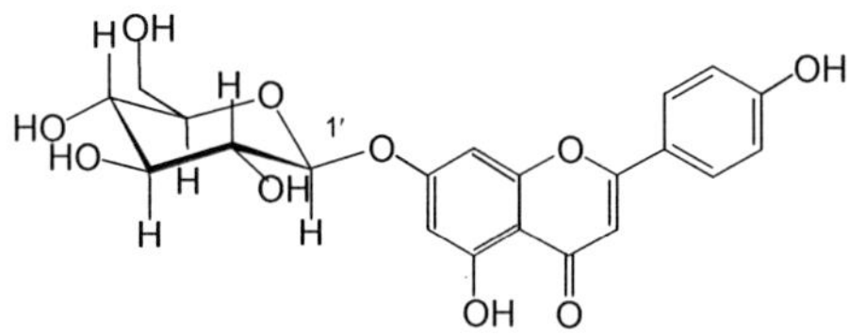

6

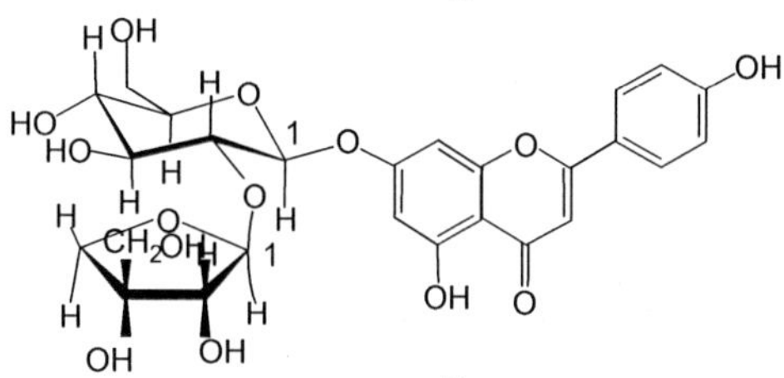

7

(1), lawsone (2), apigenin (3), luteolin (4), 2-methoxy-3-methyl-1,4-naphthoquinone (5), cosmosiin (6), apiin (7).

Table 7.1: Results of Lymphocyte Transformation (Proliferation) Assay of Total MeOH Extract, Different Solvent Fractions and Pure Compounds of Henna (*Lawsonia inermis* L.) Leaves.

Henna total methanolic extract 90% transformation)*, TC_{50} ** = 0.55 mg/ml							
Chloroform fraction*** (20% transformation), TC_{50} = 2.50 mg/ml				Ethyl acetate fraction (30% transformation), TC_{50} = 1.67 mg/ml			
Compound	c [μM]	Transformation (%)	TC_{50} [μM]	Compound	c [μM]	Transformation (%)	TC50 [μM]
1	6.09	10	30.49				
2	5.74	30	9.58	6	2.31	40	2.89
3	3.70	35	5.29				
4	3.50	50	3.50				
5	4.95	20	12.37	7	1.77	25	3.55

* Lymphocyte transformation in % at 1 mg/ml concentration is indicated in between brackets.

** Concentration showing 50% lymphocyte transformation.

*** Petroleum ether exhibited no immunomodulatory activity (0% transformation) while *n*-butanol extract elicited mild immunomodulatory activity (25% transformation, TC50 = 2.00 mg/ml), but unfortunately we were not able to isolate any compounds from it. (%) are shown in Table 7.1. The total methanolic extract as well as the different solvent fractions of henna leaves at 1 mg/ml concentration have displayed immunostimulant action as indicated by promotion of T-lymphocyte proliferative responses. It was found that the immunostimulant activity of the total methanolic extract of henna leaves (90% lymphocyte transformation) is greater than that of individual solvent fractions at the same concentration (1 mg/ml), suggesting a synergism between the different components in each fraction. Adopting the bioassay-guided fractionation, the petroleum ether extract of henna leaves was not further investigated chemically due to lack of immunoactivity. Unfortunately, we were not able to isolate any compounds from the *n*-butanol extract, despite the extract exhibited mild immuomodulatory activity (25%). This activity may be due to the presence of mucilage (highly polar polysaccharide). In order to detect whether a redox mechanism is involved in the immunomodulatory action of henna, we conducted an antioxidant screening assay. The antioxidant activity assay employed here is one of several assays that depend on measuring the consumption of stable free radicals derived from the reaction of 2,2-azino-bis (3-ethyl benzthiazoline-6-sulfonic acid) (ABTS) and manganese dioxide (MnO_2). The decrease in color intensity of the free radical solution due to scavenging of the free radicals by the antioxidant material is followed colorimetrically at a specific wavelength. The assay employs the radical cations as stable free radicals to assess the antioxidant potential of the isolated compounds. The advantage of ABTSderived free radical scavenging method over other antioxidant screening methods is that, the produced color remains stable for more than 1 h and the reaction is stoichiometric. The results of the assay in terms of inhibition (%) of the test compounds are expressed in Table 7.2. It is clear that a significant antioxidant activity was exhibited by the active constituents of *Lawsonia inermis* (henna) leaves, especially by the flavonoids and naphthoquinones. Nearly all compounds isolated from henna exhibited a free radical scavenging activity comparable with that of ascorbic acid (vitamin C) at 2 mm concentration. Compound 7 (apiin; apigenin-7-apiosyl-glucoside) has shown to be the most potent free radical scavenger. It has showed a greater antioxidant activity than the standard well-known antioxidant ascorbic acid. These results may, in part, explain the mechanism of the immunomodulatory actions of henna, which is based on its antioxidant potential. Thus, the constituents of henna act as free radical scavengers that prevent the phospholipid membrane peroxidation and protect immuno-compromised cells from free radical damage. This also may account for the previously reported hepatoprotective effect of henna against CCl4-induced hepatotoxicity, as well as for the anti-sickling activity through protecting the membrane of normal and sickle erythrocytes by reaction with a transient oxidative species.

The 13C NMR spectrum of compound 1 showed the presence of 9 carbon atom signals, their multiplicities were determined using the DEPT 135" experiment that revealed the presence of six methane signals. By subtracting DEPT 135" signals from the original 13C NMR spectrum, three signals remain that can be assigned to three quaternary carbons. The EI/MS molecular ion peak at *m/z* 164 suggested a molecular formula of $C_9H_8O_3$ and thus giving a double bond equivalent (DBE) of six, four of which were assigned to a *p*-disubstituted phenyl moiety as reflected by the strong IR band for aromatic C-H out of plane

Table 7.2: Results of ABTS Antioxidant Activity Screening Assay.

Test component (2 mM)	A_{Test}*	Inhibition (%)	DM**	IC_{50}*** [mM]
Blank	0.5	0	–	–
Ascorbic acid	0.3	40	2.1	2.5
Henna total MeOH extract	0.35	30	1.7	–
1	0.31	38	1.1	2.6
2	0.49	2	0.6	50.0
3	0.35	30	3.1	3.3
4	0.4	20	1.8	5.0
5	0.3	40	2.4	2.5
6	0.33	34	2.7	2.9
7	0.19	62	4.1	1.6

* Absorbance of test solution at λ_{max} 734 nm.

** Deviation from the mean.

*** Concertration showing 50% inhibition.

bending at 856 cmD1 and confirmed by the appearance of a two double intensity 13C NMR signal for the aromatic methines C-2,6 and C-3,5 at δ 130.7 and 116.3, respectively. This was corroborated by the appearance of two 1H NMR doublets at δ 6.78 (2H, d, *J* = 8.0 Hz) and 7.52 (2H, d, *J* = 8.0 Hz) for the *o*-coupled protons H-2,6 and H-3,5, respectively. The oxygenated quaternary carbon signal at δ 160.1 could be assigned to the hydroxylated carbon C-4 that was confirmed by the appearance of a broad IR band at 3392 cm D1. The quaternary carbon signal at δ 125.8 was assigned to C-1. Another DBE was assigned to a C7-C8 double bond that is obvious from the appearance of the two methine 13C NMR signals at δ 115.9 and 144.7 assigned to the olefinic carbons C-8 and C-7, respectively. This was assured by the appearance of two olefinic 1H NMR signals at δ 6.29 (1H, d, *J* = 16.0 Hz) and 7.49 (1H, d, *J* = 16.0 Hz) for protons H-8 and H-7, respectively. This large coupling constant suggested that the double bond is in *trans* (*E*) configuration. The ultimate DBE could be assigned to the carboxylic carbonyl carbon C-9 appearing at δ 168.5. The EI/MS mass spectrum of compound 1 confirmed the above assignments; showing a molecular ion peak [M+] and in the same time the base peak at *m/z* 164 corresponding to the molecular formula $C_9H_8O_3$. The peak at *m/z* 146 resulted from the dehydration of the parent ion [$M\text{-}H_2O^+$]. Decarboxylation of the parent ion resulted in the peak at *m/z* 119. Other fragments characteristic of the cinnamoyl moiety were those at *m/z* 91 that correspond to the 7-membered tropylium ion [$C_7H_7^+$]; subsequent elimination of a neutral acetylene molecule resulted in the fragment at *m/z* 65 which corresponds to the 5-membered ion [$C_5H_5^+$]. The above mentioned assignments and comparison with the previously reported literature data made us deduce that compound 1 is *trans*-4- hydroxy-cinnamic acid, known as *p*-coumaric acid. To the best of our knowledge, this is the first report of an isolation of such an aromatic acid from *Lawsonia inermis*.

The spot of compound 2 on TLC plates acquired an orange color that was intensified by alkalis such as ammonia, NaOH, and Na_2CO_3 and after heating with vanillin sulphuric acid spray reagent using precoated silica gel plates G60 F254 suggesting a naphthoquinone structure. It exhibited UV absorption maxima at 269 and 453 nm (MeOH solution) suggesting a highly conjugated system. Its IR spectrum showed the presence of a hydroxyl group (3410 cmD1), two α-unsaturated carbonyl bands at 1676 and 1644 cm D1 (C=O chelated with an α-hydroxyl), suggesting also a 1,4-naphthoquinone structure.The 13C NMR spectrum of compound 2 showed the presence of ten carbon signals, the multiplicities of which were determined using an APT experiment that revealed the presence of five methine signals and five quaternary carbon signals confirming the naphthoquinone 10 carbons skeleton. Four 13C NMR methane signals were assigned to four aromatic methines C-5, C-8, C-6, and C-7 at δ 126.5, 126.7, 133.1, and 135.3, respectively. The remaining olefinic methane signal at δ 110.7 could be assigned to C-3. The two quaternary carbon signals at δ 129.4 and 132.9 were assigned to C-8a, and C-4a, respectively. An oxygenated quaternary carbon signal at δ 156.3 was assigned to the hydroxylated carbon C-2. The remaining two quaternary carbon signals at δ 181.9 and 184.9 were assigned to two upfieldshifted α-unsaturated carbonyls C-1 and C-4, respectively, corroborating the 1,4-naphthoquinone structure. The 1H NMR spectrum was consistent with the above 13C NMR assignments, displaying an olefinic proton signal at δ 6.36 (1H, s) for H-3, a set of four double doublets at 7.7D 8.2 ppm that were assigned to four *m*-, *o*-coupled aromatic protons at δ 7.71 (1H, dd, *J* = 2, 10.2 Hz), 7.73 (1H, dd, *J* = 2, 10 Hz), 7.76 (1H, dd, *J* = 2, 11.2 Hz), and 8.12 (1H, dd, *J* = 2.6, 9.4 Hz) for protons H-6, H-5, H-7, and H-8, respectively. The above assignments as well as co-chromatography with the authentic sample made us to deduce that compound 2 is 2-hydroxy-1,4-naphthoquinone (2- hydroxy-1,4-naphthalenedione) known as lawsone, isojuglone, or Natural Orange.

The close similarity in the UV spectrum between compound 5 and compound 2 (lawsone) indicated that they possess one and the same chromophore (1,4-naphthoquinone moiety). The IR spectrum of compound 5 revealed two strong and sharp absorption bands at 1679 and 1652 cm D1 for C=O stretching indicating the presence of two carbonyl groups conjugated with a double bond (α,-unsaturated carbonyls) and thus endorsing the possibility of having a 1,4-naphthoquinone nucleus. A major difference from compound 2 is the lack of the IR broad absorption band around Antioxidant and Immunomodulatory.

Constituents of Henna Leaves

3500 cmD1 excluding the presence of a free hydroxyl group. This was corroborated through the 4D5 ppm upfield shifting of the 13C NMR signal for C-2. Methoxylation of C-2 was deduced from the appearance of the 13C NMR signal at 54.9 ppm for the methoxyl carbon, as well as the 1H NMR signal for methoxyl protons at 3.75 ppm. Another difference from compound 2 was the disappearance of the olefinic 1H NMR signal for H-3 indicating that it was substituted. This was confirmed by the appearance of a 13C NMR signal at 18.5 ppm for the methyl substituent at C-3 in addition to the 1H NMR signal at 1.98 ppm for methyl protons. The mass spectral data of compound 5 were very useful in elucidating its structure. The EI/MS mass spectrum assured the above assignments showing a molecular ion peak [M^+] at *m/z* 202 indicating the molecular formula $C_{12}H_{10}O_3$.

The fragment ion at *m/z* 187.9 indicated demethylation, thus suggesting the presence of a methyl group. The loss of a 31 mass unit fragment, giving the peak at *m/z* 157, indicated losing a methoxyl (–OCH_3) group. Subsequent loss of carbon monoxide moieties (28 mass units) resulted in the peak at *m/z* 129. Another pathway for fragmentation could be proposed starting from the parent ion at *m/z* 202 which loses a CO moiety leading to the fragment at *m/z* 174 followed by demethylation and deprotonation yielding the fragment at *m/z* 158. The fragment at *m/z* 174 can also lose a CO moiety resulting in the peak at *m/z* 146. Subsequent demethoxylation gives rise to the fragment at *m/z* 115. The base peak at *m/z* 105 [$C_8H_9^+$] resulted from the fragmentation of the naphthalene cation.

The above assignments made us to conclude that compound 5 is 2-methoxy-3-methyl-1,4-naphthoquinone. To the best of our knowledge, this compound is reported in henna for the first time.

The TLC spot of compound 3 attained a yellow color if visualized with NaOH or ammonia, and after heating with vanillin sulphuric acid spray reagent using precoated silica gel plates G60 F254 indicating its flavonoidal nature. Its UV spectrum in MeOH displayed absorption bands I and II at λmax 338 and 268 nm, respectively, indicating that it has a flavone nucleus. A bathochromic shift in band I of + 54 nm with increasing intensity on addition of sodium methoxide indicated the presence of a free hydroxyl group at C-4. A bathochromic shift in band I of + 44 nm with aluminium chloride shift reagent, that persisted after addition of HCl, reflected the presence of a free hydroxyl group at C-5, and the absence of 3, 4-*ortho*-dihydroxy groups in ring B. The bathochromic shift (+ 7 nm) in band II, on addition of sodium acetate, indicated the presence of a free hydroxyl group at C-7. Little (+ 2 nm) or no bathochromic shift in band II with sodium acetate/boric acid indicated the absence of *ortho*-dihydroxy groups at ring A. The above data showed that compound 3 is a flavones with free 5,7,4 hydroxyls. The flavone nucleus was confirmed from the 13C NMR signal at 181.5 ppm that was assigned to C-4. This was emphasized by 1H NMR signals at δ 6.76 (1H, s) for H-3. The two 13C NMR signals at δ 93.9 and 98.7 were assigned to C-8 and C-6, respectively, indicating that these positions are unsubstituted. The double intensive 13C NMR signals at δ 115.8 and 128.3 for carbons C-3, 5 and C-2, 6, respectively, proved that ring B is mono-substituted at position 4. This was confirmed by the 1H NMR spectrum that displayed two doublets at δ 6.9 (d, *J* = 8.7 Hz) and 7.9 (d, *J* = 8.7 Hz), each integrated for 2 protons that are corresponding to the *o*-coupled protons H-3, H-5, and H-2, H-6, respectively. The oxygenation pattern of ring A was established from the 1H NMR signals at δ 6.18 (1H, d, *J* = 1.5 Hz) and 6.47 (1H, d, *J* = 1.8 Hz) for the *m*-coupled protons H-6 and H-8, respectively, indicating that these positions are unsubstituted. Further confirmation of the *m*-oxygenation pattern of ring A came from the 13C NMR signals at δ 160.9 and 163.9 for the two oxygenated carbons C-5 and C-7, respectively. EI/MS fragments corroborated the aforementioned assignments showing a molecular ion peak which is also the base peak [M+] at *m/z* 270 corresponding to the molecular formula $C_{15}H_{10}O_5$ indicating that compound 3 is apigenin.

The spectral data of compound 4 are more or less similar to that of compound 3 yet having an additional hydroxyl group in ring B at position 3. This was corroborated by the significant bathochromic shift (+ 62 nm) in band I of the UV spectrum (MeOH) with aluminium chloride as shift reagent that declined upon addition of HCl as well as the bathochromic shift of band I (+ 21 nm) with sodium acetate/boric acid shift reagent indicating the presence of 3, 4-*ortho*-dihydroxy groups in ring B. Additional confirmation for the 3-hydroxyl function was provided by the 13C NMR signals at δ 145.6 and 149.9 for the hydroxylated carbons C-3 and C-4. This was emB.R. Mikhaeil *et al.* · Antioxidant and Immunomodulatory Constituents of Henna Leaves 473 phasized by the 1H NMR signals at δ 7.43 (1H, d, *J* = 2.1 Hz), 6.89 (1H, d, *J* = 8.1 Hz), and 7.41 (1H, dd, *J* = 2.1, 8.1 Hz) that could be assigned for the protons H-6, H-5 and H-2, respectively. EI/MS fragments of compound 4 corroborated the previous assignments showing a molecular ion peak which is also the base peak [M^+] at *m/z* 286 corresponding to the molecular formula $C_{15}H_{10}O_6$. The above assignments as well as co-chromatography with an authentic sample made us to conclude that compound 4 is luteolin.

Compound 6 is also flavonoid based on a similar basis like for compound 3. It gave a positive Molisch's test suggesting that it is glycosidic in nature.

It displayed UV and NMR spectral patterns resembling that of compound 3 suggesting that it has an apigenin aglycone. Nevertheless, the absence of a significant bathochromic shift of band II in the UV spectrum (MeOH) upon addition of sodium acetate as shift reagent reflected that the hydroxyl group at C-7 may be absent or blocked by glycosidation. Glycosidation of the 7-hydroxyl group was corroborated by the downfield shifts of about 0.5D 1 ppm in the *ortho* related C-6 and C-8 signals and 1.5D2 ppm in the *para* related C-10 signal relative to those in the aglycone (compound 3) *i.e.* apigenin. Strong acid hydrolysis of compound 6 and TLC of the hydrolysate afforded glucose. This was confirmed by the 13C NMR signal at δ 99.9 that was assigned for the anomeric carbon C-1 of glucose, and the 1H NMR signal at δ 5.05 (1H, d, *J* = 6.6 H) for the anomeric proton of the configured glucopyranose moiety as deduced from the axialaxial coupling constant. The above findings were confirmed through positiveion FAB/MS-MS (TANDEM MS) that showed a fragment ion peak at *m/z* 433 for [M^+H^+] corresponding to the molecular formula $C_{21}H_{21}O_{10}$, and at *m/z* 271 for [apigenin (aglycone)$^+H^+$], as well as through negative-ion FAB/MS-MS (TANDEM MS) that showed fragment ion peaks at *m/z* 431 for [M-HD] corresponding to the molecular formula $C_{21}H_{19}O_{10}$, and at *m/z* 269 for [apigenin (aglycone)-HD]. The aforementioned data suggested that compound 6 is apigenin-7-*O*-d-glucopyranoside known as cosmosiin which has been previously isolated from the leaf extracts of *Lawsonia inermis* L. by Muhammad *et al.*

Another apigenin-7-glycoside is compound 7 that was concluded by the same grounds as compound 6, yet the glycosyl moiety is a little bit different being formed of a disaccharide. This was deduced from the strong acid hydrolysis and TLC of the hydrolysate that afforded glucose and apiose. This was corroborated by the 13C NMR signals at δ 99.3 and 108.6 that were assigned for the anomeric carbons C-1 of glucose and C-1 of apiose and the 1H NMR signals at δ 5.14 (1H, d, *J* = 6.9 Hz), and 5.45 (1H, s) for the anomeric protons of the configured d-glucopyranosyl moiety and the configured d-apiofuranosyl moiety, respectively, as deduced from the axial-axial coupling constants. The d-apiofuranosyl moiety is attached to C-2 of glucose as reflected by the sizeable downfield shift of C-2 of glucose from 73 to 76.8 ppm.

Experimental

Materials for chromatographic study

Silica gel G60 F254 for TLC (Merck, Germany), silica gel for column chromatography (70D230 mesh) (Merck), precoated silica gel GF254 aluminium and plastic plates for TLC (Merck and Machery-Nagel, Germany) were used.

Reagents for Lymphocyte Transformation Assay

Heparinized peripheral venous blood was obtained from healthy volunteers from the blood bank of Mansoura University Hospital; Ficoll/Hypaque was obtained from Amersham Pharmacia, Uppsala, Sweden; phytohaemagglutinin (PHA) was obtained from Difco, Detroit, MI, USA; concanvalin A (ConA) was obtained from Merck, Germany; Hank's balanced salt solution (HBSS), foetal calf serum (FCS), glutamine, HEPES (*N*-2-hydroxyethylpiperazine-*N* D2-ethanesulfonic acid)-buffer and RPMI-1640 medium were obtained from Gibco BRL, Life Technologies, Pailsey, Scotland; crystalline penicillin G and streptomycin were obtained from El-Nile Pharmaceutical Co., Cairo, Egypt; *Echinacea purpurea* extract (Immulone") was obtained from Sekem Pharmaceutial Co., Cairo, Egypt; levamisole (Ketrax") was obtained from Elkahira Pharmaceutial Co., Cairo, Egypt (manufactured under license from Astra- Zeneca, Wilmington, Delaware, USA); cyclophosphamide (Endoxan") was obtained from ASTA Medica AG, Frankfurt, Germany; cyclosporine (Sandimmune Neoral") was obtained from Novartis Pharma, Switzerland. Antioxidant and Immunomodulatory Constituents of Henna Leaves.

General instrumentation

UV spectra were recorded in MeOH using a Shimadzu 1601-PC UV/Visible spectrophotometer; IR spectra were recorded on a Buck model 500 Infrared spectrophotometer; NMR spectra were recorded using a Bruker AM-300 spectrometer, Drx-400, and a Varian Mercury-300 spectrometer with CDCl3 and DMSO-*d6* as solvents and TMS as internal standard. Chemical shifts (δ) are expressed in ppm. DEPT and APT experiments were conducted under standard conditions. EI/MS were performed using a Finningan Mat SSQ 7000 mass spectrometer with a Digital DEC 3000 workstation.

Plant material

The air-dried powdered leaves of *Lawsonia inermis* L. were purchased from the local herbal stores in Mansoura, Egypt. It was identified through microscopical examination and identification of diagnostic fragments previously described by Youngken.

Extraction

The air-dried powdered leaves of *Lawsonia inermis* L. (2.0 kg) were extracted with about 15 l of methanol (by maceration) at room temperature several times until complete exhaustion. The methanolic extract was concentrated to a syrup consistency (300 g) under reduced pressure at a temperature not exceeding 45 °C, diluted in about 1 l of distilled water and then successively extracted with petroleum ether, chloroform, and ethyl acetate. The aqueous mother liquor was further subjected to partition with *n*-butanol saturated with water. The extracts, in each case, were treated with anhydrous Na_2SO_4 and evaporated almost to dryness under reduced pressure and kept for further investigation.

The obtained fractions were weighed to obtain the petroleum ether fraction (109.9 g), chloroformic fraction (34.8 g), ethyl acetate fraction (37.2 g), and finally *n*-butanol fraction (56.8 g).

Isolation and identification

Only the chloroformic and ethyl acetate fractions were investigated as explained before. The chloroformic extract (20 g) was applied onto the top of a glass column (120 cm \ 5 cm) previously packed with silica gel (300 gm; 70D230 mesh; Merck) in petroleum ether. The extract was gradiently eluted with petroleum ether containing an increasing proportion of ethyl acetate. The effluent was collected in 50 ml fractions. Each fraction was concentrated to a small volume and monitored by TLC. Fractions 1D13 revealed the presence of three spots. They were not further investigated due to poor yield. Fractions 14D15 were further purified by silica gel column chromatography (15 g, 60 cm \ 2.5 cm) using chloroform containing increasing proportions of ethyl acetate. Sub-fractions 8D12 upon crystallization yielded compound 1 (27.6 mg). Fractions 16D19 were purified by preparative TLC on silica gel using petroleum ether/EtOAc (6:4) to afford compound 2 (500 mg). Fractions 20D23 were separated by normal phase silica gel column chromatography (30 gm, 50 cm \ 2 cm column) using petroleum ether/ethyl acetate gradient elution, collecting 25 ml fractions. Sub-fractions 1D9, upon evaporation of solvent, deposited 112 mg of compound 3. Fractions 24D30 were further purified by normal phase silica gel column chromatography (30 gm, 50 cm \ 2 cm column) using petroleum ether/ethyl acetate gradient elution, collecting 20 ml fractions. Sub-fractions 8D11 upon crystallization afforded compound 4 (32 mg), whereas sub-fractions 21D27 upon evaporation of solvent and re-crystallization yielded compound 5 (30 mg).

About 20 g of the ethyl acetate extract were applied onto the top of a glass column (60 cm \ 5 cm) previously packed with silica gel (300 gm) in ethyl acetate. The extract was gradiently eluted with ethyl acetate containing an increasing proportion of a methanol/water mixture. The effluent was collected in 50 ml fractions. Each fraction was concentrated to a small volume and monitored by TLC. Fractions 1D14 revealed the presence of 3 spots in TLC, yet they were not further investigated due to poor yield. Fractions 15D17 upon evaporation of solvent and re-crystallization afforded compound 6 (264 mg) as canary yellow crystals. Fractions 18D42 upon crystallization deposited light yellow crystals of compound 7 (90 mg).

The UV, IR, MS and NMR spectral data of the isolated compounds are available upon request from the corresponding author. B. R. Mikhaeil *et al.* Antioxidant and Immunomodulatory Constituents of Henna Leaves.

Assessment of the immunomodulatory activity: lymphocyte blast transformation (mitogensis) assay

(A) Separation of Peripheral Blood Lymphocytes (PBL)

Lymphocytes were separated from peripheral human venous blood by the Ficoll/Hypaque gradient technique. For each sample, 5 ml of heparinized blood was diluted with an equal volume of Hank's balanced salt solution (HBSS) in a sterile plastic centrifuge tube. 6 ml of diluted blood were carefully overlaid on 4 ml Ficoll/ Hypaque solution gradient without allowing the solution to become mixed by keeping the pipette against the tube wall 5D10 mm above the fluid meniscus. The tube was centrifuged at 1200 rpm (200 \ *g*) at room temperature. The lymphocytes were localized as a whitish layer on the upper meniscus of the gradient solution. Using a fine pasteur pipette, the zone containing lymphocytes was taken and washed twice in HBSS, 10 min at 1200 rpm (200 \ *g*). The residue is a buffy coat of polymorphnuclear leucocytes (PMNLs).

(B) Lymphocyte Transformation Assay

The viable lymphocytes were adjusted to a concentration of 2 \ 106 cells/ml in RPMI-1640 medium supplemented with 600 μl penicillin, 0.1 ml streptomycin, 1% glutamine, 25% HEPES-buffer, and 20% foetal calf serum (FCS). The lymphocytes were plated into 96-well tissue culture plates (or Eppendorf tubes). The test solution (100 μl) in DMF (100 μl/ml) and 20 μg of the mitogen (PHA) were added to each well. Cell cultures were incubated at 37 °C in 5% CO_2 atmosphere for 72 h, during which the mitogen produces its maximal effect on DNA synthesis. After culture, cell films were stained by Giemsa stain and the average count of percentage of transformed (proliferated) blasts was determined. Aqueous *Echinaceae purpurea* extract (Immulone") and levamisole (Ketrax") were used as positive control (standard immunostimulant) while cyclophosphamide (Endoxan") and cyclosporin (Sandimmune Neoral") were used as negative control (standard immunosuppressant) at 100 μg/ml of each drug in DMSO.

8

Antistaphylococcal Activity of Henna Extracts *Lawsonia inermis*

Plant materials are used throughout developed and developing countries as home remedies. Many works have been done which aim at knowing the different antimicrobial and photochemical constituents of medicinal plants and using them for the treatment of microbial infections as possible alternatives to chemically synthetic drugs to which many infectious microorganisms have become resistant. Moreover, antibacterial pharmaceuticals are not affordable to the majority of the communities in the developing countries.

An Increase in resistance calls for new antibacterial drugs, one source of which are traditional medicinal plants. Plants may provide a natural source of antimicrobial drugs that will/or provide novel or lead compounds that may be employed in controlling some infections globally. *Lawsonia inermis* (*L. inermis*) is a scientific name of a tall shrub plant commonly known as Henna or Mehndi or mignonette tree belongs to the Kingdom: Plantae, Division: Angiospermae, Class: Dicotyledoneae, Order: Myrtales, Family: Lythraceae, Genus: *Lawsonia*, Species: *L. inermis*. Henna is a flowering plant, having a height of meters, natal to subtropical and tropical regions of the world including South Asia, Africa, oases of Sahara Dessert and even in the northern regions of Australia. Leaves of the henna plant are entire, opposite, sub-sessile, oval-shaped and smooth. The leaves have a length of 2–3 cm with 1–2 cm width. Henna shrub is highly branched and has greyish-brown barks. *Lawsonia inermis* (Henna) is used as a hair dye based on the staining properties of one of its constituents, e.g. Lawsone. Modified Henna products, such as Black Henna are also available to consumers.

The content of Lawsone among various modified Henna products may vary significantly, but these products contain some other substances for modifying the intensity of the color provided by Henna alone. *Lawsonia inermis* powder as a product of botanical origin is composed of various ingredients and cannot be examined per se for percutaneous absorption. Consequently, it is necessary to identify and select a representative lead ingredient. Since Lawsone is an important ingredient and can be analyzed easily, it has been selected as the lead ingredient. However, Lawsone is predominantly glycosidic bound and only a small amount is available in the plant powder. For practical and analytical reasons, Lawsone is therefore often added separately and mixed to the *Lawsonia inermis* powder, especially when the investigations were performed with a radiolabelled material. Main chemical constituents of henna are Lawsone

(2- hydroxynaphthoquinone), mucilage, mannite, gallic acid and tannic acid. Henna is known to be used as a cosmetic agent for dyeing hair, nails and skin. In traditional medicine, henna plant is used to treat many diseases like edema, bronchitis, menstrual disorder, rheumatism, hemorrhoids and even in jaundice, leprosy, pain, spleen enlargement, dysentery and skin problems. Henna can also be used as an astringent and antihemorragic agent and is also known for its hypertensive, cardio inhibitory and sedative effects. In addition, henna is reported to show some other properties including hypoglycemic, immunostimulant, hepatoprotective, anti-inflammatory, tuberculostatic, anti-cancer and antioxidant properties.

The present research is designed to determine the Antistaphylococcal activity of leaves of *Lawsonia inermis* against certain skin staphylococci.

MATERIAL AND METHODS

L. inermis were collected from private gardens in Basra. The leaves were left to dry at room temperature for 24 hours. The dried leaves were ground to a powder and were kept in dry containers. Various concentrations (50, 100, 250, 500, 750 and 1000) mcg/ml (mcg mean μg(microgram)) were made from aqueous and alcoholic (ethanol 100%) extracts of leaves. All techniques of plant extraction were carried out.

The antibacterial effects of henna extracts *Staphylococcus aureus* (coagulase–positive staphylococci (CoPS), *Staphylococcus epidermidis* (coagulase–negative staphylococci (CoNS), were studied. These bacteria were isolated from patients with acne vulgaris of both sexes under 20 years who attended the Dermatology outpatient clinic in Basra teaching Hospital. Identification of bacterial types was carried depending on routine laboratory techniques. Determination of the inhibition zones (mm) and minimum inhibitory concentrations (MIC). The inhibition zones (mm) of L. inermis (henna) extracts were assessed using the Agar diffusion dilution method.

Muller Hinton agar was used with different diluted extract concentrations. 0.1 ml containing 105 CFU /ml (0.5 McFarland) was spread on the agar as described in NCCLS-200015 and minimum inhibitory concentrations (MIC) (mcg/ml) of plant extracts was carried by using brain heart infusion (Difco) by tube dilution method. Tetracycline, Ampicillin, Gentamicin, cephalexin, cloxacillin and vancomycin antibiotics were used in this study to evaluate the antibacterial efficacy of *L. inermis* (henna) extracts.

The statistical differences were tested by analysis of variance (ANOVA) for each treatment and using of chi square. The analysis was carried out using SPSS program ver.

RESULTS

Staph.aureus and *Staph.epidermidis* were isolated from acne vulgaris cases as predominant bacterial pathogens. All results are shown in Tables 8.1, 8.2 and 8.3.

Table 8.1: Antistaphyloccal Activity of Various Concentrations and Determination of Minimal Inhibitory Concentrations (MICs) of Aqueous Extract of Henna (Lawsonia Inermis) on Staphylococci Species and Determination of Minimal Inhibitory Concentration (Mic). P<0.05

Staphylococcl species	Diameter of inhibition zones (mm) for various aqueous extract (mcg/ml)						MIC µg/ml
	50	100	250	500	750	1000	
Staphylococcus aureus	NE	NE	NE	NE	NE	NE	600–700
Staphylococcus epidermidis	NE	NE	NE	NE	10	17	400–500

Table 8.2: Antistaphyloccal Activity of Various Concentrations and Determination of Minimal Inhibitory Concentrations (MICs) of Alcoholic Extract of Henna (*Lawsonia inermis*) on Staphylococci Species and Determination of Minimal Inhibitory Concentration (MIC). P<0.05

Staphylococcl species	Diameter of inhibition zones (mm) for various alcoholic extract (mcg/ml)						MIC µg/ml
	50	100	250	500	750	1000	
Staphylococcus aureus	NE	NE	NE	NE	NE	NE	600–700
Staphylococcus epidermidis	NE	NE	NE	NE	10	17	400–500

Table 8.3: Diameters of Inhibition Zones of Standard Antibiotics Aganist Staph. Aureus and Staph. Epidermidis. P<0.05

Staphylococcl species	Diameter of inhibition zones (mm) for standard antibiotics					
	ampi-cillin	vanco-mycin	cloxa-cillin	tetra-cyclin	genta-micin	cepha-lexin
Staphylococcus aureus	NE	24	14	NE	20	16
Staphylococcus epidermidis	NE	28	18	16	20	20

The results found that alcoholic extracts are more efficacious than the aqueous extract of henna leaves, and the highly effects associated with increase of extract concentrations with statistical differences between treatment. P< 0.05.

The biggest diameter of inhibition zone was 22 mm recorded for 1000 mcg/ml of alcoholic extract against *Staphylococcus epidermidis* followed by 20 mm against *Staphylococcus aureus*. Aqueous extract was less efficacious on *Staphylococcus aureus* and recorded 17 mm against *Staphylococcus epidermidis*.

The ranges of minimal inhibitory concentrations were between (400-700) µg/ml and (200-300) µg/ml for aqueous and alcoholic extracts, respectively with highly statistical differences between both MICs. P<0. 05.

In comparison with standard antibiotics we can illustrate the results as follows:

Vancomycin (24, 28 mm), gentamicin (20, 20 mm), cephalexin (16,20 mm), cloxacillin (14, 18 mm), tetracycline (0,16) and ampicillin not affected, on

Staphylococcus aureus and *Staphylococcus epidermidis* respectively with statistical differences between each antibiotics. $P<0.05$.

DISCUSSION

Henna has many traditional and commercial uses, the most common being as a dye for hair, skin and fingernails, as a dye and preservative for leather and cloth, and as an anti-fungal. Henna body art is made by applying henna paste to the skin: the lawsone in the paste migrates into the outermost layer of the skin and makes a red-brown stain. Some pastes have been found to include: silver nitrate, carmine, pyrogallol, disperse orange dye, and chromium. These have been found to cause allergic reactions, chronic inflammatory reactions, or late-onset allergic reactions to hairdressing products and textile dyes. Henna contains Lawsone in about 0.5 to 1.5% of its ingredients.

Lawsone (2-hydroxynapthoquinone) is the principal constituent responsible for the dyeing properties of the plant. However, henna also contains mannite, tannic acid, mucilage and gallic acid. These substances are present in henna in the form of a mixture. Antimicrobial activity may be due to numerous free hydroxyls that have the capability to combine with the carbohydrates and proteins in the bacterial cell wall. They may get attached to enzyme sites rendering them inactive. Water extracts did not show any antibacterial activity compared to alcoholic and oily extracts. This may be due to the lack of the solvent properties which plays an important role in antibacterial efficacy.

The alcoholic extract showed the highest MICs compared to other types of extracts and this may be due to the large quantity of active substances that were precipitated during the extraction process due to the effect of the alcoholic extract itself. When compared with antibiotics, alcoholic henna extracts showed more antimicrobial activity and similar antibacterial activity compared to those of antibiotic. We concluded that henna has an in-vitro antibacterial activity against the tested bacterial strains. These findings have also been mentioned in literatures.

Medicinal and herbal plants have been used as remedies for human diseases for centuries; this is because they contain components with therapeutic properties in their parts. The antibacterial effect of several plant extracts has been proven previously. In this study, henna leaves and roselle calyxes extracted by either water or ethanol increased the inhibition zone on all of the tested bacteria; this result Confirm their antibacterial activity this is consistent.

Confirm their antibacterial activity this is consistent with confirmed their antibacterial activity. This is consistent with previous studies which conclude that the extracts of *L. alba* (henna) and *H. sabdariffa* (roselle) were shown to have promising antibacterial properties. Some studies suggested that henna has a wide spectrum of antimicrobial activity including antibacterial, antiviral, antimycotic and antiparasitic activities. With the ever increasing resistant synthesized antibiotics, the naturally available henna could be a potential alternative.

Antimicrobial activity may be due to numerous free hydroxyl ions that have the capability to combine with the carbohydrates and proteins in the bacterial cell wall. They may get attached to enzyme sites rendering them inactive. On the other hand, this study showed that ethanolic extract is more efficient than water extract for henna. This result is consistent with who found slight higher inhibition of the roselle ethanol extract against *Bacillus subtilis* and *Staphylococcus aureus* than that of water extract. Also, antibacterial activity of henna extracted by water. This may be due to the lack of solvent the solvent properties which plays an important role in antibacterial efficacy.

9

Chemopreventive Action of *Lawsonia inermis* Leaf Extract

Lawsonia inermis Linn (Henna) is a plant which grows wild in abandoned area. This plant is a worldwide known cosmetic agent used to stain hair, skin and nails. However, it is not only relevant to cosmetics. The alcoholic extract of henna leaves reported mild antibacterial activity against *Micrococcus aureus* and *E.Coli. Lawsonia inermis* was also reported to have tuberculastatic activity. The leaves are used as a prophylactic against skin disease. They are used externally in the form of past or decoction against boils, burns, bruises and skin inflammations. A decoction as used as gurgle against sore throat. The roots of this plant are useful in burning sensation, loprosy, strangury and premature greying of hairs. The major phytochemical constituents of *Lawsonia inermis*, Lawson was found to possess significant anti-inflammatory, analgestic and antipyretic activities Wound healing potential of different extracts of *Lawsonia inermis* leaves was also reported in the rat burn wound models. This compound has been reported to have the inhibitory growth effect against human colon carcinoma, HCT-16 cells. Modern pharmacological research on henna and its constituents has confirmed its antiinflammatory, antipyretic and analgesic effects. It can also be used to treat pediculosis. The active component of henna is lawsone (2-hydroxy-1,4-naphthoquinone, CAS 83-72-7), which is also the principal dye ingredient. Current research suggests that lawsone is non-problematic for external use because of its low toxicity and genotoxicity. However there is no study reported on the inhibitory effect of other skin cancer (papilloma) and melanoma tumour. Therefore we have planned to carry out this study to see the anticarcinogenic effects in *Swiss albino* mice.

MATERIALS AND METHODS

Animals

The study was conducted on random bred, 6-7 weeks old and 24-28 gm body weight bearing, male Swiss albino mice (Figure 9.1). Animals were maintained under controlled conditions of temperature and light (Light: dark, 12 hrs: 12 hrs.). They were provided standard mice feed and water ad libitum. The study protocol is approved by the Departmental Animal Ethical Committee (IAEC Ref. No. 670/225.IACE/2008).

Chemicals

The chemicals, 7, 12-dimethylbenz (a) anthracine (DMBA) and croton oil were procured from Sigma Chemicals Co., St. Louis, USA. DMBA was dissolved at a concentration of 100 μg/100 μl in acetone. Croton oil was mixed in acetone to give a solution of 1% dilution.

Extract Preparation

The identification of the plant *Lawsonia inermis* (family: *Lythraceae*) was done by botanist Dr. S. S. Khan (Voucher Specimen No: WR/102/LGOB/2006), Department of Botany, Safia Science College, Bhopal, Madhya Pradesh (India). The *Lawsonia inermis* (Henna) leaves were collected and dried for few days in shade.. The leaves were washed, air dried, powdered and extracted with double distilled water by refluxing for 36 hrs. at 60°C. On the day of experimentation, the desired amount of powder was disolved in double distilled water for the final administration.

SKIN BIOASSAY PROTOCOL

Procedure

Experiments were performed as per the method reported by Berenblum (10) A group of 6 mice (Shaved on dorsal skin two days earlier) were by the initiated single application of 104 μg of DMBA in acetone (100 μl), was began 1 week after initation *L. inermis* extract (100 μl) were applied 1 hrs before each croton oil treatment. The extract was applied to the shaved area using the micropipette. The experiment was continued for 16 weeks. Skin tumour formation was recorded weekly and the tumours greater than 1 mm in diameter were included in counting of total number of papillomas/mouse, tumor incidence and tumor yield if they persisted two weeks or more.

Group 1 (Untreated control) No treatment was given.

Group 2 (Vehicle control) 100 μl acetone 2 times /week up to 16 weeks

Group 3(DMBA alone) 104 μg DMBA was dissolved in 100 μl acetone and single application was given.

Group 4 (Croton oil alone) 1% Croton oil was applied on skin 2 times a week up to 16 weeks.

Group 5 (DMBA + Croton Oil) 104 μg DMBA was dissolved in 100 μl acetone and Single application was given afterwards 1 % Croton oil was applied on skin 2 times a week up to 16 week.

Group 6 (DMBA + *L. inermis* ext. + Croton Oil) 104 μg DMBA was dissolved in 100 μl acetone and single application was given afterwards the 100 μl dose of *L. inermis* ext. was given one hour before the each application of 1% croton oil, 2 times a week up to 16 weeks.

Group 7 (*L. inermis* extract alone): the 100 μl was given 3 times a week up to 16 weeks.

Each group's content 6 animals for skin model assay and the animals of all groups were kept under observation for gross and microscopic changes in skin.

MELANOMA SKIN BIOASSAY

Animals

The study was conducted on random bred, 6-7 weeks old and 25 ± 2 gm body weight of, C57BL hybrid mice of both sexes. These were maintained under controlled conditions of temperature (25±2°C) and light (12 light: 12 dark). They were housed in good laboratory condition and were given standard mouse pellet diet and water *ad Libitum*. 4-6 animals were housed in polypropylene plastic cages.

Procedure

Melanoma cell line was obtained from National Cell science centre, Pune and maintained in our laboratory. The C57BL mice of both sexes of the mean weight of 25 gm and 6-7 weeks old were obtained from the animal colony of our institute. They were housed in good laboratory condition and have given standard mouse pellet diet and water *ad Libitum*. All the mice were kept at controlled light and temperature condition. Cell suspensions having about 5 Lacks cell were injected to every mouse by S. C. route.

After implantation of the melanoma cell line, animal kept in observation and experiment was started after 10 days when the tumours were seen and the treatment was given for 30 days and tumour volume and survival time was recorded. The following groups were maintained.

Group 1 (Positive Control Group)

This group consisted of four animals bearing the melanoma cell line (B16F10). The dose of 300 mg/Kg body weight of Cyclophosphamide dissolved in double distilled water was given by intraperetonally route. During the treatment, the size of the implanted tumors was measured by Vernier calipers.

Group 2 (Treatment Group)

This group consisted of four mice having the melanoma cell line (B16F10).

Group 3 (*L. inermis* extract alone Group)

This group consisted of four animals bearing the melanoma cell line (B16F10). The mouse was given aqueous *L. inermis* extract orally at the dose of 1000 mg/ kg body weight during the treatment; the size of the implanted tumors was measured by Vernier calipers.

Group 4 (*L. inermis* extract + Cyclophosphamide Group)

This group consisted of four animals and the melanoma cell line (B16F10). The mice was given aqueous extract of *L. inermis* extract orally at the dose of 1000 mg/ Kg body weight and after 30 min. 0.2 ml cyclophosphamide was inject intraperetonally during the treatment, the size of the implanted tumors was measured by Vernier calipers.

RESULTS

The results of the present investigation have been summarized in Tables 9.1 and 9.2. Topical single application of DMBA at the dose of 4 mg/kg b. wt. followed by 1% croton oil produced skin papilomas the incidence of tumors reached 100% animals and the value of cumulative number of papillomas in these animals were recorded 21 and the average number of papillomas per mouse (tumor yield) was found to be 3.5.

Table 9.1: Effect of *L. inermis* (henna) Leaf Extract on DMBA Induced Skin Papilomas in Swiss Albino Mice.

S.No.	Groups	Body weight (Mean ± SE)		Cumulative Number of papillomas	Tumour Yield	Tumour Incidence
		Initial	Final			
1.	No Treatment	25.8 ± 1.2	28.9 ± 1.1	00	00	0/6
2.	Vehicle alone	27.7 ± 1.6	29.3 ± 1.9	00	00	0/6
3.	DMBA alone (1 application)	28.0 ± 1.3	30.0 ± 1.3	00	00	0/6
4.	Croton oil alone	26.7 ± 2.2	29.8 ± 1.8	00	00	0/6
5.	DMBA + Croton oil	27.0 ± 1.3	29.9 ± 1.4	21	3.5	6/6 (100%)
6.	DMBA + *L. inermis* + Croton oil	27.7 ± 2.1	29.5 ± 1.6	10	1.6*	4/6(66%)
7.	*L. inermis* alone	28.1 ± 1.6	30.1 ± 1.4	00	00	0/6

*Level significance as compared to carcinogen control group at $p < 0.05$.
Carcinogen control v/s L. inermis experimental

Table 9.2: Effect of *L. inermis* (henna) Extract on B16F10 Melanoma Tumors

S.No.	Group	Tumour Volume	VDT (days)	I R %	ILS %
1.	Control (Un treated)	2.550 ± 0.49	3.5 ± 1.19	–	23.50
2.	Cyclophosphamide alone (Positive control)	0.710 ± 0.045*	5.50 ± 2.08*	25.73	28.23
3.	*L. inermis* ext. + CP	0.620 ± 0.273*	8.50 ± 0.57*	35.14	50.33
4.	*L.inermis* ext. alone	0.855 ± 0.078*	2.10 ± 0.05*	10.56	30.89

*denotes statistically significant as compared to untreated group at $p<0.05$.
VDT– Volume doubling time, IR - Inhibition rate, ILS - Increase in life span.

The mice which received *L. inermis* extract showed a significant decrease in the number and incidence of tumor as compared with that of the DMBA + croton oil group. When *L. inermis* extract was topically applied at the dose of 0.6 g/kg b. wt. for 16 weeks to the skin of animals the tumor incidence was found to be 66% (Grp.6), and the value of cumulative number of papillomas in these animals were recorded 10 and the average number of papillomas per mouse (tumor yield) in this group was found to be 1.6 respectively, The differences in the values of the results of experimental groups were statistically analyzed and found to be significant in comparison to the control group (Grp. 5) ($p< 0.05$). Vehicle Control, No treatment, *L. inermis* extract alone, Croton oil alone and DMBA alone groups did not show any tumor incidence.

Histopathology of Skin Tumour

The animals which received the treatment of DMBA + Croton oil for 16 weeks showed the infiltration nests of neoplastic squamous epithelium were observed. Tumour cells exhibited a high nuclear cytoplasmic ratio. Moderate cytoplasm and dense clumped chromatin were also seen. Adjacent epithelium showed marked hyperkeratosis.

This is suggestive of kerating squamous cell carcinoma grade II. When the *L. inermis* extract was applied along with the DMBA and Croton oil malignant tumours were not seen as compared to DMBA + Croton oil group. In the case of this group only four mice having tumours and the histopathology report suggest in these animals were having papillomatous hyperplasia, papilloma, extracellular keratin and epithelial hyperplasia with mild displasia was reported and the remaining animals showed the normal skin.

The present studies with the melanoma tumour model shows the effect of cyclophosphamide alone, *L. inermis* alone and cyclophosphamide with *L. inermis* extract on B16F10 melanoma tumour bearing mice.

The preventive effect of *L. inermis* extract was calculated using the parameter of inhibition rate (IR), Increase the life span (ILS), and Volume of tumour doubling time (VDT).The inhibition rate was 10.56% and 25.73% in *L. inermis* extract and cyclophosphamide (CP) treated group as compared to 35.14% in *L. inermis* + cyclophosphamide group. The life span was also increase in *L. inermis* extract + cyclophosphamide group (50.53%) as compared to cyclophosphamide alone (28.23%) and 30.89% in *L. inermis* extract alone group. The volume of tumour doubling time of CP alone group was 5.50 ± 2.08 (days), *L. inermis* extract alone group 2.10 ± 0.05 (days) and *L. inermis* extract + CP group volume of tumour doubling time was recorded 8.50 ± 0.57 (days) respectively. The differences in the values of the results of experimental groups were statistically analyzed and found to be significant as comparison to the control group ($p< 0.05$).

DISCUSSION

The present study demonstrates that when *L. inermis* extract was given one hour before the each application of croton oil, the incidence and the number of skin papillomas was significantly decreased. The appearance time of papillomas was also prolonged in the *L. inermis* experimental group in comparison to the carcinogen treated group. The reduction in tumour count may be due to effect in the promotional phase of tumourgenesis which prevent the reduction of free radicals. This compound has been reported to have the inhibitory growth effect against human colon carcinoma, HCT-16 cells. Active constituent of *L. inermis,* lawsone is non-problematic for external use because of its low toxicity and genotoxicity. Topical application of TPA (active constituent of croton oil) has been reported to increase production of free radicals. This is perhaps due to the free radical oxidative stress that has been implicated in the pathogenesis of a wide variety of clinical disorders. Many antioxidants and anticarcinogenic compounds appear to have major effect on the detoxification of the carcinogens by the induction of Phase II detoxification enzymes since these enzymes divert carcinogens to react with critical cellular macromolecules. The exact mechanism of anticarcinogenecity of *L. inermis* extract is not fully understood but it may be possible the free radicals scavenging activity. The anticarcinogenic effect of *L. inermis* (henna) leaf extract suggest its role in chemoprevention of skin cancer. These results are important because this plant is a worldwide known cosmetic agent used to stain hair, skin and nails. It may an important drug for chemotherapeutic treatment of cancer.

10

Correlation Between the Phytochemical Constituents and Anthelmintic Activity of *Lawsonia inermis* Leaf Extracts

Plant materials have been used for the treatment of serious diseases throughout the world before the advent of modern clinical drugs. The use of medicinal plants still plays an important role to cover the basic health needs in the developing countries. Several top selling drugs of modern times such as Quinine, Artemisinin, Shikonin, etc. are obtained from plants. Most of the phytochemicals, secondary metabolites of plants, are physiologically active. The plants are known to provide a rich source of botanical, anthelmintic, antibacterials, and insecticides. Helminths are recognized as a major problem to livestock production throughout tropics. Most diseases caused by helminths are of a chronic and debilitating in nature; they probably cause more morbidity and greater economic and social deprivation among humans and animals than any single group of parasites. The parasitic gastroenteritis is caused by mixed infection with several species of stomach and intestinal worms, which results in weakness, loss of appetite, decreased feed efficiency, reduced weight gain and decreased productivity. Most of the existing anthelmintics produce side effects such as abdominal pain, loss of appetite, nausea, vomiting, headache and diarrhoea. Chemotherapy is the only treatment and effective tool to cure and control helminth infection, as effective vaccines against them have not been developed so far. Indiscriminate use of synthetic anthelmintics can lead to resistance of parasites. Herbal drugs have been in use since ancient times for the treatment of parasitic disease in human and could be of value in preventing the development of resistance. Some investigators have mentioned the importance of some phytochemicals like alkaloids, glycosides, terpenoids, tannins and flavonoids for showing anthelmintic activity of plants.

Natural drugs are obtained from the plant, animal or mineral kingdom. The plant kingdom is the store house of the organic compounds. *Lawsonia inermis* Linn (Family- Lythraceae) is commonly known as henna and mehendi. It is a small shrub to a height of 6 m. The branches of this plant are lateral with leaves that grow in pair which are 2-4 cm long. The flowers are fragrant and red rose like. Henna leaves contain an important pigment called "lawsone". It contains tannic acid, gallic acid, mucilage and napthaquinone. It is also known as good medicinal plant which is said to have properties of astringent, antihaemorrhagic, intestinal, neoplastic, hypotensive and sedative effects. Useful parts of the plant are leaf, flower, bark, root and seed. The leaf used for alleviating jaundice, skin disease, veneral disease and small pox. Seeds are effective against dysentery, liver disorders and associated problems. Bark is used for burn scald. Root is considered as a potent medicine for gonorrhoea and herpes.

Some workers have mentioned that the in vitro anthelmintic potency of the petroleum ether extract (obtained by maceration method) of *Lawsonia inermis* leaves using Indian earthworm (Phretima posthuma). Considering it as a potential anthelmintic agent, we undertook a study to know the anthelmintic property of the methanolic and ethanolic extracts of *Lawsonia inermis* leaves.

MATERIALS AND METHODS

Plant Material

The leaves of the plant *Lawsonia inermis* were collected from Chhend, Rourkela, during December 2011. The sample was authenticated by Dr. Prativa Sahoo, Botanist, Rourkela Autonomous College, Rourkela. The shade dried leaves were powdered and stored in a dessicator.

Preparation of Extracts

The powdered leaves were passed through a sieve (No. 40) and stored in a dessicator. Then the powder (10 gm) of *Lawsonia inermis* were extracted by using maceration method. The powdered leaves were macerated in 60 ml of ethanol for 3 days at room temperature. The resulting extract was filtered through a filter paper. The residue was further extracted using the same procedure. The filtrates obtained were combined and then evaporated to dryness under reduced pressure. Instead of using ethanol, the above mentioned procedure was conducted separately for methanol.

Phytochemical Screening

Following chemical tests were performed for testing different chemical groups present in both the extracts:

Alkaloids

Mayer's test: To 2-3 ml of the extract, few drops of the Mayer's reagent (1.36 gm of Mercuric chloride and 5 gm of Potassium iodide in 100 ml distilled water) were added. Formation of a cream colour precipitate indicated the presence of alkaloids.

Amino Acids

Millon's test: To 2 ml of the test extract about 2 ml of Millon's reagent (Mercury nitrate) was added. White precipitate indicated the presence of amino acids.

Carbohydrates

Molish test: To 2 ml of the test extract, at first, few drops of alcohoholic α-napthol were added. Then through sides of test tube, few drops of concentrated sulphuric acid were mixed with it. Purple to violet colour ring appeared at the junction indicated the presence of carbohydrates.

Flavonoids

Alkaline reagent test: To 2 ml of the test extract, few drops of sodium hydroxide solution were added. At first, intense yellow colour was formed, which was subsequently turned to colourless, on addition of few drops of dilute acid indicated the presence of flavonoids.

Glycosides

Borntrager's test: The test extract was boiled with 1 ml of sulphuric acid in a test tube for 5 minutes. While hot it was filtered, then it was cooled. Shaking of the mixture was done with equal volume of chloroform. Two layers of solution were formed. The lower layer of chloroform was separated. Then that layer was shaken with half of its volume of dilute ammonia. Production of a rose pink to red colour suggested the presence of glycosides.

Saponins

Froth formation test : 2 ml of the extract was shaken vigorously with water in a test tube. Formation of persistent foam indicated the presence of saponins.

Tannins

Gelatin test : To 2 ml of the extract, 1% gelatin solution containing 10% sodium chloride was added. Formation of a precipitate suggested the presence of tannins.

Proteins

Warming test : 2 ml of the extract was heated in a boiling water bath. Proteins get coagulated due to heating.

Steroids and Triterpenoids

Salkowski test : The test extract was treated with few drops of concentrated sulphuric acid. Red colour at lower layer indicated the presence of steroids, whereas formation of yellow colour at the lower layer suggested the presence of triterpenoids.

Anthelmintic Activity

The anthelmintic activity was performed on adult Indian earthworm Pheritima posthuma due to its anatomical and physiological resemblance with the intestinal roundworm parasite of human beings. Indian adult earthworms, collected from moist soil and washed with normal saline to remove all fecal matter, were used for anthelmintic activity. Different concentrations of the dried extracts (10-25 mg/ml in distilled water with tween 80) were prepared. 10 ml of each concentration of ethanolic extract was delivered into a Petridish.

Then six worms (same type) were placed in it. Similarly, for each concentration of methanolic extract, 6 worms were used. Time for paralysis was noted when the worm did not revive even in normal saline. Time for death of worms were also recorded when the worms lost their motility followed by fading away of their body colour (when dipped in warm water of 50°C). Piperazine citrate (15 mg/ml in distilled water) was used as positive control.

Statistical Analysis

Data were analysed using one way factorial ANOVA tests followed by Dunnett's t-tests on each group. P values under 0.001 were considered highly significant.

RESULTS

While amino acids, flavonoids, glycosides, saponins, proteins and triterpenoids were found in the ethanolic extract, alkaloids, flavonoids, glycosides, saponins, proteins and triterpenoids were available in the methanolic extract. In the ethanolic extract, alkaloids, carbohydrates, steroids and tannins were absent. On the other hand, amino acids, carbohydrates steroids and tannins were not found in the methanolic extract (Table 10.1).

Considering the time for paralysis and death of the worms, it was found that both methanolic and ethanolic extracts were more or less equally potent. The anthelmintic activity revealed the concentration dependant nature of the extracts. We found that ethanolic as well as methanolic extracts were better than the positive control (piperazine citrate 15 mg/ml) as far as their anthelmintic activity was concerned (Figure 10.1). Negative control (distilled water with Tween 80) did not show any activity against earthworms (Table 10.2).

Table 10.1: Qualitative Analysis of Various Leaf Extracts of *Lawsonia inermis* Phytoconstituents Ethanolic Extract Methanolic Extract

Phytoconstituents	Ethanolic extract	Methanolic extract
Alkaloids	–	+
Aminoacids	+	–
Carboyhydrates	–	–
Flavonoids	+	+
Glycosides	+	+
Saponins	+	+
Proteins	+	+
Steroids	–	–
Tannins	–	–
Triterpenoids	+	+

'+' = Present, '–' = Absent

Table 10.2: Anthelmintic Activity of the Leaf Extracts of *Lawsonia inermis* and Controls

Treatment	Group	Concentration (mg/ml)	Time of paralysis (min) ± SEM	Time of death (min) ± SEM
Distilled water with Tween 80 control	I	–	–	–
Piperazine citrate	II	15	97 ± 0.57	116 ± 1.15
Ethanolic extract	III	25	57 ± 0.57***	63 ± 1.15***
	IV	50	35 ± 1.15***	40 ± 1.15***
Methanolic extract	V	25	56 ± 1.52***	65 ± 0.57***
	VI	50	35 ± 1.15***	42 ± 1.52***

Values are expressed as mean ± standard error mean (SEM). Values are calculated by using ONE way ANOVA followed by Dunnett's t–test. ***Values are highly significant i.e., more potent than controls at ($p<0.001$).

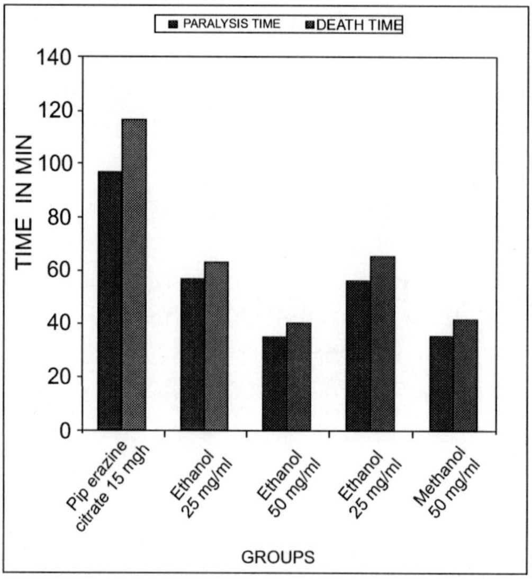

Fig. 10.1: Anthelmintic Activity of *Lawsonia inermis* leaf extracts

DISCUSSION

While some investigators have mentioned the importance of some phytochemicals like alkaloids, glycosides, terpenoids, tannins and flavonoids for showing anthelmintic activity of plants, we have seen the presence of flavonoids, glycosides, saponins, proteins, triterpenoids, amino acids and alkaloids in the extracts used in this study (Table 10.1). It seems that glycosides, terpenoids and flavonoids were responsible phytochemical constituents for demonstrating anthelmintic activity of the ethanolic extract. On the other hand, the anthelmintic activity of the methanolic extract was probably due to the presence of alkaloids, glycosides, terpenoids and flavonoids. Although

Bairagi et al. reported that petroleum ether extract of *Lawsonia inermis* leaves displayed anthelmintic activity, we have seen both methanolic and ethanolic extracts were having potent anthelmintic activity. Moreover, those extracts were more effective (highly significant) than the positive control as per as their anthelmintic activity was concerned (Table 10.2).

CONCLUSION

It can be concluded that the phytochemical constituents responsible for anthelmintic activity are present in the ethanolic and methanolic extracts of leaves of *Lawsonia inermis*. To identify the actual phytochemical constituents that are present in the crude drug extracts of this plant which are responsible for anthelmintic activity, should be studied thoroughly. It would be even better to conduct further research on pure chemical constituents of the plant to critically evaluate their activity on many animals.

11 Effect of Hydroalcoholic Extract of Henna (*Lawsonia inermis*) on Liver Enzymes

Different studies shown that women tend to use more botanical drugs, and frequently used them for relieve of problems like dysmenorrhea, minimizing menopause symptoms, menstrual disorders, prevention of osteoporosis and also pregnancy related problems. Pregnant women also assumes that natural remedies are not problematic and do not lead to complications for the mother and the fetus; so they attempt to cure pregnancy related problems with herbal ingredients.

Henna or arghan (*Lawsonia inermis*) is a tall shrub or small tree form myrtales order and lythraceae family, standing about 5-6 meter tall. The leaves are glabrous, lanceolate, oval, and grows opposite each other on the stem, with 2-3 cm length and flowers are fragrant, white, and paired. The medicinal part of the plant is its leaves. The henna plant is native to tropical regions of Africa and Asia. It is cultivated in Kerman, Hormozgan, and Baloochestanprovince of Iran. Henna leaves contain a pigment called Lawson or 2-hydroxy-1, 4-naphthoquinone (1-1.4%), flavonoids such as apigenin, luteolin, quercetin, several phenolic glycosides, coumarin, xanthone, quinoids, glycosides, beta-cytostrol, terpenoids, 6% lipid, 2-3% resin, 7-8% tannin, catechin and 1.2% essence. Other compounds derived from henna leaves are 5-7 glycosides derivatives, gallic acid, acastin glycoside, 1,4-naphthoquinone, laxanthon 1 and 2, and small amount of alkaloids. There are mannitol and mucilage in henna in addition to above components. Henna leaves have hemolysis capacity due to a compound called lawsone with chemical name of 2-hydroxy-1, 4-naphthoquinone which has oxidation property. It is used topically for the treatment of fungal disease and rheumatoid pain. It is also used as pigment especially for coloring skin and hair. The leaves have narcotic effects and high doses led to headache and poisoning.

Henna has antioxidant and regenerative properties as well as neutralizing the free radicals. Henna leaf extract has antioxidant and immunomodulatory (immune modulation) activities. It also has a protective effect in preventing protein oxidation and glycolisation.

In traditional medicine, henna has been used for treating joint pains, rash and sores. It and has been used as a coloring agent for hair and skin too. Lawson temporarily slowing the heart rate and increased the amplitude of heart muscle contraction. Anti-diarrheal effect of Lawson is due to lowering the tone and peristalsis of the intestines. Lawson has been shown anti-inflammatory, analgesic and antipyretic effects with dose of 500 mg/kg. The liver is the largest gland in the body and second largest organ in the body after skin. It is modified variety of foreign substances and results of body metabolism and compounds such as ammonia and various hormones; also liver is a storage place for various materials such as triglycerides, vitamins and sugar and the main place of gluconeogenesis. Hepatic enzymes are involved in the processes of detoxification and inactivation various materials and toxins through bio-transformation procedures. One of the indicative tests for liver function condition is measurement of transaminase, which is responsible for transfer of amino group between aspartate and alanine to alpha - Ketoglutarat. Every qualitative and quantitative changes in various hepatic enzymes is reflecting the health or disease state of liver and a representation of the severity of liver necrosis.The most sensitive and the most widely used hepatic enzymes are the aminotransferases, including aspartate aminotransferase (AST) and alanine aminotransferase (ALT). ALT is an aminotransferases enzymes that transfer amine group and catalyze conversion ofalpha ketoacid to the amino acid.Combination of oxaloacetate and alanine and production of glutamate and pyruvate which is a duplex reaction, catalyzed by the ALT and provide a more specific and sensitive indictor in the assessment of liver function enzymes than AST. Liver damage would lead to increased leakage of ALT and AST from the hepatocyte into the blood stream. ALP raises in pathological conditions and the liver and bone disorders. Thus, the blood level of this enzyme is one of the health indicators of the liver. Studies have shown that the methanol extract of the roots of henna has abortion inducing effects. And there are reports indicating that, henna parboil is used to induce abortion in pregnancy. But so far, the effects of this herb during pregnancy has not been studied on the baby's liver scientifically. Therefore, present study was conducted with main purpose of assessing the effects of the henna plant on liver enzymes and some blood biochemical factors and also changes in liver tissue of male newborn rats.

MATERIAL AND METHODS

Sampling and Required Equipment

Animals used in this study consisted of 40 male newborn rats of the Wistar genus, weighing approximately 100 g and 22 days old. Their mothers were under care in the animal infirmary of the Islamic Azad University, Kazerun Branch, and henna extract has been prescribed to them during pregnancy, the male pups were separated from their mothers after birth and have been kept at the same center. Animals were kept at fixed ambient temperature of 22 ± 2°C and fixed photoperiod of 12 h darkness and 12 hours light. Indirect and consistent light was come through the windows. Animals were held in polycarbonate cages with 40 × 25 × 15 cm dimensions with steel grid ceiling. Cage floor was carpeted by wood chips. Air conditioning system in the laboratory was active and in good condition. Mice drink water from municipal tap water and their mothers were feed by compressed rat food supplied by Pars cooperative company of livestock and poultry feed, newborn was fed by breast milk. Liver enzymes measuring kits were purchased from Pars Azemoon in Iran.

Extract Preparation Method

Henna leaves have been collected from Yazd surroundings, then dried in the sun for one week and extraction was performed using maceration technique. 100 g of plants powder was mixed in 1000 ml solvent (ethanol 70%) and after 48 h sleep at 37 °C, the resulting solution was filtered through Watman no.1 filter paper. The filtered solution was converted to extract powder through using a rotating evaporation device (Rotary) and under vacuum conditions. It should be noted that alcoholic content of the solution would be evaporated and has no impact on the results of the experiment. Then dry powder kept in the refrigerator for later use. In the day of experiment, fresh solution of 100, 200 and 400 mg/kg were prepared and used.

Procedure

In this experimental study, 40 head of the baby Wistar rats were divided into 5 groups of 8 heads, and each kept in the separate cage but same condition. The control group consisted of 8 male infants of mothers who have spent a normal and extract free course of pregnancy. The placebo group was consisted of 8 male infants who born from mothers with normal pregnancy and daily dose of 0.3 ml solvent (distilled water). There was three treatment groups consisted of 8 male infant each, who born from mothers of treatment groups 1, 2, 3 who received 100, 200, 400 mg/kg henna extract, respectively. The LD50 of henna was 2000 mg/kg and intra peritoneal injection of extract for 21 day were used as study intervention on treatment groups. After birth and at the end of the 22-days of neonatal period, blood samples have been collected from all the groups. Sampling was done from the heart. Tubes containing blood were centrifuged for 15 minutes at a speed of 5000 RPM, then serum aliquot was separated and kept at –20°C until enzymatic assays. For measurement of the enzymes level of activity, samples were transferred to the lab, then tested using the enzyme assay kits from the Pars Azemoon, Iran and also with the help of the US made Technicon RA–1000 device. After collection of 100 blood samples, animal's liver were dissected and fixed in 10% formalin solution, and after passing the stages of the slicing and staining, tissue slides were prepared.

Statistical Analysis

Data collected throughout the study was analyzed by SPSS Ver. 20 software package using comparison of means and variance analysis tests. $P \leq 0.05$ was considered statistically significant.

RESULTS

The study results shown that there was not any significant statistical differences between two groups of control and placebo. Comparison of the results related to the ALT, AST and ALP enzyme in 100, 200, 400 mg/kg groups shown a significant increases than control group. The amount of serum protein in groups receiving a dose of 200 and 400 mg/kg have significant increases than control group. There was not any significant change in other variables compared with control group (Table 11.1 and 11.2).

Table 11.1: The Plasma Level of Hepatic Enzymes (U/L) in Different Groups

Groups	ALT	AST	ALP
Control	92.87 ± 6.91	360.50 ± 38.32	600.37 ± 26.92
Placebo	76.575 ± 17.71	424.83 ± 63.22	602.50 ± 95.85
Treatment 1 100mg/kg	121.85 ± 10.15*	500.42 ± 158.19*	750.85 ± 53.05*
Treatment 2 200mg/kg	148.075 ± 17.90*	518.00 ± 67.91*	899.00 ± 50.81*
Treatment 3 400mg/kg	150.00 ± 6.67*	621.25 ± 45.68*	963.37 ± 44.75*

* There was significant difference with control group ($p<0.05$)

Table 11.2: Some Biochemical Factors in Blood (Albumin, Protein), Liver Weight and Infant Weight

Groups	Infant Weight (g)	Liver Weight (g)	Albumin (mg/dl)	Protein (mg/dl)
Control	73.33 ± 1.84	3.90 ± 0.19	3.42 ± 0.05	5.95 ± 0.15
Placebo	79.55 ± 3.48	4.57 ± 0.38	3.55 ± 0.06	5.60 ± 0.04
Treatment 1 100 mg/kg	72.20 ± 3.39	3.95 ± 0.40	3.58 ± 0.01	6.22 ± 0.10
Treatment 2 200 mg/kg	87.75 ± 7.31	3.60 ± 0.41	3.42 ± 0.09	6.71 ± 0.18*
Treatment 3 400 mg/kg	87.66 ± 7.05	3.76 ± 0.27	3.57 ± 0.05	6.83 ± 0.24*

Results of Histologic Studies

In this research study, in histological studies on the liver paranchymal cells, it was observed that the liver paranchymal cells were normal in both control and placebo group. Comparing liver paranchymal cells in different treatment group who received the extract (100, 200 and 400 mg/kg) with control group, the rate of necrosis was higher in the treatment groups than control group with progressive increase corresponding with the consumed extract dose (Figures 11.1 to 11.5, respectively). It can be said that the amount of liver tissue necrosis increase is consistent with dose increases. There was large number of binuclear cells and picnotic bodies in the sinusoids, large number of degenerated macrophages and red blood cells in the liver of treatment groups who received extract. Moreover, basophil levels in the cytoplasm of groups who received the extract was higher than the control and placebo group.

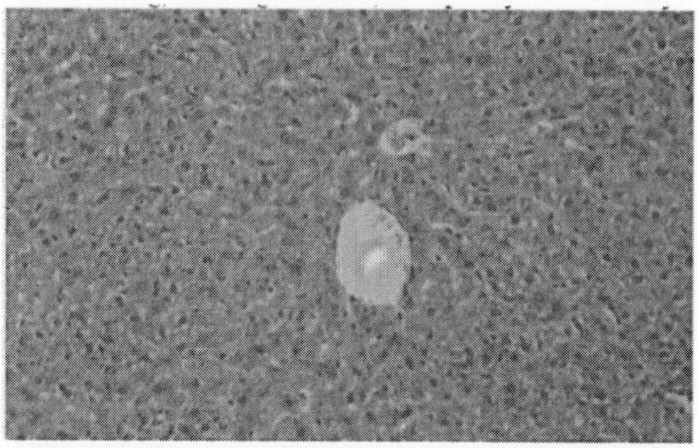

Fig. 11.1: Photomicrograph of liver tissue in control group - the longitudinal sections with hematoxylin - eosin staining, 20x magnification; all hepatocytes are healthy.

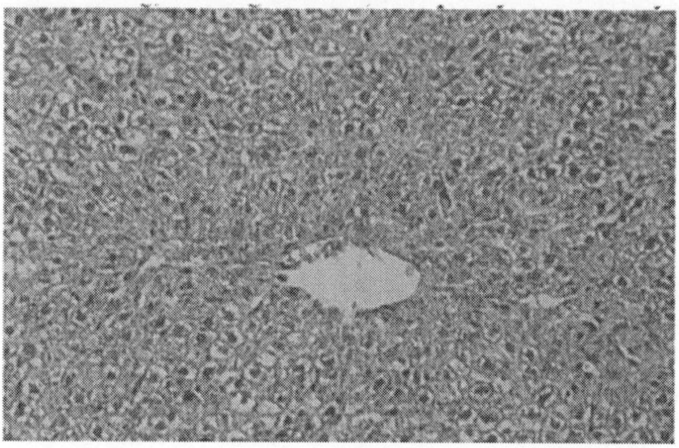

Fig. 11.2: Photomicrograph of liver tissue in treatment group - the longitudinal sections with hematoxylin - eosin staining, 20x magnification; all hepatocytes are healthy.

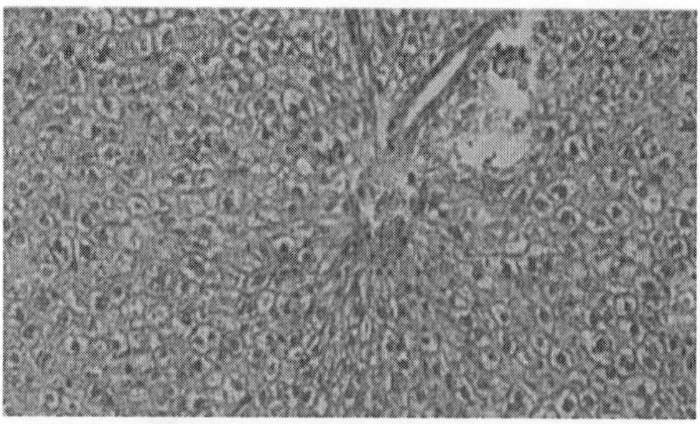

Fig. 11.3: Photomicrograph of liver tissue in treatment group 1 - the longitudinal sections with hematoxylin - eosin staining, 20x magnification; arrow shows the necrotic tissue.

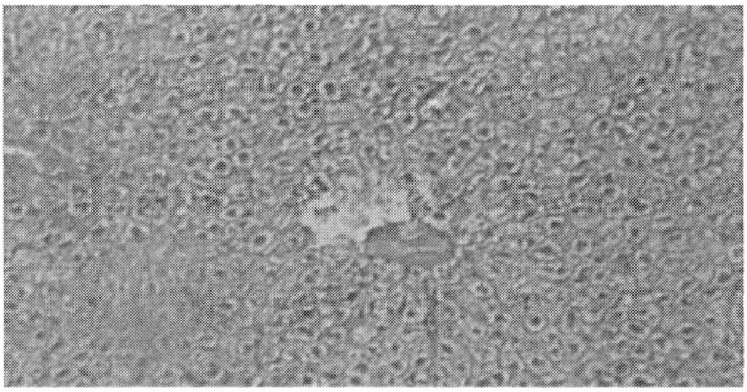

Fig. 11.4: Photomicrograph of liver tissue in treatment group 2 - the longitudinal sections with hematoxylin - eosin staining, 20x magnification; arrow shows the necrotic tissue.

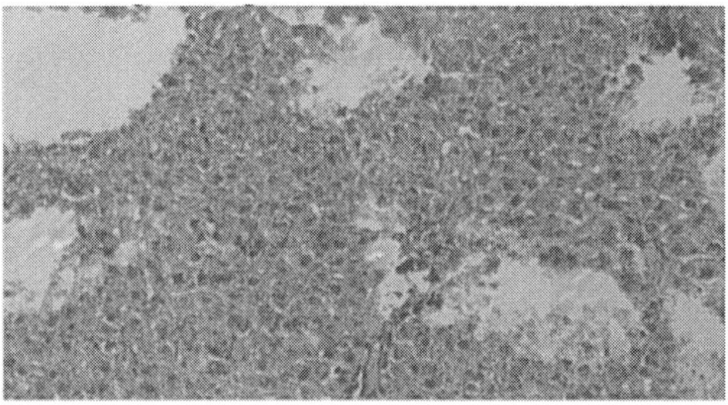

Fig. 11.5: Photomicrograph of liver tissue in treatment group 3 - the longitudinal sections with hematoxylin - eosin staining, 20x magnification; arrow shows the necrotic tissue.

DISCUSSION

According to tissue studies, considering high number of binuclear cells in the liver of treatment groups, and extreme abnormal nuclear divisions; it was clear that henna extract has teratogenic effects on liver tissue. Previous studies have shown that wild tea has teratogenic effects due to the presence of two compounds called apigenin and alpha-pinene. On the other hand, it has also been shown that henna extract contain large amounts of apigenin. There is also a high rate of pyknotic bodies in the sinusoids, and relatively large numbers of degenerated macrophages and red blood cells which proved the presence of hemolysis due to the henna effects. 2-hydroxy-1, 4naphtoquinon (Lawson) found in henna extract could induce hemolysis due to its oxidant properties. This material is metabolism in the liver and convert to a toxic metabolite, which crosses the placenta and influences the sensitive period of organogenesis and embryonic development.Liver enzymes Such as ALT AST and ALP are enzymes that specifically reflect necrosis of hepatocytes and cholestasis, and are used frequently in diagnosis of severe liver disease. Dog, cat, rabbit and rat ALT was specific to cytosol of hepatocytes, which is increase in blood plasma following changes in liver function. In addition, AST has been suggested for diagnosing liver failure. ALP is a glycoprotein attached to the membrane, which is found in various tissues such as liver, bone and lesser in kidney, intestine and placenta; and it is a worthy biochemical markers in diagnosis of osteoporosis and disorders of the liver, bile and fatty liver disease. In the current study, ALT, AST and ALP levels have shown a significant increases in the treatment groups than control group. Mohamed A. and his colleagues studies showed that the aqueous extract of the seeds of henna increased liver enzymes and necrosis of hepatocytes in mice, and these changes are attributed to addition of the henna pigment (Lawson) to other henna's compounds (flavonoids and terpenoids), but no specific mechanism was studied in this study. In a research study on a species of the genus Satureja (savory) called Macrantha, the toxicity caused by this type of plant was attributed to terpenoid compounds especially triterpenes, which possesses strong toxic effects. So we can conclude that at least one of the factors that are likely to cause toxic effects of henna in our study can be terpenoid compounds. Research has shown that methanolic extracts of henna root cause repeated abortion in mice, rats and guinea pigs, and this effect was attributed to the most existing composition in hydro alcoholic extract, apigenin. It also has been shown that apigenin metabolism is quiet slow, and the slow uptake and excretion phase of this material could lead to flavonoid accumulation in the body. Histopathological changes in the liver tissue of groups treated by henna extract showed that presence of hepatic necrosis may be due to effects of apigenin in occurrence of apoptosis. apigeninincrease reactive oxygen species, cytochrome C production and release from mitochondria into the cytosol, and consequently, cause processing and subsequent induction of prokaspaz and finally apoptosis through induction of caspase activity and rapid reduction of trans-membrane potential. Although antioxidant activity of chemical compounds of plants is well known, but under certain conditions, such as high doses or in the presence of metal ions can exhibit the peroxidant activity, this peroxidant activity or antioxidant compounds of plants have closed relationship with its prescribed concentration, which consistent with liver pathological lesions observed in our study. However, studies on cellular models have shown that many antioxidant polyphenols such as quercetin, catechin and gallic acid have peroxidative activity. High concentrations of flavonoids cause cell toxicity, DNA damage and apoptosis. It was proven that flavonoids can increase reactive oxygen species production through auto-oxidation. However, reactive oxygen species, hydrogen peroxide, superoxide anion and hydroxyl radical are important cell injury mediator, which can react with macro molecules such as lipids, proteins, nucleic acids, carbohydrates and unsaturated fatty acids in cell membranes, and after initial reaction, continued as chain-like reaction which cause cell damage and death. Also, studies have shown that compounds such as quercetin and acacetincan cause cell damage through inhibition of cytochrome P450 activity. Thus, livre damage was observed in the groups treated with henna extract. Because liver plays a major role in metabolic pathway and the regulation of numerous materials, including drugs (activation and detoxification), and excretion of exogenous and endogenous material. The results of serum protein levels shown a significant increase in the different groups receiving the extract compared to the control group. Studies shown that henna extract lead to increase in total protein concentration of serum, which is consistent with current study. Various pathological factors increase or decrease the total protein. The main cause of the increase in total protein is dehydration. In cases such as acute tissue injury, necrosis, surgery, or tumors, total protein increase was seen due to increased protein in acute phase, and chronic antigenic stimulation such as chronic inflammatory diseases and immune-related diseases, due to increased gamma globulin.According to histological studies carried out in present research, which is show liver tissue damage in groups receiving the extract, as well as the presence of darker cytoplasm and high rate basophils in the cytoplasm, which reflects more ribosomal activity in the production of proteins, we can attribute the increase in serum proteins to above mentioned reasons.

CONCLUSIONS

It can be concluded that henna extract increases the liver enzymes and liver damage according to the results of enzymatic and histopathological tests conducted in the current study.

12 Hepatoprotective Activity of *Lawsonia inermis* Linn

Role of free radicals in the causation of diseases has been well established. Several substances have been known to produce excessive free radicals and thereby produce tissue damage. Since liver is the major organ involved in the detoxification of xenobiotics, it is the main target of tissue injury produced by these chemicals and their metabolites. Reactive oxygen species produce deleterious effect on membrane lipids of the cellular components thereby producing peroxidation of lipids which leads to cell death. An association of reactive oxygen species with collagen synthesis and fibrosis has also been reported.

Many of drugs, useful against diseases are known to produce severe side effects. Antitumour drugs are known to produce myelosupression, nephrotoxicity and hepatotoxicity which are mainly caused by free radical generation 6. Scavengers of free radicals can reduce side effects of these drugs. Plant kingdom posses several non toxic compounds that can scavenge free radicals and boost the antioxidant defense mechanism in body and have a protective role against tissue damage induced by several chemicals and drugs.

The Plant *Lawsonia inermis*, commonly known as Mehendi, belongs to the familyof Lythraceae. It is a shrub and cultivated throughout India, Bangladesh and Pakistan. The leaves are greenish brown to brown, about 2.5-5 cm long, the margine entire and venation pinnate. Topical application of Henna reduced severity of Handfoot Syndrome caused by capecitabaine used for cancer treatment.This effect of Henna reported to have anti inflammatory, antipyretic and analgesics activities.

An ointment prepared from the leaves was used to cure ulcers and wounds. The astringent stem bark of *L. inermis* is traditionally used in India for the treatment of jaundice, enlargement of liver and spleen. It has been reported to posses anti inflammatory, antimicrobial and anticancer activity. One of the major active constituents of leaves of *Lawsonia inermis* are flavanoids. Hepatoprotective activity of ethanolic extract of leaves of *Lawsonia alba* has been reported. But detailed study of hepatoprotective activity has not been done. The present study has been undertaken with aim to determine the hepatoprotective activity of the warm aqueous leaves extract of *Lawsonia inermis* in animal models by estimating numbers of parameter.

MATERIALS AND METHODS

Plant Material and Preparation of the Extract

The leaves of *Lawsonia inermis* were collected from Durgapur, Burdwan district, West Bengal. They were authenticated by Botanical Survey of India, Shibpur, Howrah district,West Bengal and a voucher specimen(CNH/I I/274/2008/Tech. II/316, dated 17-11-2008) was deposited at the Institutes's Herbarium.

The leaves were washed thoroughly in tap water, shade dried and powdered. The powder (100 gm) was dissolved in 1000 ml of luke warm distilled water and was allowed to macerate for 48 hours at room temperature with constant stirring. The extract was filtered and the the residue was pressed out through clean linen, and added to the filtrate. The filtrare was evaporated to dryness in a shaker water bath at 42°C. The yield was found to be 2.2 gm. This crude extract was referred to as WAELI (warm aqueous extract of *Lawsonia inermis*). It was reconstituted in 0.25% CMC, to desired concentrations and used for experiments.

Animals

Wistar albino rats, males (270-300g) and Swiss albino mice, males (25-30g) were obtained from the Institute's Animal House. They were housed under standard conditions (temperature 24-28°C, relative humidity 60-70% and 12 hr dark light cycles), fed commercial rat feed (Lipton India Ltd., Mumbai, India) and boiled water *ad libitum*. All experiments involving animals were carried out according to National Institute of Health guidelines, after getting the approval of the Institute's Animal Ethics Committee (Reg No 955/A/06/ CPCSEA, 2006).

Toxicities Studies

Mice of either sex, weighing 20-25 g were used for acute toxicity studies. Acute toxicity study for WAELI was performed by Miller and Tainter method 20 to determine lethal dose (LD50). CMC (0.025%) was used as vehicle to suspend the extracts and the suspension was administered intraperitoneally. One tenth of the LD50 was used as a maximum dose of extracts tested for acute toxicity. The dose was selected for evaluation of hepatoprotective activity i.e. 400 mg/ kg i.p.

Hepatotoxins and Test Substances

All the test substances including silymarin were suspended in vehicle i.e. 0.025% CMC for administration. CCl_4 at a dose level of 1.25 ml/kg diluted in liquid paraffin (1:1) was administered intraperitoneally.

Carbon Tetrachloride Induced Hepatotoxicity 21

Rats were divided into 4 groups of 6 each, control, CCl_4, silymarin and test group.The rats of control and CCl_4 group received three doses of 0.025% CMC (1 ml/kg, po) at 12 hr intervals (0 hr, 12 hr and 24 hr). The rats of CCl_4 group received a single dose of CCl_4 (1.25 ml/kg, ip) diluted in liquid paraffin (1:1) 30 minutes after the administration of first dose of vehicle. The animals in silymarin and test group received three doses of respective test substances (silymarin 100 mg/kg; WAELI 400 mg/kg, i.p.) at 0 hr, 12 hr and 24 hr. CCl_4 (1.25 ml/kg i.p.) was administered 30 minutes after the first dose of the respective test substances. After 36 hr of administration of CCl_4, the animals were sacrificed by mild ether anaesthesia. Blood samples were collected and serum was separated at 2500 rpm for 15 min and biochemical investigations were carried out. Liver was dissected out and used for biochemical determinations and liver tissue slices were collected for histopathological studies.

Biochemical and Histopathological Studies

Biochemical parameters like serum glutamate pyruvate transaminase (SGPT), serum glutamate oxaloacetate transaminase (SGOT), serum alkaline phosphatase (SAKP) and serum bilirubin (SB) were assayed according to standard methods. Animals were sacrificed to remove liver. The liver was fixed in Bouin's solution for 12 hr, and then embedded in paraffin using conventional methods, cut into 3 μm thick sections and stained using haematoxylin eosin dye. The sections were then observed for histopathological changes.

Assesment of Lipid Peroxidation

The antilipid peroxidant effect of WAELI was studied in vitro, following modified methods 26, 27. Briefly, 0.5g of the rat liver tissue was sliced and homogenized with 10ml of 150 m*M* KCL Tris HCL buffer (*p*H 7.2). The reaction mixture was composed of 0.25 ml of liver homogenate, Tris HCL buffer (*p*H 7.2), 0.1 m*M* asborbic acid (AA), 4 m*M* $FeCl_2$ and 0.05 ml of various concentrations of WAELI extract. The mixture (in triplicate) was incubated at 37°C for 1 hr in capped tubes. Then, 0.1 N HCL, 0.2 ml of 9.8% sodium dodecyl sulphate (SDS), 0.9 ml of distilled water and 2 ml of 0.6 thiobarbituric acid (TBA) were added to each tube and vigorously shaken. The tubes were placed in a boiling water bath at 100°C for 30 min. After cooling, the flocculant precipitate was removed by adding 5 ml of n butanol and they were centrifuged at 3000 rpm for 20 min. The absorbance of the supernatant was measured at 532 nm.

DPPH Radical Scavenging Activity

DPPH radical scavenging activity was measured by the spectrophotometric method 28. To a methanolic solution of DPPH (200 μ*M*), 0.05 ml of the test compound dissolved in ethanol were added at different concentrations (100 500 μg/ml). An equal amount of ethanol was added to the control. After 20 min, the decrease in absorbance of test mixture (due to quenching of DPPH free radicals) was read at 517 nm and the percentage inhibition calculated by using the formula 29 given below:

$$\text{Inhibition \%} = \frac{\text{(Control-Test)}}{\text{Control}} \times 100$$

Behavioural and Toxic Effects

Seven groups of ten mice were treated with WAELI extract, (500, 1000, 2000, 3000, 4000 and 5000 mg/kg i.p). They were observed continuously for 1 hr for any gross behavioural changes, symptoms of toxicity and mortality if any and intermittently for the next 6 hr and then again, 24 hr after dosing with WAELI extract.

Statistical Analysis

The mean values ± SEM were calculated for each parameter. For determining the significant inter group difference one way analysis of variance was carried out and individual comparisons of the group mean values were done using Dunnett's test.

RESULTS

Effect of WAELI on Serum Hepatic Enzyme Levels

There was a significant increase in hepatic enzymes SGPT, SGOT, SAKP activity of CCl_4 treated groups when compared with that of normal control (Table 12.1). Free treatment of *Lawsonia inermis* leaf extract (Group IV and Group V) could

Table 12.1: Effect of Warm Aqueous Extract of Lawsonia Inermis Leaf on (WAELI) on Rat Serum Enzymes After CCl_4 Administration [values are mean ± SD of 6 animals]

Groups	SGOT (IU/L)	SGPT (IU/L)	SAKP (KA units/ 100ml)	SB (IU/L)	TP (IU/L)	Liver wt in (g/100g body weight)	Lipid pero- xides (µM of MDA/ mg of protein	GSH (µg/ mg of pro- tein)
Group Normal control (0.025% CMC, ml/kg)	97.60 ± 1.67	65.68 ± 1.47	24.57 ± 191	2.35 ± 0.20	7.61 ± 0.40	2.17 ± 0.22	118 ± 1.68	314 ± 1.9
GroupII CCl_4 treated (1.25 ml.kg)	181.25 ± 0.95	181.25 ± 0.95	68.59 ± 2.26	3.04 ± 0.04	3.63 ± 0.35	5.49 ± 0.39	471.4 ± 3.0	220 ± 4.03
GroupIII CCl_4 + Silymarin (100mg/kg)	107.13 ± 0.85**	65.93 ± 1.48**	26.80 ± 1.80**	1.35 ± 0.01**	6.90 ± 0.45**	3.99 ± 0.39**	135.7 ± 1.28**	335.60 ± 2.95**
GroupIV CCl_4 + WAELI (400mg/kg)	141.5 ± 1.42**	76.77 ± 1.95**	36.13 ± 1.31**	1.83 ± 0.02**	6.20 ± 0.27**	4.08 ± 0.24**	290.6 ± 2.60**	333 ± 3.0**

** significance p <0.01, compared to CCl_4 control

significantly reduced SGPT, SGOT and SAKP activities of serum total bilirubin in the group II animals was significantly increased when compared with the group I animals. Pretreatment with *Lawsonia inermis* leaf extract decreased the bilirubin level (Table 12.1) the total protein and glutathione in group II animals was significantly decreased when compared with that of Group I animals. Pretreatment with *Lawsonia inermis* leaf extract increased the total protein and glutathione level (Table 12.1).

The lipid peroxidation in liver tissue of untreated control animals was 471.40± 3.0 which was significantly higher when compared with that of normal control level (118±1.68). This increased level was found to be significantly lowered in the extract treated groups (Table 12.1).

Table 12.2: Inhibitory Effect of Warm Aqueous Extract of *Lawsonia inermis* leaf on (WAELI) on $FeCl_2$ –ascorbic acid (AA) induced Lipid Peroxidation in Rat Liver Homogenate *in vitro* [values are mean ± SD of 6 animals]

Groups	WAELI Concentrations (μg/ml)	MDA (nmol/g wet liver)	MDA Inhibition (%)
Normal control	–	1.32±0.58	–
$FeCl_2$– AA control	–	2.28 ± 0.02	–
$FeCl_2$ –AA + WAELI	25	1.82 ± 0.02	22.02
$FeCl_2$ –AA + WAELI	50	1.37 ± 0.02	39.98
$FeCl_2$ –AA + WAELI	100	0.84 ± 0.02**	62.54**
$FeCl_2$ –AA + WAELI	200	0.90 ± 0.01**	59.33**

**$P < 0.01$, compared to $FeCl_2$ –AA control

Effect of WAELI on in vitro lipid peroxidation

WAELI showed very potent inhibition of FeCl2 AA stimulated rat liver lipid peroxidation in vitro at concentrations of 100 & 200 μg/ml. There was a significant increase of malondialdehyde (MDA) in $FeCl_2$ – AA treated rat liver homogenate, Compared to normal control without $FeCl_2$ –AA. (Table 12.2).

Effect of HH on DPPH free radical scavenging activity

WAELI showed maximum inhibition (90.75%) of DPPH free radical at 400 ug/ml. 25 μg/ml dose failed to evoke significant response & it was observed that the free radical was scavenged in a concentration dependent manner up to 400 μg/ml. (Table 12.3)

Toxicity Studies In the acute toxicity studies, the WAELI extracts was found to be toxic (5/10 mice died) at the dose of 4000 mg/kg, but it was found to be safe up to 2000 mg/kg. The LD50 of WAELI was therefore 4000mg/kg i.p, in mice (data not shown).

Table 12.3: Effect of Warm Aqueous Extract of Lawsonia Inermis Leaf on (WAELI) on DPPH Radical Scavenging Activity [values are mean of 3 experiments]

Conc. (μg/ml)	DPPH (% inhibition)
25	40.25
50	62.85
100	68.35
400	90.75
800	88.23

DISCUSSION

In recent years, many studies have been undertaken with traditional medicines, in an attempt to develop new drugs for hepatitis. In the present study, we used animal models including CCl_4 for liver damage induction to investigate whether the plant extract WAELI could decrease efficiently the toxicity produced by these hepatotoxicants.

CCl_4 has been one of the most intensively studied hepatotxicants to date & provides a relevant model for other halogenated hydrocarbons that are used widely. A single exposure of CCl_4 can lead to severe centizonal necrosis and steatosis. The changes associated with CCl_4 induced liver damage are similar to that of acute viral hepatitis. CCl_4 is transformed by Cytocrome P 450 system to produce trichloromethyl free radicals. These free radicals may again react with oxygen to form trichloromethyl peroxyl radicals which may attack lipids on the membrane of endoplasmic reticulum to elicit lipid peroxidation, finally resulting in cell necrosis and consequent cell death.

Marked increase in release of hepatic enzymes into the blood stream is often associated with massive necrosis of liver. CCl_4 is known to cause marked elevation of serum enzymes. In the present study, a significant increase activity of SGOT, SGPT, SAKP, SB, Lipid peroxides, Liver weight and decrease content of TP and Glutathione was observed within 24 hr of exposure to CCl_4 indicating considerable hepatocellular injury. Our results indicated that WAELI at 400 mg/kg doses tested significantly prevented the increased serum enzyme activity and decreased TP and Glutathione content induced by CCl_4, indicating improvement of the functional status of the liver by this herb. $FeCl_2$ – ascorbic acid mixture is known to stimulate lipid peroxidation in microsomes of rat liver in vitro. In the present study, WAELI prevented the rise of lipid peroxides (MDA production), showing its significant anti lipid peroxidant effects.

DPPH radical is widely used as the model system to investigate the scavenging activities of several natural compound. DPPH is scavenged by antioxidants through the donation of proton forming the reduced DPPH which can be quantified by its decrease of absorbance. WAELI significantly quenched

DPPH radicals indicating its potent free radical scavenging activity, in the present study.

The result also revealed the non toxic nature of WAELI up to 4000 mg/kg in mice and was not surprising as it is extensively used in tribal medicine of Orissa to treat various ailments. Major active constituents of henna leaf are flavonoids which have been shown to possess various biological properties related to antioxidant mechanisms. Perhaps the triterpenes and flavonoids present in WAELI extracts are responsible for its hepatoprotective effects. The findings of the present study therefore support the reported therapeutic use of *Lawsonia inermis* in tribal medicine of Orissa to treat liver ailments. The probable mechanism of action of *Lawsonia inermis* appears to be its effect as a free radical scavenger & inhibitor of lipid peroxidation of the liver plasma membrane. Further studies are in progress in our laboratory to explore its chemical constituents & detailed mechanism of action.

13

Evaluation of Spermicidal Property of Aqueous Ethanolic Extract of *Lawsonia inermis* linn. Leaves

Herbal medicine is a major component of all indigenous people's traditional medicine and is so important that World Health Organization in assessing the health care systems in developing countries suggested that common medicinal plants could be utilized as substitutes for drugs to reduce overdependence on importation of allopathic drugs. However, there is need for proper scientific verification of their efficacy and systemic effects, particularly on reproduction. Herbal contraceptives are in popular demand because they are cost effective, readily available from local sources and have fewer side effects. However, herbal medicines may impair fertility in male and female animals or humans. Whilst some medicinal plants tested for their antifertility properties caused reduction in sperm counts and altered the motility of the sperm cells, others altered hormone levels and the histoarchitecture of the testis. Many plants used as contraceptives or sterility agents decrease spermatogenesis, impair implantation or are spermicidal. Some research findings have confirmed the spermicidal properties of *Cestrum parqui, Carica papaya* and *Hymenocardia acida* Global search for antifertility agents as an alternative to resolve population explosion has continued to receive attention especially in developing countries. For decades, efforts have been made to develop safe and effective contraceptives from natural sources. Plants having folkloric reputation have been identified and evaluated for their contraceptive efficacy. In recent years, there is a renewed interest in the control of fertility by using plants as male contraceptives. Although *Lawsonia inermis*, a popular medicinal and cosmetic plant of the family Lythraceae widely cultivated in tropical and subtropical regions of Africa, has been evaluated for its antifertility effect in female, its spermicidal property has not yet been reported. The aim of the present study was to evaluate the spermicidal property of aqueous ethanolic extract of *Lawsonia inermis* leaves.

MATERIALS AND METHODS

The leaves of *Lawsonia inermis* were collected within Makurdi metropolis, Benue state, Nigeria and authenticated at the College of Forestry, University of Agriculture, Makurdi. Voucher specimen was deposited at the College herbarium. The leaves were washed, air dried at room temperature, pulverized and stored in airtight container until required. One hundred grams of powdered material was soaked in 500 ml of 70% ethanol and stirred intermittently for

48 hours at room temperature. The material was filtered using sterile cotton wool and Whatman (No. 1) filter paper; the residue was re-suspended in the same amount of solvent and then filtered three more times. The filtrates obtained were dried at room temperature under the electric fan to obtain a crude extract. The extracts were stored in airtight containers at 4 °C until needed.

Animals

White albino rats (Wistar strain) were kept in polypropylene cages under room temperature, with 12-hour light and 12-hour dark cycle and were allowed to acclimatize for two weeks. The animals were provided commercial feed (Grand Cereals and Oil Mills Ltd, Bukuru, Jos, Nigeria) and clean water freely. Protocols for this experiment were in accordance with the guidelines on the care and well-being of research animals and were approved by the Ethics Committee.

Experimental design

The rats were anaesthetized using diethyl ether. A scrotal incision was made to exteriorize the testis and epididymides. The epididymides were carefully dissected out of the testes and blotted free of blood. To prepare sperm suspension, epididymal sperm were obtained by teasing the cauda epididymides placed in prewarmed beaker containing 2 ml of physiological saline (maintained at 37 °C). Sperm suspension obtained from each rat was used for the *in vitro* immobilization activity as previously described. Briefly, ten micro litres of the plant extract dissolved in physiological saline solution at varying concentrations (1%, 2%, 4%, 8% and 16 %) were mixed with epididymal sperm suspension (1:1 v/v) and tested for their effects on sperm motility. A drop of the evenly mixed sample was immediately placed on a clean and dry glass slide covered with cover slip and mounted on a prewarmed stage. This slide was then examined under the binocular microscope (Olympus, Japan) at magnifications of x10, x40. At least five fields were rapidly examined and 100 spermatozoa were counted. For the control, 10 μl of physiological saline was used instead of plant extract. The motility of spermatozoa was observed at various time intervals (15, 30 60, 90, 120 and 180 seconds).

Statistical Analysis

The results were analyzed and expressed as mean ± S.E.M using Graph Pad Prism Version 3.0 for Windows (Graph Pad Software, San Diego, California).

RESULTS

The effect of aqueous ethanolic extract of *Lawsonia inermis* leaves on sperm motility at different times (duration in seconds) is shown in Table 13.1. The extract caused significant decreases ($P < 0.05$) in spermatozoa motility in a concentration-dependent manner. An instant immobilization of spermatozoa was observed when 16% concentration was applied.

DISCUSSION

The present study evaluated spermicidal properties of aqueous ethanolic extract of *Lawsonia inermis* leaves and revealed a concentration-dependent reduction ($P < 0.05$) in the motility of sperm cells (Table 13.1). A similar study on the extract of *Hymenocardia acida* stem bark caused instant immobilization of the rat epididymal spermatozoa at 10% concentration.

However, the extract of *Lawsonia inermis* immobilized sperm cells immediately on application at 16% concentration. The result of the present study is in agreement with the findings of Lohiya and others who showed that partially purified compounds of ethyl acetate sub-fractions of *Carica papaya* seeds when administered at 2% concentration reduced motility of spermatozoa. An impaired motility was reported as index of spermicidal activity of *Achyranthes aspera* and *Stephania hernandifolia*. As was observed with *Cestrum parqui,* aqueous ethanolic extract of *Lawsonia inermis* leaves possesses *in vitro* spermicidal effect on rat sperm cells.

Different phytochemicals in plants screened for their spermicidal or sperm immobilization property were reported to contain saponins, flavonoids and phenol compounds. Most plant derived spermicides which caused sperm immobilization in animals and humans were confirmed to contain saponins The extract of *Lawsonia inermis* leaves revealed the presence of saponins and other phytoconstituents (data not shown). The result of this study showed that aqueous ethanolic extract of *Lawsonia inermis* leaves has spermicidal effect. However, the efficacy of *Lawsonia inermis* as spermicidal agent need to be further investigated.

Table 13.1: Effect of *Lawsonia inermis* Leaves Extract on Spermatozoa Motility (expressed as percentage).

Concentrations	0 Seconds	15 Seconds	30 Seconds	60 Seconds	120 Seconds	180 Seconds
Normal saline	75.70 ± 1.56	74.70 ± 1.90	73.70 ± 1.25	70.80 ± 2.34	66.21 ± 2.75	61.30 ± 2.90
10 mg/ml	26.90 ± 0.00	26.90 ± 0.00	26.53 ± 0.37	25.68 ± 0.90	25.00 ± 0.97	23.85 ± 1.40
20 mg/ml	20.10 ± 0.30	20.50 ± 0.40	20.23 ± 0.35	19.58 ± 0.70	17.58 ± 2.07	16.05 ± 2.28
40 mg/ml	12.70 ± 0.00	13.10 ± 0.40	12.43 ± 0.71	12.40 ± 0.55	11.90 ± 0.52	11.43 ± 0.63
80 mg/ml	9.20 ± 0.00	9.80 ± 0.50	9.73 ± 0.35	9.60 ± 0.28	9.34 ± 0.34	9.17 ± 0.33
160 mg/ml	0.00 ± 0.00	0.00 ± 0.00	0.00 ± 0.00	0.00 ± 0.00	0.00 ± 0.00	0.00 ± 0.00

14 Corrosion Treatment of Industrial Cooling Water by the Passivation Process using *Lawsonia inermis*

At present the Malaysian Government has focused its attention on improving and upgrading the existing water system and facilities, which are considered inadequate in terms of the treatment efficiency. In many cases, the quality of the effluent does not meet with the effluent standards required by the authorities. Untreated and inadequate treatment of wastewater has been the major factor in causing severe pollution in rivers and at shoreline areas due to the rapid industrialization and urbanization programmes since the 1980s. The polluted water in the rivers and surrounding seas has consequently increased health hazards for the Malaysian population who live in these areas and depend on these waters. The Government's latest policy is to change the numerous poorly equipped sewerage treatment plants to fewer, larger and more efficient centralized wastewater treatment plants to meet the effluent standard1. In the industrial plants, a cooling water system plays a major role in the manufacturing activities and in controlling the internal environment. Naturally occurring impurities in the water cooling system can leave the equipment vulnerable to fouling, scale formation, corrosion or rusting and growth of microorganisms. If left uncontrolled, any of these conditions can cause a loss of efficiency and shorten the life-span of the equipment. This problem will also involve, costs, time, reduce production and cause other aggravation. Corrosion is an electrochemical process by which a metal returns to its natural state where it forms oxide when in contact with oxygen. The major factors that influence corrosion are chlorine, total dissolved solid (TDS), conductivity and temperature. Chlorine and conductivity can be related to TDS or total suspended solid (TSS) to form corrosion. This is due to the presence of chlorine in water which reacts with the moisture in the air to produce hydrochloric and hypochlorous acids that corrode steel. The higher the TDS or TSS values, the higher would be the conductivity of water and in turn the probability for corrosion to occur would also be higher. Passivation is a process of making a material "passive" in relation to another material prior to using the materials together. Passivators act as anodic inhibitors. They prevent the corrosion of the metal by shifting it in a "noble direction", where they themselves get reduced at the anodic sites on the metal surface producing the current density necessary for passivation. The problems of scaling and corrosion are common phenomena in the industrial water cooling systems especially in the open cooling systems. This study was performed with the main aim of measuring water quality and metal content from wastewater samples from cooling tower. Moreover, performance of the passivation process using *Lawsonia inermis* (Henna) (a natural antioxidant) on the corrosion of mild steel was also investigated.

MATERIAL AND METHODS

Industrial Cooling Water

The present study was carried out at the Gebeng Industrial Park, Kuantan, Malaysia. The region was selected due to its rapid industrial growth and numerous factories that are equipped with cooling towers. In addition, there are large amount of wastewater being discharged daily into the nearest river and lake ecosystems that no longer support the full biological diversities. Other than that, Gebeng is the nearest petrochemical industrial area to Universiti Malaysia Pahang (UMP), where the chemical analysis was performed. Wastewater samples were taken from two industrial plants that use cooling tower; Flexsys Chemicals (M) Pvt. Ltd. and Cargill Palm Products Pvt. Ltd., Malaysia.

Chemical Analysis

The water samples were collected using plastic bottles at three locations: (*a*) at the basin of the cooling system, (*b*) at the surface area, and (*c*) at an interval of one meter up to three meters of depth. These samples were taken to the laboratory in UMP, for chemical analysis. The laboratory analysis included chemical oxygen demand (COD), total organic carbon (TOC), Iron (Fe), Nitrite (NO_3), and Lead (Pb), all according to Standard Methods6. The wastewater quality analysis was based on the Standard B of the Environmental Quality Act (1974). The effluent quality of any discharge from a sewage treatment process into inland water (other than one having an ocean outlet) should meet the minimum requirements of the Environmental Quality Act (EQA) (1974) set by the Environmental Quality.

Natural Antioxidants

The second phase of the study was devoted to investigate the corrosion effects on the cooling tower pipes. Accordingly, an attempt was made to examine the treatment performance using a passivation process by natural antioxidants (corrosion inhibitor). There are several antioxidants that can be obtained in the form of phytonutrients, which are found in nature's whole foods, in fruits and vegetables.

The deeper the color, the richer the anti-oxidant content would be. Some examples of antioxidants are; red apples, cherries, grapefruit, red grapes, raspberries, red plums, strawberries, tomatoes, watermelons, asparagus, green capsicums, broccoli, cucumbers, green grapes, spinach, cabbage, cauliflower and celery. Henna extract (*Lawsonia inermis*) was selected in the present study due to its main constituent's (lawsone, gallic acid, d-Glucose and tannic acid) that act as an inhibitive on the corrosion of mild steel.

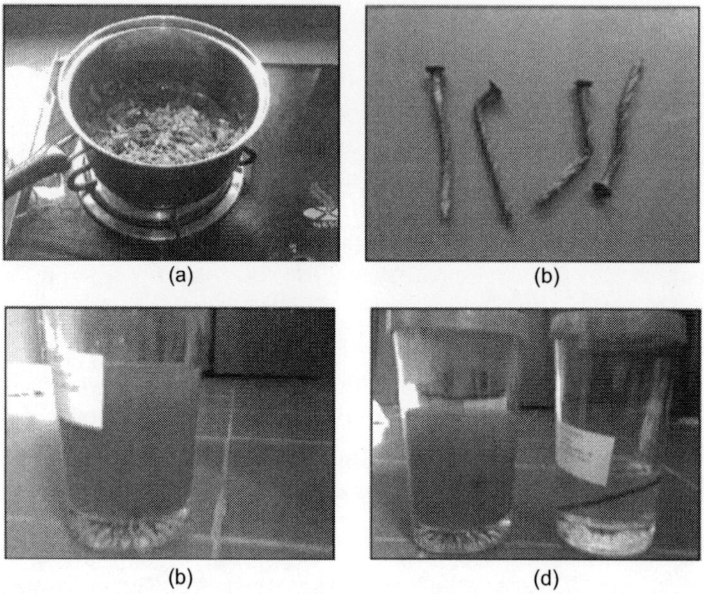

Fig. 14.1: Experimental preparation for passivation process; (a) boiled and crushed *Lawsonia inermis*, (b) corroded nails used in study, (c) *Lawsonia inermis* solution, 1(d) corrode nails immersed in *Lawsonia inermis* solution

Experimental Preparation

Initially, *Lawsonia inermis* was crushed and extracted in hot water for 20 min (Figure 14.1a) and then the required concentration was prepared8. The corroded nails (Figure 14.1b) which had the nominal composition of 0.179% C, 0.165% Si, 0.439% Mn, 0.203% Cu, 0.034% S and Fe were used as the mild steel specimens. A corroded nail, 50 mm in length and 2.5g in weight was used for the weight loss8. The extracted solution of the henna was filtered and the water from the extract allowed evaporating. About 50 ml of the wastewater (cooling water) solution was used to immerse the corroded nails (Figure 14.1c and d). The *Lawsonia inermis* extract had a concentration of 0.2 - 1.2 g.L-1 8. The experimental study was performed at 27, 40, 50 and 60°C with different concentrations of henna extract. The immersion time for the weight loss was 6 h. The results of the weight loss experiment was from the mean of three runs; each with a fresh specimen and a 50 ml fresh waste water solution. The corroded nails were weighted before and after the immersion period and then the percentage of the Inhibition Efficiency (IE) was calculated using the following equation:

$$IE\% = \frac{W_2 - W_1}{W_2} \times 100 \qquad ...(1)$$

W2 and W1 are the weight loss of the corroded nails in the presence and absence of the inhibitor, respectively.

RESULTS AND DISCUSSION

The results from this study were presented in two categories; water quality analysis of the industrial wastewater (cooling tower) and treatment using the passivation agent. The results were compared to the standard discharge limit stipulated in the Environmental Quality Act (1974). The comparison was made between the wastewater from the cooling tower and specifications of Standard B. For the passivation process, the performance was evaluated in terms of weight loss and surface analysis of the nails.

Water Quality Analysis

In this section, results of the wastewater (cooling water) quality analysis from Flexsys Chemicals and Cargill Palm Products industries were presented. The characteristics of the wastewater was evaluated in terms of total dissolved solid (TDS), chemical oxygen demand (COD), total organic carbon (TOC), turbidity, nitrite, iron, lead and pH. Details of the results are given below:

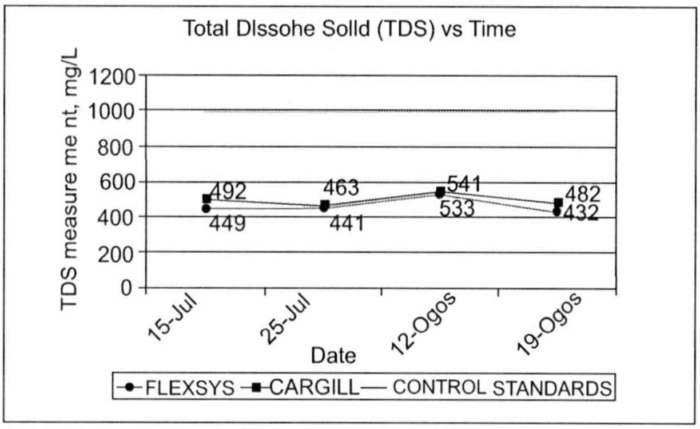

(a)

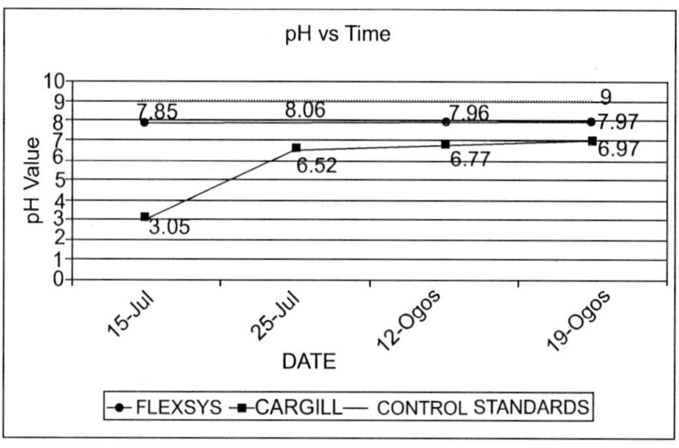

(b)

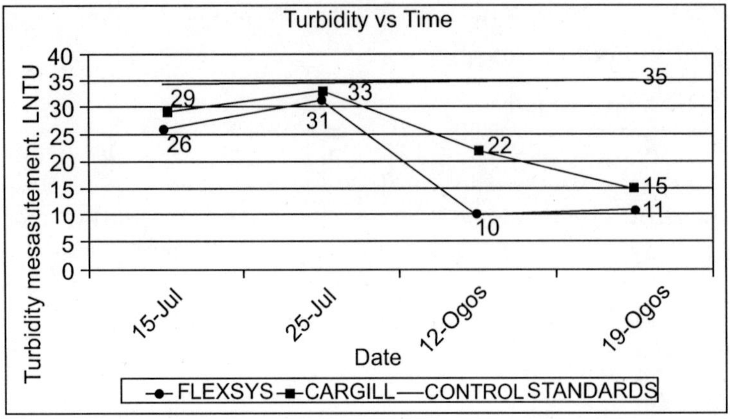
Turbidity vs Time
Turbidity mesasutement. LNTU
40
35
30
25
20
15
10
5
0
29
26
33
31
35
22
15
11
10
15-Jul
25-Jul
12-Ogos
19-Ogos
Date
FLEXSYS
CARGILL
CONTROL STANDARDS

(c)

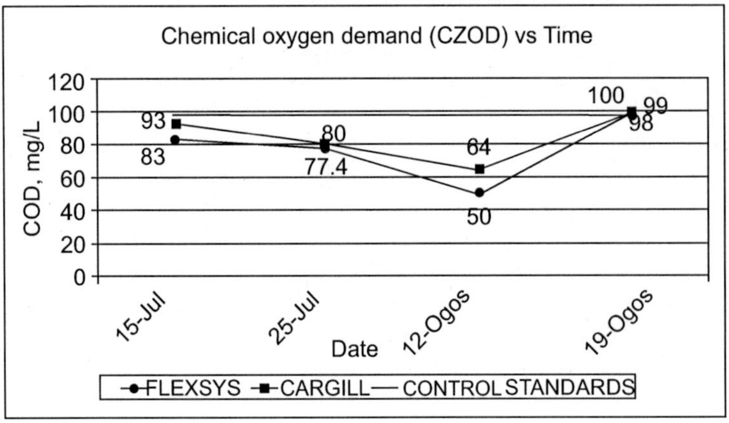
Chemical oxygen demand (CZOD) vs Time
COD, mg/L
120
100
80
60
40
20
0
93
83
80
77.4
64
50
100
99
98
15-Jul
25-Jul
12-Ogos
19-Ogos
Date
FLEXSYS
CARGILL
CONTROL STANDARDS

(d)

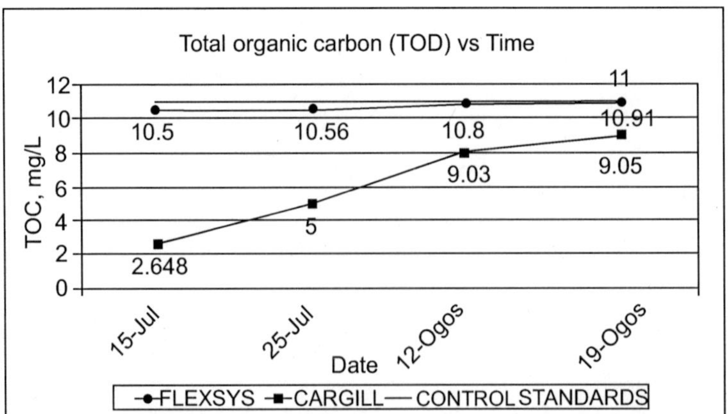
Total organic carbon (TOD) vs Time
TOC, mg/L
12
10
8
6
4
2
0
11
10.5
10.56
10.8
10.91
9.03
9.05
5
2.648
15-Jul
25-Jul
12-Ogos
19-Ogos
Date
FLEXSYS
CARGILL
CONTROL STANDARDS

(e)

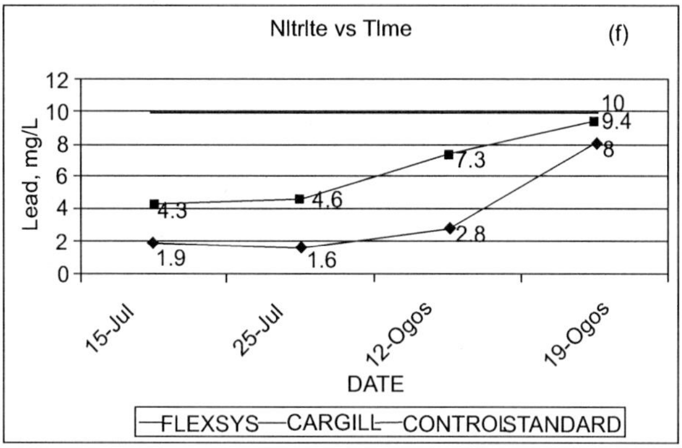

(f)

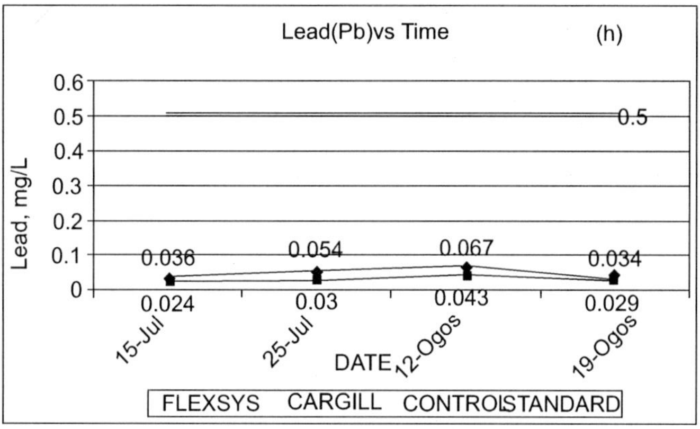

(g)

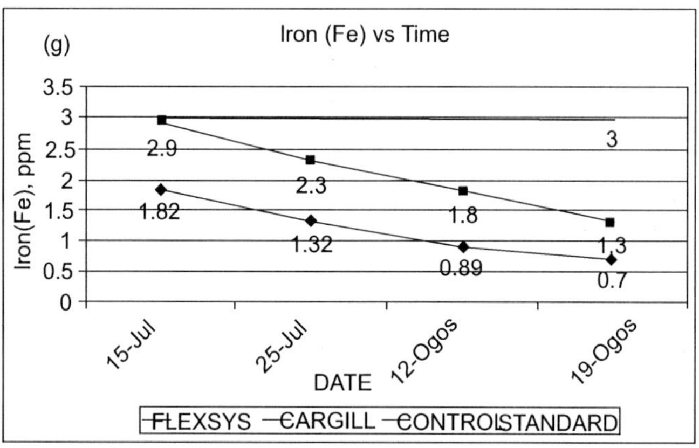

(h)

Fig. 14.2: Results of the wastewater quality analysis

Figure 14.2a shows the maximum TDS (533 and 541 mg.L-1) detected from the wastewater collected from Flexsys Chemicals and Cargill Palm Products, respectively. The TDS concentration for all the experimental period (4 d) complies with the Standard B requirement (1000 mg.L-1). It should be pointed out here is that the TDS concentration should be below 1000 mg.L-1 since it has the ability to increase the biological oxygen demand (BOD) of the receiving water. Moreover, it also facilitates microorganisms to escape disinfection and could clog soil absorption field in onsite systems. This is of particular concern because some industrial wastewater contains high amounts of salt, dissolved solids that may require expensive pretreatment to prevent harming the microorganisms that are the main agents for treating wastewater. The pH results for Flexsys Chemicals were 7.85, 8.06, 7.96, and 7.97, whereas for Cargill Palm Products it was 3.05, 6.52, 6.77 and 6.97 (Figure 14.2b). The pH detected was relatively stable (6 - 9) for all the experimental period, except for 15 July. In general, for any wastewater effluent, the pH should be between 6.6 - 7.8 for satisfactory treatment process. Microbial groups involved in treatment process have a specific pH region for optimal growth and values outside this range can be quite detrimental to the process. Therefore, maintaining a suitable and stable pH of the wastewater influent should be a major priority for ensuring efficient treatment performance. The changes in the pH profile for both industries may be attributed by the different properties of the product. Acids and other substances from the industrial or commercial resources may affect the wastewater treatment process. Similar trend was also observed for turbidity analysis for both Flexsys Chemicals and Cargill Palm Products (Figure 14.2c) where it complies with Standard B (less than 35 NTU). The highest turbidity was measured at 31 and 33 NTU for Flexsys Chemicals and Cargill Palm Products, respectively. It was thought that the different measurements of turbidity from both industries were caused by the products they produced. For instance, Cargill Palm Products produces oily substances which may release impurities to the effluent wastewater. The turbidity of a wastewater is not merely associated with TSS, but also due to plankton and other organisms. The turbidity itself is not of a major health concern, however high turbidity can interfere with disinfection and provide a medium for microbial growth. It may also indicate the presence of microbes. The concentration of COD was measured in the current experiment and the results were presented in Figure 14.2d. It can be seen that the COD concentration was in the range of 83 - 98 mg.L-1 (Flexsys Chemicals) and 64 - 100 mg.L-1 (Cargill Palm Products). The highest COD concentration measured was 99 mg.L-1 and it complies with the standard requirement. In general, COD is the equivalent amount of oxygen required to chemically oxidize the organic matter contained in a known volume of wastewater using a standard test in which a strong oxidant (potassium dichromate) is used. Nearly all the organic material is typically oxidized in this test. COD are non-biodegradable organics which are resistant to biological degradation. For example, constituents of woody plants, such as tannin and lignic acids, phenols, and cellulose, are found in natural water systems and are considered refractory (resistant to biodegradation).

15 Method for the Treatment of Itching

Itching is a symptom, commonly associated with dermatitis, caused by various insults in mammals. Insect bites, exposure plants or foods, skin diseases and skin disorders are examples of the kind of insult which can result in itching. Pruritus may also be caused by systemic diseases (such as obstructive bilary disease) or be of unknown origin.

Itching of the skin caused by foods, plants or other insults discussed above is frequently caused by the direct contact of irritants and the skin. However, indirect transfer of irritants, such as by ingestion of foods etc., and transport internally through the body to the skin is also believed to occur and to lead to itching. In the art, compounds which induce itching, dermatitis, or both can be referred to as allergens or allergenic compounds, sensitizing or sensitizer compounds, elicitor compounds, irritants or other similar names. In this description, no distinction is made between any of these names, but for convenience they are generally referred to simply as "irritants."

Plant irritants are exemplary of the irritants which come into contact with the skin and lead to itching. For example, itching is commonly associated with contact dermatitis induced by irritants present in plants of the Anacardiaceae and Ginkgoaceae families. Included among these plants are the Toxicodendrons, e.g., poison ivy (T. radicans), Eastern poison oak, (T. quercifolium), poison sumac (T. vernix), and Western poison oak (T. diversilobum). Also included are manzanillo (Rhus striata), Japanese lac (R. verniciflua), Mango tree (Mangifera indica), India ink tree, (Semicarpus anacardum), ginko tree (Ginko biloba L.), and the cashew tree (Anacardium occidentale).

One such group of plant-borne irritants is a mixture of alkyl-catechols known as the urushiols. Urushiols are present in, e.g., poison ivy and Japanese lac, and are known to induce the contact dermatitis commonly known as "poison ivy" rash. One to two million people are said to be afflicted with varying degrees of poison ivy rash each year. It has been estimated that as many as 150,000 working days are lost annually to urushiol induced contact dermatitis.

The mechanism of action of urushiols in inducing contact dermatitis has been described in the literature. Allergic contact dermatitis caused by naturally occurring quinones. It is believed that the mechanism of action of the urushiols may be general to many irritants that lead to itching. Briefly, the process leading to urushiol-induced contact dermatitis, or poison ivy rash, is reported to be as follows. Urushiols are transmitted from the plant to the skin and are oxidized in vivo to ortho-quinones. The ortho-quinones are thought to interact with proteins and form quinone-protein conjugates which act as the actual antigens. Next, the conjugates are reported to be presented to inexperienced T-lymphocytes by epidermal macrophages. The exposed lymphocytes can develop into immunologically competent lymphocytes which are capable of reacting to subsequent exposure to the urushiols. At this point a mammal is said to be sensitized to the urushiols. The subsequent exposure of these competent lymphocytes to urushiol (ortho-quinone)-protein conjugates is thought to lead to the release of lymphokines and the manifestation of urushiol induced contact dermatitis—the poison ivy rash.

Poison ivy rash starts with a reddening of the skin and itching. The itching intensifies with time and watery blisters appear. The itching typically causes afflicted mammals to scratch the affected area. This can delay healing and can spread urushiols to a wider area of the skin or other parts of the body.

The widespread occurrence of poison ivy induced dermatitis has led to the proposal of many treatments to prevent or alleviate the symptoms of the poison ivy rash. Methods reported to prevent the rash include the use of desensitizing materials, urushiol absorbing materials, and forming protective layers on the skin to block irritants. Reportedly useful methods for alleviating symptoms include applying plant extracts, corticosteroids, and enzymes including catechol oxygenase or p-diphenol oxidase, washing irritants from the skin with polyglycol ethers, thymopentin therapy and the use of topical anesthetics.

In addition, there are numerous purportedly effective ethnobotanical treatments for alleviating itching, including the itching associated with poison ivy. However, the use of plant material or crude plant extracts in therapeutic methods, compositions and kits can have undesirable drawbacks. These include the presence in the final composition of unknown or undesirable irritants that can exacerbate itching, dermatitis, or both. Compositions can also vary widely in components and component concentrations depending on factors such as method of preparation or plant growth conditions, e.g., soil type, nutrient supply, season, water supply, etc. Other drawbacks and dangers of applying plant materials to dermatitis include the potential presence of excess bulk; irritating bits of leaf, stem or root; soil; insect parts and infectious microorganisms.

One such ethnobotanical cure purported that jewelweed was an effective plant in the treatment of itching associated with poison ivy rash. However, publications have dismissed the value of treatments using this plant.

DESCRIPTION

It has been discovered that 1,4-naphthoquinones, wherein the hydroxyl group is at position 2 or 3, and juglones (a class of 1,4 naphthoquinones that are not so substituted) are useful in alleviating the itching generally associated with any irritation or allergic reaction. These compounds are useful in alleviating pruritus, e.g., the itching associated with contact dermatitis. For example, these compounds are useful in alleviating the itching induced by ortho-quinone forms of various cyclic irritants or from itching caused by any irritant or allergic reaction.

It is reported in the art that urushiols are members of a class of irritant compounds that exist as, or are oxidized in vivo to, ortho-quinones and that these ortho-quinone forms are responsible for the allergenic nature of these compounds. Urushiols appear to be the most studied of these irritants due to the impact of the poison ivy induced contact dermatitis in humans. It is also generally reported that the ortho-quinone forms of the urushiols and other irritants are important in the overall pathology of contact dermatitis.

Without wishing to be bound by any particular theory, it is postulated that the 1,4-naphthoquinone compounds useful as taught herein act by blocking an activity or binding of ortho-quinones and other irritants that causes itching and other symptoms of contact dermatitis. It is possible that the 1,4-naphthoquinones can alleviate itching by blocking the interaction of ortho-quinones and other irritants with histamine receptors, or by otherwise inactivating histamine receptors.

A general class of 1,4-naphthoquinones compounds useful in the present invention are characterized by a hydroxyl group at the 2 or 3 position. This general class of 1,4-naphthoquinones can exist in equilibrium with 1,2-diketo or 2,3-diketo forms. For example, a 2-hydroxy-1,4-naphthoquinone can exist in equilibrium with the 1,2-diketo as: ##STR11## The diketo forms can mimic ortho-quinones and other irritants that cause itching and trigger contact dermatitis, e.g., urushiols. The 1,4-naphthoquinones are thereby postulated to compete with and or block the activity or binding of allergenic ortho-quinones and other irritants.

A useful class of compounds in this invention are juglones, for example, 5-hydroxy-1,4 naphthoquinone. This compound is similar in action to the lawsone derivatives (2-hydroxy-1,4 naphthoquinone) in structure and will react with proteins in the same manner. Essentially, in nature, the reaction of the keto forms of both will react with the amino groups of proteins even though the spacing between the formed carbonyls is different. In the lawsone the 2-hydroxy becomes a carbonyl and the 1,2-dicarbonyl derivative is bioactive. In solution, the 5-hydroxy group of juglone becomes a carbonyl. The 4,5-dicarbonyl is again bioactive, even though there is one ring carbon between the two carbonyls. It has been observed that this compound (juglone) has a more powerful anti-itch property than lawsone. Juglone is a natural product found in walnuts (genus Juglans).

Many of the general class of 1,4-naphthoquinones described herein are not seen to be generally sensitizing in mammals either generally or at effective concentrations useful in this invention. For example, lawsone, a 2-hydroxy-1,4-naphthoquinone, and its derivatives have been used in contact with human skin for hundreds of years as hair coloring. Lawsone and derivatives are also used applied to the skin as skin colorant or protectant from UV radiation. Lapachol, a 3-hydroxy-1,4-naphthoquinone is also known to exhibit very low sensitizing activity (see e.g., Lepoittevin and Benezra, incorporated above). Another example is phthiocol, a compound found in Tabebuia avellanedae Lor. ex Griseb. and now also considered to be an oxidative artifact of K vitamin synthesis. Phthiocol is also believed to be non-sensitizing or allergenic at concentrations that would be effective to relieve itching.

It should be noted that the subset of 1,4-naphthoquinones where both the 2 and 3 positions are hydroxyl can be photosensitizers. If these compounds are used one should be aware that exposure of skin to, for example, sunlight, treated with these compounds can lead to inflammation and increased discomfort.

The 1,4-naphthoquinone compounds useful to alleviate itching as described herein can form dimers, or other oligomers, in solution. Dimers, or other oligomers, can be formed by interactions between carbons 5-10 of two 1,4-naphthoquinone molecules. (see, e.g., Lepoittevin and Benezra, incorporated above). No difference in the action of the compounds useful in this invention has been noted due to the presence of oligomers.

Similarly, these 1,4-naphthoquinone compounds can exist in nature, and be isolated or purified therefrom as 1-glucosyl-, 4-glucosyl- or 1,4-diglucosyl forms. For example, 2-hydroxy-juglone (2,6-dihydroxy-p-naphthoquinone) can occur as a hydrojuglone glycoside. The sensitizing capacity of naturally occurring quinones—Experimental studies in Guinea pigs. I. Naphthoquinones and related compounds.. 1,4-Naphthoquinones useful in this invention can be natural compounds or synthetic compounds—the latter including synthetic derivatives made from natural compounds. Synthetic and natural compounds can be equivalently used in this invention. For example, lawsone, 2-hydroxy-1,4-naphthoquinone, is commonly isolated or purified from Lawsonia alba and related species, e.g. L. inermis. The chemical synthesis of lawsone is also known and synthetic lawsone is commercially available. In a method, kit, or composition of this invention, either natural or synthetic lawsone can be used.

As will be recognized by those skilled in the art, derivatives of the 1,4-naphthoquinones described herein can be made and used in the method, compositions and kits of this invention. The 1,4-naphthoquinones have an aromatic ring that can optionally carry one or more substituents X: ##STR12## wherein either R or R′ may be a hydroxyl or a methoxy group and the other one of R or R′, is selected from the group consisting of hydrogen, hydroxyl, methyl, methoxy, quaternary amine, cycloalkyl group containing 3 to 7 carbon atoms, and alkyl, 1-alkylaminoalkyl, 1-alkenyl or alkanoyl groups of 2 to 3 carbons, and wherein the aromatic ring of the 1,4-naphthoquinone is unsubstituted. Alternatively, is substituted with one or more groups which do not adversely affect the effectiveness of the 1,4-naphthoquinone, thus the ring substituent X, ca be any ring substitution which does not adversely affect the effectiveness the 1,4-naphthoquinone, e.g., a ring substitution can alter, but not abolish the therapeutic activity of the 1,4-naphthoquinone compound. The ring substituent X, can be chosen from a variety of chemical groups. For example, X can be selected from halogens such as Cl, Br & F, or from oxygenated groups including phosphates, nitrates, sulphates, or from methoxy, carboxy, carboxylate or carboxy-lower alkyl group, or from hydroxy or hydroxylates, or from quaternary amines, or from glucosyl or glucosylamine, or from a variety of branched or straight chain alkyl groups or methyl.

One or more ring substitutions can be a useful means to increase or decrease solubility as deemed desirable for suitable use in this invention. As is apparent to one skilled in the art, a hydrophilic substituent should increase solubility while a hydrophobic substituent should decrease solubility.

Herein, these derivatives are referred to as being a member of the 1,4-naphthoquinone of the source material, or having a chemical backbone thereof. For example, a ring substitution derivative of lawsone are referred to as one of the "lawsones," a ring substitution derivative of lapachol are referred to as one of the "lapachols," and so on. In cases of named compounds that carry ring substituents as named, an example being juglone having a hydroxyl group on the aromatic ring, a derivative is a compound with at least one additional ring substitution.

EXAMPLES

Example 1. Compositions.

For solid compositions, compounds useful in this invention can be provided separately or can be compounded with conventional nontoxic solid carriers such as, for example, pharmaceutical grades of mannitol, lactose, starch, magnesium stearate, talcum, cellulose, glucose, sucrose, magnesium carbonate, and the like. Liquid pharmaceutically-administrable topical compositions can be prepared, for example, by dissolving the a 1,4-naphthoquinone and optional pharmaceutical adjuvants in an aqueous carrier, such as, for example, water, aqueous dextrose, and the like, to thereby form a solution or suspension. If desired, the pharmaceutical composition to be administered can also contain minor amounts of nontoxic auxiliary substances such as pH buffering agents and the like, for example, sorbitan monolaurate, triethanolamine, sodium acetate, triethanolamine oleate, etc. Compositions can also be prepared as creams, sols or gels in aqueous bases.

A 1,4-naphthoquinone or derivative may be solubilized in an appropriate solvent, e.g., 5-10% ethanol when preparing a compound.

1,4-Naphthoquinones can vary in their stability in a topical composition. As when formulating any composition, compositions of this invention should be tested for shelf-life. For example, the composition used in a clinical trial described below is 2-hydroxy-1,4-naphthoquinone mixed in water. It has been found that this composition is most effective if used within about three days of mixing. It has been noted that once mixed into water, the effectiveness of the topical composition gradually decreases over about three days and then levels off.

Example 2. Method of Treatment of Itching.

The method of this invention is simply performed by applying a topical composition containing an effective amount of an 1,4-naphthoquinone to the skin of a mammal in need of treatment because the mammal is afflicted with pruritus, which can also be associated with dermatitis.

The amount of a 1,4-naphthoquinone which is effective can be determined via standard experimental techniques known in the art of dosage formulation. Briefly, one can begin by preparing topical compositions containing from 0.1 to 100.0 ppm (parts per million) of a particular 1,4-naphthoquinone in a pharmaceutically acceptable carrier. The topical compositions are then tested by applying them to the skin of an afflicted mammal and scoring the relief from itching provided by the composition. One can proceed to test concentrations of a 1,4 naphthoquinone above and below the aforementioned ranges as necessary to arrive at an effective amount, i.e., one can prepare compositions ranging up to 200, 500, 750 or 1000 ppm for compounds or formulations that are relatively less effective and down to 0.05, 0.025, 0.01, 0.0075, 0.005, 0.0025 or more with compounds or formulations that are relatively more effective. The concentration may also be determined by weight of the compound, e.g., not less than 2-10 μg/ml.

For example, if the mammal is a guinea pig a topical composition can be applied to a shaved portion of the mammal's skin in which a contact dermatitis has been induced and the animal can be observed for behavioral changes indicating relief from itching. If the mammal is a human, the topical composition can be applied to the skin of the person and the person can be asked directly to subjectively assess the relief conferred by the composition.

Once the range of effective amounts has been determined, a topical composition containing an effective amount can be prepared on demand for conducting the method of treatment of this invention.

Example 3. Kits to Facilitate Performing the Method of Treatment.

A kit is a useful means of conducting the method of treatment described herein. A kit can provide a container in which at least one, or a plurality, of a predetermined amount of a 1,4-naphthoquinone is provided to a user to facilitate performing the method. The user can employ the kit to perform the method on themselves or on another.

The predetermined amount of 1,4-naphthoquinone compound can be conveniently provided in many different formulations in a kit. The 1,4-naphthoquinone can be provided dry to allow the user to prepare the topical composition shortly before use. If dispensed under prescription, a pharmacist could prepare the topical composition shortly before dispensing to a patient. If the compound is not provided in a dry form, a topical composition can be conveniently formulated in a pharmaceutically acceptable carrier suitable to use with the particular 1,4-naphthoquinone. For example, if lawsone is the 1,4-naphthoquinone, water or a water soluble gel, sol or cream is an acceptable carrier. The addition of water allows the hydroxy and diketo states of lawsone to be in equilibrium.

Several convenient compositions of 1,4-naphthoquinone are particularly useful. A powdered composition of or containing 1,4-naphthoquinone can be used to provide predetermined amounts of 1,4-naphthoquinone. It is useful to provide these compositions in kits in containers of various types including pouches, capped vials or bottles, spray bottles etc. If a pouch is provided the user can prepare a topical composition by adding the contents of the pouch to an amount of an liquid carrier. If a container is provided in the kit the user can prepare a topical composition simply by adding an aqueous carrier to the container and shaking. Various other means of providing powdered formulations for the preparation of topical compositions are known, or will be apparent, to those of ordinary skill in the art.

When using a kit, a desired final concentration of a 1,4-naphthoquinone in a topical composition can be realized in many ways. For example, the final concentration can be achieved by adding a predetermined amount of aqueous carrier to the composition, e.g., a container can contain a composition and have a fill line to indicate that a predetermined amount of aqueous carrier should be added. Instructions can be provided directing a user to add a particular amount of an aqueous carrier to a particular amount of a composition.

Alternatively, a final concentration can be achieved by relying on the solubility of a particular 1,4-naphthoquinone in a topical composition. For example, lawsone is soluble in water at up to about 100 micrograms per milliliter. If the particular 1,4-naphthoquinone is lawsone and the topical composition is lawsone in water, then the solubility limit of lawsone in the carrier water can limit the final concentration of the 1,4-naphthoquinone in the topical composition. It should be noted that additional components in a topical composition can affect the solubility of the 1,4-naphthoquinone. Therefore, if one desires to rely on solubility limits to determine the final concentration of the 1,4-naphthoquinone in a topical composition a simple solubility test can be performed with the particular 1,4-naphthoquinone in a particular topical composition.

Example 4. Dissolving tablets.

A 1,4-naphthoquinone can be formulated into tablets that will dissolve in an aqueous carrier to create a topical composition containing an effective amount of an 1,4-naphthoquinone. The tablets can be added to an amount of an aqueous carrier and mixed to dissolve and form a topical composition. Effervescent tablet formulations can also be used and can avoid an need to mix to form the topical composition. As described above, the final concentration can be controlled by adding a predetermined amount of a formulation to a predetermined amount of carrier, by directions or by solubility.

Example 5. Clinical Evidence of Lawsone Effectiveness.

A clinical trial was held to assess the effectiveness of 1,4-naphthoquinones in the treatment of itching. Lawsone, 2-hydroxy-1,4-naphthoquinone was chosen as the 1,4-naphthoquinone tested in the clinical trial because it is readily available and has been used uneventfully in contact with human skin for cosmetic purposes. Other 1,4-naphthoquinones can be tested in a similar manner.

Lawsone was obtained as an orange powder from Sigma Chemical Co., St. Louis, Mo. 1994 catalog number H0508. The powder was divided into containers in predetermined amounts of about 10 milligrams for the convenience of the subjects.

The subjects were human volunteers presenting with symptoms of contact dermatitis caused by poison ivy. The volunteers gave their informed consent to the treatment tested in the clinical trial.

The subjects were provided with the 1,4-naphthoquinone and directions to prepare a topical composition as follows: The subjects were instructed to place approximately one half of the powder into a cup or beaker and to add tap water, preferably not hot water. Because lawsone is only soluble in water up to about 100 micrograms per milliliter the subjects were instructed that the powder would not completely dissolve into solution and some should be present in the bottom of the cup after mixing.

The solubility limit of lawsone in water acted as an internal control on final concentration, removing any requirement that the subjects accurately measure the amount of powder they used and ensured that similar concentration, about 100 micrograms per milliliter, was used by all subjects receiving lawsone. The subjects were further instructed to save the solution remaining after a treatment and to add additional water for the next treatment. The subjects were told not to add additional powder unless the powder dissolved completely.

The volunteers were instructed to apply the topical composition to about one half of the affected area(s) of their skin by, e.g., dabbing the composition onto the skin with a cotton ball, a cloth, paper tissue, paper towel, or the like. The remaining one half of the affected area(s) was considered a control area and was treated only with water.

The subjects were instructed to self-administer the solution as follows: On the first day the subjects were instructed to apply a freshly made solution to the affected area of their skin. A second application was to be made when the itching returned. On the second and following days two or three treatments were recommended but self-administration was unrestrained.

For comparative purposes, the subjects were asked to treat a portion of their affected areas only with water. However, if that area was very uncomfortable the subjects were asked to withhold the 1,4-naphthoquinone treatment for only the first day.

The subjects were provided with sufficient lawsone to make a topical composition for at least several days, if not weeks, of applications. The subjects treated themselves and recorded the effects of the topical composition by filling out a questionnaire. If the lawsone was used on the control area from the second day onward the subjects noted this on the questionnaire.

All subjects receiving lawsone during the trial indicated that the topical composition provided complete relief from the itching of poison ivy, induced dermatitis. The relief was reported to last from one to six hours. At this point the subjects could reapply the topical composition. No relief was demonstrable from the water applied to control areas in the trial. Additionally, about one third of the subjects reported accelerated healing of the affected areas of their skin. However, in this study controls were not in place to distinguish the effects of the topical composition from the effects of the subjects refraining from scratching affected areas.

Example 6. Clinical Evidence of Effectiveness with Additional Naphthquinones.

In this example a clinical trial is conducted essentially as described above except that the 1,4-naphthoquinones selected from the lapachols, phthiocols, 2-hydroxy-juglones, 3-hydroxy-juglones, flaviolins, lawsones and other related compounds are used as the test compounds. These 1,4-naphthoquinones are obtained from commercial sources and prepared for distribution in predetermined amounts to be used in topical compositions of predetermined final concentrations. The final concentrations should be well below the amounts that can be sensitizing or irritating in humans. Simple pretesting of skin can be required to assess irritation (e.g., allergenicity). If a compound is too irritating it is not recommended for use in the method, composition or kits described herein.

Subjects are obtained from human volunteers presenting with contact dermatitis with itching. The subjects are divided into treatment groups receiving each of the test compounds and one or more control groups receiving a placebo compound. Each subject is instructed in the conduct of the clinical trial.

The subjects are instructed in the preparation of and self-administration of topical compositions containing a test compound (or a placebo). The subjects self administer the topical composition one or more times the first day of treatment as needed and for one to three days thereafter. The volunteers record the effectiveness of the tested compounds in relieving the itching associated with the dermatitis by responding to a questionnaire.

The results of the trial are analyzed by review of the questionnaires and the effectiveness of the tested compounds in providing relief from itching is determined.

16 A Process of Preparing A Herbal Filler Composition for Bidi Cigarette

Bidi, cigarette or cheroot made from tobacco contains nicotine and such bidi, cigarette or cheroot when lighted and smoked are deleterious to the health of smokers. The harmful nature of nicotine is universally known. Nicotine exists in tobacco in formation with maleic acid or citric acid. It is a colourless oily liquicl, which contains low oxide. It is volatile and water-soluble. It smells like tobacco and becomes brown when exposed to air. It is strong poison, since two or three drops will be fatal for human. Even a small amount in the lungs causes drowsiness, headache and dizziness. Excessive long term smoking causes clumsiness and stomach and eye disorders.

Nicotine has been implicated as a carcinogenic substance by many cancer research organizations through out the world. For example, in the 1978 and 1982 journals of international agencies for research on cancer, it is said that nicotine is a major factor in the cause of cancel.

People have smoked tobacco for a long time. Many people enjoy smoking at the present time and many people have died as a result of lung cancer caused by nicotine.

It has been reported that it is 6-10 times more likely for smokers to die from lung cancer than for non-smokers. Smoking prohibition has been initiated everywhere and there is a widespread anti-smoking campaign. Although such prohibitions and campaigns may have some degree of effectiveness, it is not the best way to solve the problem. The population of smokers is increasing. Children start smoking as early as 11 or 12 years old. Clearly, the initiation of smoking at such a young age will have deleterious effect on their health. It is therefore highly desirable to remove nicotine from bide, cigarettes and the like.

The object of this method is to make bidi, cigarette or cheroot non-toxic and nicotine free by replacing the tobacco with herbal composition and yet have the same feeling as bidi or cigarette or cheroot with tobacco.

To achieve the said objective this invention provides a process of preparing herbal filler composition for bidi, cigarette and the like comprising : shredding the shade dried leaves of *Lawsonia inermis* L. and Ocimum santum L. separately and mixing them in the ratio I : 0. 72-1 on weight /weight basis, tying the mixture with a sieve and placing it on the mouth of a pot containing the boiling sugar syrup, -keeping said mixture for 20-30 minutes on said sieve, rotating said mixture continuously in the sieve, removing the mixture from the sieve and air drying the material, and - cooling said mixture in shade.

The sugar syrup is prepared from 500 (Ylll gur in 1 liter water.

The sieve and the pot used in the process are khadi cloth and earthen pol respectively.

The above process further comprises mixing extracts of Saussaurea lappa, /7heck catechu, and Terminalia catappa in the range 0. 1-0. 5%, 0.1-0.3% & 20-30% respectively.

The flavouring agents like lemon grass oil, methanol and Eucalyptus oil are included in the herbal filler composition in the range 0. 0004-0. 0008%.

The extract of Sanssaurea lappa is prepared by : washing dry roots of Saussaurea lappa with water till the soil particles are removed, drying said washed roots ulldel-shade till the moistut-e contelll is reduced upto 10%, crushing said roots to fine powder, extracting said crushed roots with food grade ethanol for 5-8 hours, filtering said extract through a sieve, drying said filtrate at temperature below 50 °C until said ethanol is evaporated and a semi solid substance is obtained.

The crushing of roots to fine powder is done by a pulverizer.

The extracting of crushed leaves is carried out by 100% food grade ethanol for 5-8 hours using a reflux condenser.

The said sieve is a muslin cloth.

The extract of Areca catechu is prepared by : -peeling the outer fibrous layer of Areca catechu to obtain round shaped seeds, crushing said seeds to fine powder, extracting said powder with food grade ethanol for 4-6 hours, filtering said extract through a sieve, and drying said filtrate at temperature below 50°C until said ethanol is evaporated and a powdery mass is obtained.

The crushing of seeds to fine powder is done by a pulverizer.

The extracting of crushed seeds is carried out by 100% food grade ethanol for 4-6 hours using a reflux condenser.

The sieve is a muslin cloth.

The extract of Terminalia catappa is prepared by: removing the midribs of fresh Terminalia catappa leaves, drying said leaves till ! moisture reduces to 15-18%, crushing said leaves to powder using a pulverizer, -sieving said powder through a sieve to obtain material having particle size of more than 800 microns.

The said sieve is a 0. 8 mm sieve.

The invention further provides a herba ! fitter composition for bidi, cigarette and the tike comprising sugar coated dried leaves of L awsonia inermis L. and Ocimum scantum L. in the ratio f : 0. 72-1 on weight l weight basis.

The said herbal filler composition further comprises extracts of Saussaurea lappa, Areca Catechu, and Terminalia catappa in the range 0.1-0. 5%, 0. I-0. 3°, 20-30% respectively.

The flavouring agents, like lemon grass oil, methanol and Eucalyptus oil are included in the herbal filler composition in the range 0.0004-0. 0008%.

The invention also provides a cigarette prepared from the herbal filler composition of claim 1 comprising sugar coated dried leaves of *Lawsonia inermis* L. and Ocimum santum L in the ratio 1: 0.72 on wt/wt basis.

The instant invention further provides a bidi prepared from the herbal fitter composition of claims 1 to 5 comprising'L. awsonia inermis L. and Ocimum santum L. in the ratio 1 : 0. 72-1 on weight/. weight basis and extracts of Saussaurea lappa, Ai-eco and Terminalia catappa in the range 0.1-0. 5%, 0. 1-0. 3% and 20-30% respectively.

The invention further relates to a herbal filler composition for bidi, cigarette and the like comprising: 75% of sugar coated dried leaves of *Lawsonia inermis* L. and Ocimum santum L., – 25% of Terminalia catappa coated with Saussaurea lappa, Areca C.'aleclrrr and lemon grass oil.

25% of Terminalia catappa is coated with 0. 3% of Saussaurea lappa, 0. 2% of Areca Catechu and 0.0006% of lemon grass oil.

Details of Plants Used in Place of Non-tobacco Materials for Filling in Cigarettes and Beedis

1. *Lawsonia inermis* L.

Vernacular names : Sans : Madayantika, Hindi : Mehendi, Beng : Mehedi; Tam: Maruthani; Eng : Henna.

Occurrence & Distribution : Cultivated throughout India for its leaves and as a hedge-plant; found wild in Western India.

Description : A glabrous shrub, with angular branchlets, sometimes spinescent.

Leaves coriaceous, elliptic or ovate-elliptic from a cuneate base. Flowers greenish-yellow, cream-coloured or white, very fragrant, borne m terminal paniculate cymes.

Capsules depressed, globose, irregularly dehiscent, with numerous angular seeds.

Flowers and fruits during April-July.

Parts used : Leaves

Uses : given in leucorrhoea, menorrhagia and externally in headache, paste (with vinegar or lime guice) applied as poultice over the soles to relieve the troublesome burning sensation of the feet; (with water) in rheumatism; decotion is astringent and beneficial in burns, bruises, inflammation and sprains, uses as a gargle in cases of ulcer in the mouth, juice mixed with milk prescribed in spermatorrhoea; an ointment from the leaves useful as a cure of wounds and ulcers.

Generla chemical constituents : 7- and 3'- glucosides of luteolin, 2-hydroxy-α - naphthaquinone (lawsone); esculetin, fraxetin, scopoletin (leaves); 5-allyloxy-7-hydroxycoumarin, 1-hydroxy-3, 6-diacetoxy-7- methoxy xanthone and 1-hydroxy- 3, 7-dimethoxy-6-acetoxy-xanthone, 1,3-dihydroxy-6, 7-dimethoxy-xanthone isolated from the plalit.

2. *Ocimum sarzturn* L.

Vernacular names: San: Surasah, Tulasi; Hin: Kalatulsi, Tulsi; Tam : Tulasi; Eng: Holy basil.

Occurrence & Distribution: Throughout India, as well as cultivated Description: An erect much branched softly pubescent undershrub, 30-60 cm high with red or purple subquadrangular branches; leaves simple, opposite, ellilptic, oblong, obtuse or acute, entire, serrate or dentate, pubescent on both sides, minutely gland dotted, petioles slender, hairy; flowers purplish in elongate racemes in close whorls, stamens, exerted, upper pair with a small bearded appendage at the base; fruits nutlets, smooth, not mucilagninous when wetted.

Parts used: Leaves Uses: The plant is bitter, acrid, aromatic, stomachic, demulcent, diaphoretic, digestive, diuretic, expectorant, febrifuge, vermifuge and alexeteric. It is useful in cardiopathy, haemopathy, leucoderma, asthma, bronchitis, catarrhal fever, ota) gia, hepatopathy, vomiting, lumbago, hiccough, ophthalmia, gastropathy in children, genitor-urinary disorders, ringworm, verminosis and skin diseases.

General chemical constituents: Leaves contain 0. 075% of oil. Cadinene, 1, 8-cineole, eugenol, limonene and methylchavicol are found in leaf oil. Leaves afforded β-carotene and ursolic acid.

3. *Terminalia catappa* L.

Vernacular Name : Sans : Batada; Hindi & Bengali : Gangli; Tamil : Nattu badam, vadam; Eng : Indian Almond Tree Occurrence and Distribution : Largely planted on Road sides towards the warmer parts of India including the Andamans.

Description : A Medium sized tree with branches in horizontal whorls. Leaves clustered towards ends of the branches, 15-20 cm) long; deciduous in the cold season, obovate, spikes axillary, solitary, grey or rusty tomentose; the upper flowers male, the tower hermaphrodite, fruits ellipsoidal, slightly compressed. Flowers during April-June and Fruits during October-December Parts Used: Leaves.

Uses : sudorific, applied to rheumatic joints, ointment made from juice useful in scabies and other cutaneous affections.

General ctiemical constituents : Ellagic acid, chebulagic acid, corilagin, 1-desgalloyl-eugenin, geraniin, punicalgin, granatin B, punicalin, tercatin, terftavins A and B, tergallagin and 2,3-[(S)-4,4′,5,5′,6,6′-hexahydroxy diphenoxyl]-D-glucose.

4. Saussurea lappa

Hindi-Kuth; Eng.-Costus Family: Composite Occurrence and distribution : Grows in high mountainous regions at 2400 to 3900m altitude. It is cultivated in Lahaul-Spiti valley of Himachal Pradesh and Garhwal of Uttar Pradesh and wildly grown in Kashmir valley.

Description : The plant is a tall, herbaceous, perennial growing upto 2.4 m with radical leaves and a robust stem bearing a cluster of several bluish-black tlower heads. Roots stout often upto 60 cm lon, possessing a characteristic penetrating odour. Seeds for propagation are collected in September from the standing crop by harvesting the flowering stalk, just before the seeds are ripe, stacked in sun for a week and thrashed.

Parts used : Roots Uses: The roots are employed to protect woolen fabrics against insect attack by the locals and lcm piece is eaten raw to alleviate knee joint pain and fever.

General chemical constituents : Essential oil (1.5%). Essential oil constituents (Aplotaxena 20%, Sesquiterpenes (60%), Saussurine alkaloid, Kushtin, Lactones, Costunolide, Palmitic Acid, Dihydrodehydrocostus, lactone, propyl'acetate, lauric acid.

5. Arecal catechu

Eng: Arecanut tree, Betelnut tree; Hin: Supari; Kan : Adike; Mal : Kavunnu, Kamuku; San: Pugah; Tam : Pakkumaram; Tel : Vakka, Poka Family: Arecaceae Occurrence and Distribution : Cultivated throughout India.

Description : A tall slender unbranched palm with a crown of leaves, stem annulate; leaves pinnate with a conspicuous sheath; flowers in spadix, male many at the upper portion, female much larger and few at the base; fruits 3. 8-5 cm long, smooth, orange or scarlet when ripe.

Parts used: Seed (kernel) Uses: The nuts are used either raw or cured. They are cooling, astringent, diuretic, digestive, anthelmintic, aphrodisiac, nervine tonic and emmenagogue.. They are useful in urinary disorders, anorexia and general debility. Chewing of nuts facilitates salivation and prevents decay of teeth; but its continued use blackens and loosens them. The constant use of this nut might result in oral carcinoma. The juice of tender nuts in small doses is a good laxative. The burnt nut is often used as dentifrice.

General chemical constituents : Kernels contain catechu, tannin 15%; gallic acid; oily matter, gum and alkaloids namely arecoline 0.07%, arecaine 1%, arecaidine and guvacoline, guvacaine and choline (occurs in traces only). li.

PLANT SPECIFICATIONS 1. Lawsonia Name of the plant Henna Vernacular names Mehndi Botanical name *Lawsonia inermis* L.

Part required Dried leaves Physical characters Colour brown Texture Free flowing Odour Characteristic Taste Aromatic Chemical character Moisture content < 5% Purity and Identity Foreign matter < 2% Total ash < 5% Acid insoluble ash < 3% Alcohol soluble extractive > 6% Water soluble extractive > 13% TLC identification As per specifications 2. Ocimum Name of the plant Sacred Basil Vernacular names Tulasi Botanical name Ocimum sanctum L.

Part required: Dried leaves Physical characters Colour Green Texture Free flowing Odour Characteristic Taste Astringent Chemical character Moisture content < 5% Purity and Identity Foreign matter < 2% Total ash < 19% Acid insoluble ash < 3% Alcohol soluble extractive > 6% Water soluble extractive > 13% TLC identification 10 spots on Toluene : Ethyl acetate & vanillin-sulphuric acid reagent Heavy metal analysis Lead < 10 ppm Cadmium < 1 ppm Arsenic < 2 ppm Mycotoxin analysis Aflatoxins < 5 ppb 3. Te7 » Name of the plant Indian almond tree Vernacular names Gangli Botanical name Terminalia catappa L.

Part required Mid rib removed crushed leaves Physical characters Colour Green Texture Smooth in the upper portion of the leaf Odour Characteristic Taste Characteristic Mesh size 800-1000 micron Chemical ! character Moisture content Between 10 and 15 % Purity and Identity Foreign matter < 2% Total ash < 11% Acid insoluble ash < 2% TLC identification as per specification Heavy metal analysis Lead < 10 ppm Cadmium < I ppm Arsenic < 2 ppm Mycotoxin analysis

Aflatoxins < 5 ppb 4. Saussaurea Name of the plant Costus Vernacular names Kuth Botanical name Saussaurea lappa 10 Part required Methanolic extract of the root Physico-chemical analysis Colour dark brown Texture soft paste Odour Characteristic Taste Aromatic Moisture content < 10% w/w Ash content < 9% \v/Nv Acid insoluble ash < 3% w/w 5. Au-eco 15 Name of the plant Betel nut tree Vernacular names Supari Botanical name Areca cafechil L.

Part required. Nut Physical characters : Colour light brown Texture Fresh nut (not dried) Odour 20 Characteristic Taste Characteristic Purity and Identity Foreign matter < 2% Total ash < 5% Acid insoluble ash < 2% TLC identification as per specification 25 Heavy metal analysis Lead < 10 ppm Cadmium < I ppm Arsenic < 2 pupil7 30.

Processing and Preparation of Herbal Extracts

1. Processing of Terminalia catappa Mid ribs are removed manually when the leaves are fresh and kept in direct sunlight as a single layer for 8 hours or in an electric oven till the moisture content comes down to 15 to 18%. The material is then crushed using a pulveriser and sieved (800 35 microns). The material having the particle size of more than 800 microns is taken for further processing. Terttiin. Processing of Saussaurea lappa The dried roots are washed thoroughly with water till all the soil particles are removed and

dried under shade until the moisture content comes to 10%. The roots are then crushed to fine powder using a pulverizer and extracted with 100% food grade ethanol for 6 hours using a reflux condenser. The extract is filtered through muslin cloth and the filtrate is dried with the help of a flash evaporator under vacuum (-600mmHg) with temperature below 50°C until all the alcohol gets evaporated and a semisolid substance is obtained.

The above herbal filler composition further includes the extracts of Saussaurea lappa, Areca Catechu, and Terminalia catappa to have taste of bidi, for instance :

3.03 gm of the semisolid substance of Saussaurea lappa is dissolved in 20 ml of 100% food grade ethanol and mixed with 2. 5 gm of powdery mass of KS (dissolved earlier in 5 ml of 100% food grade ethanol). 12.5 microliter of Lemon grass oil is then added to the mixture. This mixture was coated thoroughly on 250 gm kg of the processed Terminalia catappa leaves using a tine sprayer. To the 25Ugm of the processed leaves, 750 gm of above herbal filler composition is added.

1. For making Beedis: MT 5 and MT 6 are used for making beedis. The MT 5 and MT 6 prepared as stated above are air dried under shade or dark for 12 hours. Then the leaves are rolled in beedi leaves and dried in hot air oven at 80°C for 5 minutes. The beedis thus made are allowed to cool and packed.
2. For making Cigarettes : MT 1 and MT 4 are used for making cigarettes. The MT I and MT 4 prepared as stated above are air dried under shade or dark for 12 hours. Then the leaves are dried in hot air oven at 80°C for 3-4 minutes to remove any moisture. The leaves thus obtained are allowed to cool in shade and used for making cigarettes.

17 Antibacterial Deodorizing Compositions

Body odor is formed when fresh perspiration, which is odorless per se, is decomposed by microorganisms. This process takes place principally, though not solely, in the axilla, and a number of microorganisms are involved, each having different activity and leading to body odor of different strength and unpleasantness. The most prominent odor-producing microorganisms include aerobic diphtheroids, primarily Corynebacterium species and coagulase negative cocci such as Micrococcaceae.

Various microorganisms are found in different proportions in different individuals, and this is a reason for the fact that different individuals exhibit different body odors.

The commercial cosmetic deodorants are based on different active principles. The formation of perspiration is suppressed according to the known art by astringents, predominantly aluminum salts such as aluminum hydroxychloride. Apart from the denaturation of the skin proteins, however, the substances used for this purpose clog the pores, interfere drastically with the heat regulation of the axillary region, may cause cancer and other diseases, and should at best be used in exceptional cases. According to another accepted prior art method, the bacterial flora on the skin is reduced by antimicrobial substances. Finally, body odor can also be concealed by fragrances, which, however, is the least able to meet the aesthetic needs of the consumer, as the mixture of body odor and perfume fragrance smells rather unpleasant.

According to a recent patent on this subject, deodorants should fulfill the following conditions:

1. The biological processes of the skin must not be impaired.
2. The deodorants should have no distinct intrinsic odor.
3. They must be harmless in the case of overdosage or other unintended use.
4. They should not concentrate on the skin after repeated use.
5. It should be possible to incorporate them easily into commercial cosmetic formulations.

Those which are known and usable are both liquid deodorants, for example aerosol sprays, roll-ons and the like and solid preparations, for example deodorant sticks, powders, powder sprays, intimate cleansers etc.

U.S. Pat. approaches the problem by employing antibiotics, which are said to be specific microbiocides which predominantly destroy odor-forming microorganisms.

All the prior art methods suffer from severe drawbacks: they require the masking of body odor which has already formed prior to the application of the deodorant, because the destruction of axillary microorganisms does not remove already formed odor. They require the use of antimicrobial agents which must have a long-lasting activity on the skin, because the skin flora is not completely exterminated by their application, and, quite importantly, they very often leave unpleasant stains or halos on the cloths, particularly at and around the axilla. Also the safety of many antiperspirants is dubious, due to the presence of potentially harmful components, and the result is often unpleasant, because of the unnatural odor obtained.

Notwithstanding the many efforts made during many years, and the magnitude of the problem involved, the art has failed to provide deodorizing compositions which are convenient and safe to use, which are effective for a long time. The inventors have now surprisingly found, and this is an object of the invention, that the aforesaid goals can be achieved by using a well known harmless and effective natural agent: Henna.

Henna (*Lawsonia inermis*) is a small shrub growing in Arabia, North Africa, Iran and the East Indies. Dried leaves are a source of green powder used in cosmetics. Although henna paste has been used as a remedy for boils, wounds and some mycotic infections, there are few data on the activity of extracts.

S. S. Bhatnagar et al. examined antibacterial, antitubercular and antifungal action of 351 Indian plants. The extraction method was first using petrol (b.p. 40-60° C.), followed by extraction of the extracted powder with either 90% or 10% methanol. They found that henna powder was active against all three categories, although they did not list the kind of extracts which were active. One of the few scientific papers discussing extraction of henna for antibacterial activity is that of F. Malekzadeh. He studied aqueous extracts and found that while both Gram + and Gram – bacteria were inhibited, inhibitory action was greatest against Bacillus anthracis and least against Staphylococcus aureus.

One known component of henna is lawsone, a napthoquinone pigment which has antibacterial activity against oral species.

While henna has been used since biblical times as a colorant, and has been mentioned anecdotally as an antiperspirant and antibacterial agent and as a source of gallic acid which inhibits "Streptococcus aureus" slightly, the direct use of henna extract has been always limited due to its high staining power, which is undesirable both to skin and clothing.

Z. F. Mahmoud et al. isolated seven crystalline compounds from Egyptian henna leaves. They write that henna has been used for preserving mummies, and has been used for skin diseases and tinea of the legs. They extracted powdered leaves at room temperature with ethanol. The ethanolic extract was concentrated under vacuum and partitioned between chloroform and water. The aqueous layer was successively extracted with ethyl acetate, etc. They cite that the lawsone, the dyeing principle of henna has bacteriostatic properties, citing the work of Karawya et al.

Karawya et al. did not actually check antibacterial activity, but rather established a simple method for estimating the quantity of lawsone. They also mention antifungal and antibacterial properties, citing the work of Hoffman et al.

Black Henna, according to the information given by Alban Muller International, is a mixture of henna powder, and black powder from the plant Indigofera tinctoria. According to Anand et al., I. tinctoria is an annual herbaceous shrub 4-6 feet high found throughout India. It was cultivated in India, China and other countries of the east as a source of Indigo (a colorant that dates back to biblical times, according to B. Chisik in his book in Hebrew, "Treasure of plants". The extract of the plant is used in epilepsy, nervous disorders and bronchitis. The authors extracted the aerial part of the plant (powdered) with 50% alcohol. They then checked and found marked antihepatotoxic effect in animals.

In another paper, the authors presented histological evidence for protection of liver cells, against carbontetrachloride induced hepatotoxicity using a 50% ethanolic extract.

In another article by R. Han, the author reports that indirubin from Indigofera tinctoria is useful for the treatment of chronic myelocytic leukemia.

The fact that henna extracts have never been considered for use in respect of body odor control is probably related, inter alia, to the fact that henna extract retain a high staining power and thus any composition containing such extract is inherently deleterious to clothing and is not to be considered for application to the skin in the vicinity of clothing.

It is an object of the present invention to provide body-odor controlling compositions containing henna extracts, which are efficient to control skin microorganisms which are responsible for body odor.

It is another object of the invention to provide such deodorizing composition based on henna extracts, which can be used to control body odor, without incurring the risk of staining clothing.

It is yet another object of the invention to provide deodorizing compositions which are selective toward specific skin microorganisms, and that therefore permit to control body odor without harming the natural flora of the skin.

It is still another object of the invention to provide a method for deodorizing human or animal skin, and for preventing the formation of body odor.

It is a further object of the invention to provide a process for manufacturing a deodorizing composition of the invention.

Other objects and advantages of the invention will become apparent as the description proceeds.

DESCRIPTION

The above and other characteristics and advantages of the invention will be more readily apparent through the following examples of preferred embodiments thereof

General Procedures

The extraction process: One ml of solvent was added to 0.1-0.2 gr of henna powder. The mixture was vortexed for 10 min and the samples were centrifuged for 30 min at 10000 rpm. The supernatant was collected and referred to as the extract. The extract was then filtered through a 0.22 or a 0.45 μm filter.

Following centrifugation, the extract was allowed to stand at room temperature. It was noted that despite the previous centrifugation and filtration, a fine dark precipitate slowly collected towards the bottom of the aliquots. The amount of precipitate decreased as the percentage of alcohol increased. When this was observed, it was decided to check whether this precipitation resulted in a difference in antibacterial activity. The extract was centrifuged for an additional 30 min at 10000 rpm, and the upper layer (relatively free from precipitate) and the lower layer (rich in precipitate) were separated and tested separately for antibacterial activity. Almost no difference was found between the diameter of the inhibition zones, although the lower phase (rich in precipitate) formed a more transparent inhibition zone.

Inhibition test: The antimicrobial activity of the various extracts was examined by applying samples (5 μl) onto lawns of axillary bacteria. Following incubation of 24 hours at 37° C., inhibition was determined by measuring the diameter of the growth inhibition zone (in cm). In the tables, "+" indicates full growth inhibition(transparent zone), "–" indicates lack of inhibition, and "+/"" indicates partial inhibition (translucent zone).

Comparative Testing

For the purposes of comparative testing, 5 μl aliquots of either red or black henna extracts (20% w/v in 20% v/v ethanol) are applied to the bacterial lawns.

Red henna extract is considered active when:

1. (*a*) it inhibits the growth of *C. xerosis*,

(*b*) the inhibition zone is transparent or translucent, and

(*c*) the diameter of the inhibition zone is greater then 0.5 cm, and

2. it does not inhibit the growth of *S. epidermidis* (although in some cases, a translucent "inhibition" zone is seen).

Black henna extract is considered active when:

1. (*a*) it inhibits the growth of *C. xerosis*,

(*b*) the inhibition zone is transparent or translucent, and

(*c*) the diameter of the inhibition zone is greater then 0.5 cm, and

2. (*a*) it inhibits the growth of *S. epidermidis*,

(*b*) the inhibition is transparent, and

(*c*) the diameter is bigger then 0.5 cm.

Some purified components of henna (according to the specification sheet given by Alban Muller International) were tested, and no activity similar to that described herein was found. Solutions of lawsone, 1,4-naphthoquinone and gallic acid were tested for growth inhibition of Staphylococcus eidermidis and Corynebacterium xerosis.

The results are detailed in Table 17.1 below:

Table 17.1

Component	Solvent	Inhibition of S.epidermidis	Inhibition of *C. xerosis*
lawsone 0.2%	ethanol 20%	–	–
lawsone 0.02%	ethanol 20%	–	–
lawsone 0.01%	ethanol 20%	–	–
1,4–naphthoquinone 0.2%	ethanol 20%	+, 1.4 cm	+,0.8 cm
1,4–naphthoquinone 0.02%	ethanol 20%	–	–
1,4–naphthoquinone 0.01%	ethanol 20%	–	–
gallic acid 0.4%	ethanol 20%	+/31	–
gallic acid 0.2%	ethanol 20%	–	–
lawsone 1.0%	hot water	–	–
lawsone 1.0%	ethanol 50%	–	–
lawsone 1.0%	ethanol 100%	–	–

Although 1,4-naphthoquinone which is supposed to be found in henna leaves inhibits the growth of the two strains, it seems that the activity which the inventors have found is not due to this component as the extract of red henna of the invention inhibits only *C. xerosis*.

Example 1. Operating as in the General Procedures above, commercial extracts of henna were tested against *S. epidermidis* and *C. xerosis*. The results are shown in Table 17.2. It can be seen that all extracts were active against *C. xerosis*, but only the first extract (which is a blend of *Lawsonia inermis* and Indigofera tinctoria) caused a full growth inhibition of *S. epidermidis*.

Table 17.2

Source and Color of Henna	Extraction Conditions, Solvent and Extract Color	Inhibition of S.epidermidis	Inhibition of C.xerosis
Alban Muhler black henna AMI watersoluble	no data, water/ propylene glycol, brown	+2.0	+, 0.8 cm
H&R– Cremogen henna neutral	no data, water/ dipropylene glycol, dark brown	–	+/–, 1.0 cm
Gattefosse– Vegetol henna	prolonged maceration of the leaves in Water/propylene glycol. brown	–	+, 0.7 cm
Vege–Tech henna neutral	no data, water, Amber +/–,	1.2 cm	+, 2.0 cm

Example 2. In order to ascertain the effect of the extracting agents ethanol and methanol employed in the extractions, the inhibition of *S. epidermidis* and *C. xerosis* by these solvents was tested. The results are shown in Table 17.3.

Table 17.3

Ethanol of Content	Inhibition of C.xerosis	Inhibition of S.epidermidis	Methanol of Content	Inhibition of C.xerosis	Inhibition of S.epidermidis
5%	–	–	5%	–	–
10%	–	–	10%	–	–
15%	–	–	15%	–	–
20%	–	–	20%	–	–
25%	–	–	25%	–	–
30%	–	–	30%	–	–
35%	–	–	35%	–	–
40%	+/–, 0.2 cm	–	40%	–	–
45%	+/–, 0.2 cm	–	45%	+/–	–
50%	+/–, 0.6 cm	–	50%	+/–	–
55%	+/–, 0.6 cm	–	55%	+/–	–
60%	+/–, 0.8 cm	–	60%	+/–, 0.8 cm	–
65%	+/–, 0.8 cm	–	65%	+/–, 0.8 cm	–
70%	+/–, 0.8 cm	–	70%	+/–, 0.8 cm	–
75%	+/–, 0.8 cm	–	75%	+/–, 0.8 cm	–
80%	+/–, 0.8 cm	–	80%	+/–, 0.8 cm	–
90%	+, 1.1 cm	–	90%	+/–, 0.8 cm	–
100%	+, 1.3 cm	–	00%	+/–, 0.8 cm	–

The results show that some inhibition of *C. xerosis* is caused by ethanol, above 40% (v/v) in water, and by methanol above 45%, while no inhibition was found for *S. epidermidis*.

Example 3. Operating as in the General Procedures above, ethanolic extracts of black henna were tested against *S. epidermidis* and *C. xerosis*. The results are shown in Table 17.4.

Table 17.4

Source & Color of Henna	Extraction Conditions and Extract Color	Inhibition of *S. epidermidis*	Inhibition of C.xerosis
Market	water, black	+, 0.8 cm	+/–
B1–black	ethanol 10%, dark	+, 0.2 cm	+, 0.8 cm
henna	brown + black powder		
powder	ethanol 15% dark	+, 2.2 cm	+, 0.8 cm
	brown + black powder		
	ethanol 20%, dark	+, 2.0 cm	+, 0.8 cm
	brown + black powder		
	ethanol 25%, dark	+, 2.0 cm	+, 0.8 cm
	brown + black powder		
	ethanol 30%, dark	+, 2.0 cm	+, 0.8 cm
	brown + black powder		
	ethanol 35%, dark	+, 2.0 cm	+, 0.8 cm
	brown + black powder		
	ethanol 40%, brown	+, 1.0 cm	+, 0.8 cm
	ethanol 45%, brown	+, 1.0 cm	+, 0.8 cm
	ethanol 50%, brown	+, 1.0 cm	+, 0.8 cm
	ethanol 55%, brown	+, 1.0 cm	+, 0.8 cm
	ethanol 60%, dark brown	+, 1.0 cm	+, 0.8 cm
	ethanol 65%, dark brown	+, 1.0 cm	+, 0.8 cm
	ethanol 70%, dark brown	+, 1.0 cm	+, 0.8 cm
	ethanol 75%, dark brown	+, 1.0 cm	+, 1.1 cm
	ethabol 80%,	+, 1.0 cm	+, 1.1 cm
	brown–black		
	ethanol 85%,	–	+, 1.1 cm
	brown–black		
	ethanol 90%,	–	+, 1.1 cm
	brown–black		
	ethanol 100%,	–	+, 1.1 cm
	brown–black		
Market B2–black henna powder	ethanol 20%, brown + black powder	+, 0.8 cm	+/–, 0.8 cm

Example 4. Operating as in the General Procedures above, methanolic extracts of black henna were tested against *S. epidermidis* and *C. xerosis*. The results are shown in Table 17.5.

Table 17.5

Source & Color of Henna	Extraction Conditions and Extract Color	Inhibition of *S.epidermidis*	Inhibition of *C. xerosis*
Market B1– black henna powder	methanol 5% dark brown + black powder	+, 0.5 cm	+/–, 0.3 cm
	methanol 10%, dark brown + black powder	+, 0.5 cm	+/–, 0.4 cm
	methanol 15%, dark brown + black powder	+, 0.8 cm	+/–, 0.9 cm
	methanol 20%, dark brown + black powder	+, 1.3 cm	+/–, 0.9 cm
	methanol 25 %, dark brown + black powder	+, 1.3 cm	+/–, 0.9 cm
	methanol 30 %, dark brown + black powder	+, 1.3 cm	+/–, 1.1 cm
	methanol 35%, dark brown + black powder	+, 1.3 cm	+/–, 1.0 cm
	methanol 40%, brown + black powder	+, 1.1 cm	+/–, 1.1 cm
	methanol 45%, brown + black powder	+, 1.1 cm	+/–, 1.1 cm
	methanol 50%, brown + black powder	+, 0.8 cm	+/–, 0.9 cm
	methanol 55%, brown	+, 0.7 cm	+, 0.8 cm
	methanol 60%, brown	+, 0.8 cm	+/–, 0.5 cm
	methanol 65 %, brown	+, 0.8 cm	+/–, 0.5 cm
	methanol 70%, brown	+, 0.8 cm	+/–, .5 cm
	methanol 75%, dark brown +, 1.1 cm	+/–, 0.5 cm	
	methanol 80%, brown–black	+, 0.9 cm	
	methanol 90%, brown–black	+, 0.9 cm	+, 0.8 cm
	methanol 100%, brown–black	+, 0.8 cm	+, 0.7 cm

Example 5. Operating as in the General Procedures above, ethanolic extracts of red henna were tested against *S. epidermidis* and *C. xerosis*. The results are shown in Table 17.6.

Table 17.6

Source and Color of Henna	Extraction Conditions and Extract Color	Inhibition of *S. epidermidis*	Inhibition of *C. xerosis*
Market R1–red henna powder	water, orange	+/–, 0.2 cm	+/–, 0.2 cm
	ethanol 5% orange	–	+/–, 0.2 cm
	ethanol 10% orange	–	+/–, 0.5 cm
	ethanol 15% orange	–	+/–, 0.5 cm
	ethanol 20% orange	–	+, 0.8 cm
	ethanol 25% orange	–	+, 0.5 cm
	ethanol 30% orange	–	+, 0.9 cm
	ethanol 35% orange	–	+, 0.9 cm
	ethanol 40% orange- +/–, 0.2 cm brown	+, 1.0 cm	
	ethanol 45%, orange- +/–, 0.3 cm brown	+, 1.0 cm	
	ethanol 50%, orange-brown	–	+, 1.0 cm
	ethanol 55%, orange- +/–, 0.2 cm brown	+, 1.1 cm	
	ethanol 60%, orange- +/–, 0.2 cm brown	+, 1.1 cm	
	ethanol 70%, brown + – black powder	+, 1.1 cm	
	ethanol 75%, dark	–	+, 1.1 cm
	brown + black powder		
	ethanol 80%, dark	–	+, 0.5 cm
	brown + black dark		
	ethanol 90%, black	–	+, 0.3 cm
	ethanol 100%, black	–	+, 0.7 cm

Example 6. Extracts of red and black henna and blue indigo were tested against *C. xerosis, S. epidermidis,* Staphylococcus aureus and Micrococcus luteus. The results are shown in Table 17.7.

Table 17.7

Source & Color of Powder	Extraction Conditions	Inhibition of *C. xerosis*	Inhibition of *S. epidermidis*	Inhibition of *S. aureus*	Inhibition of *Micrococcus luteus*
Market R1-red henna powder	water	+/–, 0.5 cm	+/–, 0.3 cm	+/–, 0.6 cm	–
	ethanol 15%	+, 0.6 cm	–	+/–, 0.5 cm	–
	ethanol 30%	+, 0.6 cm	–	+/–, 0.5 cm	–
	ethanol 50%	+, 0.8 cm	–	–	–
	ethanol 70%	+, 1.2 cm	+/31, 0.6 cm	+/–, 0.2 cm	–

Market B1-black henna powder	water	+/31, 0.6 cm	+, 1.7 cm	+, 2.1 cm	–
	ethanol 15%	+, 0.8 cm	+, 2.4 cm	+, 2.1 cm	+, 1.3 cm
	ethanol 30%	+, 1.1 cm	+, 2.2 cm	+, 2.4 cm	+, 2.0 cm
Bengal blue Indigo	ethanol 20%	+, 1.2 cm	+, 1.0 cm	+, 0.7 cm	+, 0.8 cm

Example 7. Operating as in the General Procedures above, dipropylene glycol extracts of black henna were tested against *S. epidermidis* and *C. xerosis*. The results are shown in Table 17.8.

Table 17.8

Extracting Solvent	Inhibition of C. xerosis	Inhibition of S. epidermidis	Extraction Conditions of Black Henna and Extract Color	Inhibition of C. xerosis	Inhibition of S. epidermidis
10 % DPG	–	–	10% DPG, dark brown + black powder	+, 0.5 cm	+, 0.7 cm
20 % DPG	–	–	20% DPG, dark brown + black powder	+, 0.6 cm	+, 0.8 cm
30 % DPG	–	–	3.0% DPG, dark brown + black powder	+, 0.6 cm	+, 1.0 cm
40 % DPG	+/–,	–	40% DPG, dark brown + black powder	+, 0.7 cm	+, 1.2 cm
50 % DPG	+/–, 0.6 cm	–	50% DPG, dark powder	+, 0.7 cm	+, 0.8 cm
60 % DPG	+/–, 0.7 cm	–	60% DPG, dark brown	+, 0.8 cm	+, 0.9 cm
70 % DPG	+/–, 0.7 cm	–	70% DPG, dark brown	+, 0.7 cm	+, 1.0 cm
80 % DPG	+/–, 0.7 cm	–	80% DPG, dark brown	+, 0.7 cm	+/–, 0.6 cm
90 % DPG	+,0.9 cm	–	90% DPG, brown–green	+/–, 0.9 cm	+/–, 0.6 cm'
100% DPG	+, 1.1 cm	–	100% DPG, green	+/–, 1.1 cm	–

Example 8. Operating as in the General Procedures above, dipropylene glycol extracts of red henna were tested against *S. epidermidis* and *C. xerosis*. The results are shown in Table 17.9.

Table 17.9: Control Experiment

Extracting Solvent	Inhibition of C. xerosis	Inhibition of S. epidermidis	Extraction Conditions of Red Henna and Extract Color	Inhibition of C. xerosis	Inhibition of S. epidermidis
10% DPG	N.D.	–	10% DPG, orange	+, 0.4 cm	–
20% DPG	N.D.	–	20% DPG, orange	+, 0.6 cm	–
50% DPG	+, 0.4 cm	–	50% DPG, orange	+, 0.6 cm	–
70% DPG	N.D.	–	70% DPG, brown-orange	+, 0.7 cm	–
100% DPG	+, 0.5 cm	–	100% DPG, green	+, 0.7 cm	–

Example 9. Operating as in the General Procedures above, isopropanol extracts of black henna were tested against *S. epidermidis* and *C. xerosis*. The results are shown in Table 17.10.

Table 17.10: Con Experiment

Extracting Solvent	Inhibition of *C. xerosis*	Inhibition of *S. epidermidis*	Extraction Conditions of Black Henna and Extract Color	Inhibition of *C. xerosis*	Inhibition of *S. epidermidis*
10% IP	–	–	10% IP, dark brown + black powder	+, 0.5 cm	+/–, 0.5 cm
20% IP	+/–, 0.6 cm	–	20% IP, dark brown + black powder	+, 0.6 cm	+/–, 0.5 cm
30% IP	+/–, 0.9 cm	–	30% IP, dark brown + black powder	+, 0.8 cm	+, 1.2 cm
40% IP	+/–, 1.1 cm	–	40% IP, dark brown + black powder	+, 1.1 cm	+, 1.6 cm
50% IP	+, 1.3 cm	–	50% IP, green brown + black powder	+/–, 1.1 cm	+/–, 1.0 cm
60% IP	+, 1.0 cm	–	60% IP, dark green	+, 1.3	+/–, 0.8 cm
70% IP	+, 1.2 cm	–	70% IP, dark green	+, 1.4	–
80% IP	+, 1.2 cm	–	80% IP, dark green	+, 1.4	–
90% IP	+, 1.4 cm	–	90% IP, dark green	+, 1.5	–
100% IP	+, 1.4 cm	–	100% IP, green	+, 1.7	–

Example 10. Operating as in the General Procedures above, isopropanol extracts of red henna were tested against *S. epidermidis* and *C. xerosis*. The results are shown in Table 17.11.

Table 17.11: Control Experiment

Extracting Solvent	Inhibition of *C. xerosis*	Inhibitiion of *S. epidermidis*	Extraction Conditions of Red Henna and Extract Color	Inhibitiion of *C. xerosis*	Inhibitiion of *S. epidermidis*
10% IP	N.D.	–	10% IP, orange	+/–, 1.0 cm	–
20% IP	N.D.	–	20% IP, orange	+/–, 0.6 cm	–
50% IP	+, 1.0 cm	–	50% IP, brown powder	++, 1.2 cm	–
70% IP	N.D.	–	70% IP, brown–green	+, 0.9 cm	–
100% IP	+, 0.6 cm	–	100% IP, green	+, 1.0 cm	–

Example 11. A group of ten individuals performed the following experiment. Prior to evening shower, the individuals rubbed their right armpits with a deodorizing composition comprising an oil plus Benzalkonium chloride and red henna and following three minutes showered as usual. Microbial counts were estimated directly before application, and the following morning. Individuals as well as independent judges also scored their own armpit odors and recorded them. The results showed a reduction of 1.5-2 orders of magnitude in bacterial counts in the experimental (right armpit), as compared to no reduction in the control (left armpit).

Similar reductions were observed by the participants in scoring the odor from the armpits, i.e., that the experimental armpit was free or almost free of odor the morning following application, wherease the control armpit had substantial odor.

The results show that this concept is highly effective in long-lasting (ca. 8 hours) reduction of microbial counts and odor levels.

All the above description and examples have been given for the purpose of illustration and are not intended to limit the invention in any way. Many modifications can be made in the compositions of the invention. For instance, different henna powders or purified henna components can be used, many different additives can be incorporated in the compositions of the invention, be they antibacterially active or not, and many different extraction solvents can be used, to provide compositions of different activity, all without exceeding the scope of the invention.

The suitable extraction solvents or solvent combinations are those that when used as described in the extraction process yield an inhibition zone of not less than 3 millimeters when tested on lawns of susceptible bacteria.

18 Novel Anti-fungal Composition

Fungal borne infections or mycoses are most common infections among humans and animals. A variety of environmental and physiological conditions can contribute to the development of mycoses. Mycoses can be localized to skin or specific organs such as lungs, intestine or can cause serious life threatening systemic infections, which depends on various factors including immune status, virulence of infecting fungi and so on. Mycoses can be classified in to superficial, cutaneous, subcutaneous and systemic mycoses based on the site of infection. Fungal species causing infections can be structurally multicellular mold, unicellular yeast or dimorphic in nature. Opportunistic fungal infections are most difficult to treat especially with increase in drug resistance. Candidiasis, cryptococcosis and aspergillosis are frequently observed opportunistic fungal infections among immunocompromised patients.

Among the opportunistic fungal infections, Candidiasis, especially invasive Candidiasis, form the most common cause of global morbidity and mortality. Invasive Candidiasis has an attributable mortality rate of 10-49%. Candidiasis accounts for 8-10% of the total systemic nasocomial infection in United States. Similar trend was observed in India where invasive Candidiasis dominates among the opportunistic mycosis and is the second vital cause for the co-morbidity in HIV infected patients. Studies conducted at different locations in India confirm that around 40% of the HIV infected patients have Candidiasis as secondary infection. Patients with lower CD4+ cells were reported to have oral Candidiasis [66%] and pulmonary TB [60%]. Mortality in candidemia patients in India ranges from 28-71.4% and attributable mortality rate falls between 17% and 33%. Virulence of Candida sp. is attributed to many factors such as hyphal formation, surface recognition, phenotypic switching and extracellular hydrolytic enzyme production. Secreted aspartyl proteinases(Sap), phospholipase B enzymes, and lipases are the 3 most important extracellular hydrolytic enzymes produced by C. albicans. Many of the pathogenic Candida species have been shown to produce active extracellular proteases, including C. albicans, C. dubliniensis, C tropicalis and C. parapsilosis. Such proteases are responsible for digesting or distorting host cell membranes to facilitate adhesion and tissue invasion of this dimorphic opportunistic pathogen Candida. Another heterogeneous group of enzymes that share the ability to hydrolyze one or more ester linkage in glycerol phospholipids are called phospholipases. Although all phospholipases target phospholipids as substrates, each enzyme has the ability to cleave a specific ester bond and accordingly they are classified as A, B, C and D. Phospholipase C (PLC) hydrolyzes the phosphor-dieter bond in the phospholipids backbone to yield 1,2- diacylglycerol and, depending on the specific phospholipid species involved, phosphatidylcholine, phosphatidyl ethanolamine, etc. Inhibition of these two hydrolytic enzyme activity is confirmed to reduce the pathogenicity of Candida and can also prevent invasive candidiasis.

Antifungal treatment options have been classified into three classes, Viz, azoles, polyenes and 5-fluorocytosine. Azoles are class of compounds that inhibit the synthesis of ergosterol (the major fungal cell wall sterol component). Polyenes interact with fungal membrane sterols and 5-fluorocytosine inhibits macromolecular synthesis. Candida sp. was found to develop resistance to these antifungal agents through various drug resistance mechanisms. These mechanisms include alteration in drug target, alteration in sterol biosynthesis, reduction in the intercellular concentration of target enzyme, and over expression of the antifungal drug target.

Lawsonia inermis, also popularly known as Henna, is a small desert tree, but can also be grown as a houseplant. The henna plant is native to northern Africa, western and southern Asia; northern Australasia and tropical areas. Historically, henna was used for cosmetic purposes in Ancient Egypt or Carthage, as well as other parts of North Africa, the Horn of Africa, the Arabian Peninsula, and South Asia. The lawsone molecules in the henna leaves are responsible for the color that stains the skin. Different types of solvent and aqueous leaf extracts of *Lawsonia inermis* also known as Henna were tested earlier for antifungal activity. Many of the aqueous extracts failed to exhibit antifungal activity. Solvent extracts tested included alcohols (methanol, ethanol), chloroform, benzene, ether and hexane. Among these, alcoholic extracts shows some promise, still they weren't tested further for its specific effect on Candida sp, other than inhibitory activity. One study with ethyl acetate extract of henna on Candida sp. concluded that there isn't appreciable activity of this extract and lawsone on Candida sp (13).

However, none of the prior arts discloses the extract of abundantly available *Lawsonia inermis* possessing significant antifungal activity with unique mode of action that can be safely used for fungal infections caused by resistant fungi in various groups of patients.

Therefore, there remains a need in the art to develop a herbal composition that is safe, cost effective and can effectively tackle fungal resistance in a human and/or animal.

Accordingly, the objective of the present invention is to provide a potential successor in the field of drugs, biopharmaceuticals and nutritional/dietary supplements, for human and/or animal application in the treatment of fungal infections including candidiasis.

Description of Drawings

Figure 18.1: Anticandidal activity of Lawsone against Candida albicans.

Figure 18.2: Germ tube inhibitory activity of Henna ethyl acetate extract on Candida albicans.

Figure 18.3: TLC analysis of Henna extract and standard Lawsone (Dimension of plate 4X9, Rf = 0.70

Figure 18.4: HPLC analysis of standard Lawsone (Rt: 8.68 mins)

Figure 18.5: HPLC analysis of Henna extract with Lawsone peak (Rt: 8.41 mins

Figure 18.6: Effect of Henna extract and Lawsone on the Protease enzyme activity of C. albicans.

Figure 18.7: Native gel-PAGE profile of aspartate dehydrogenase activity of *Lawsonia inermis* treated C. albicans in comparison with control and DMSO control treatment.

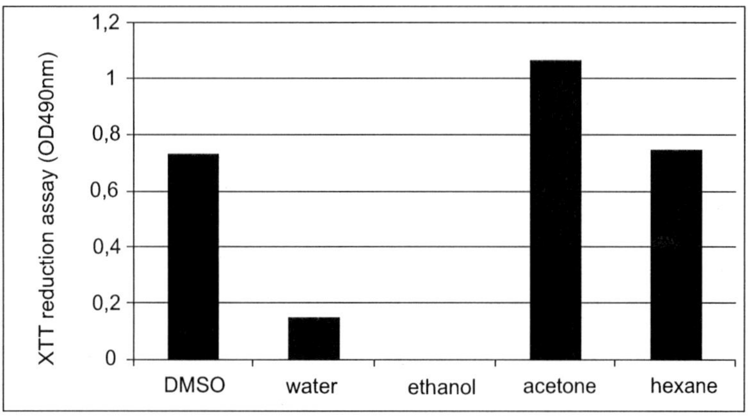

A

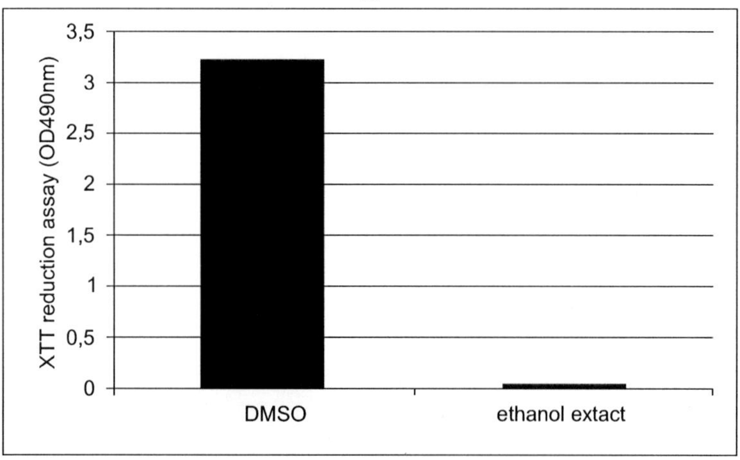

B

Fig. 18.1

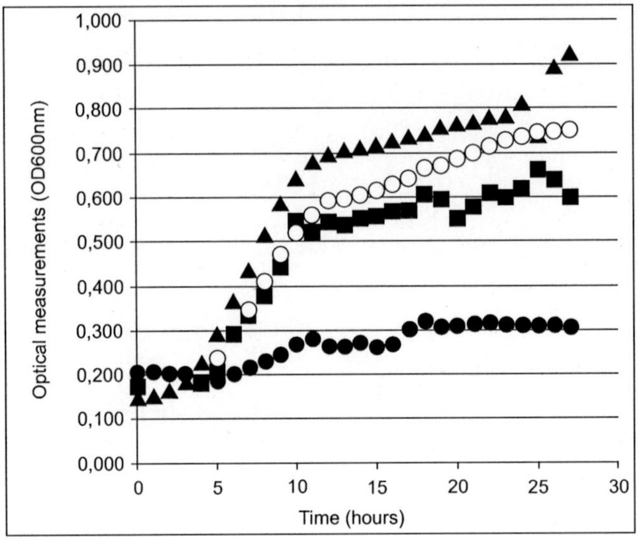
Optical measurements (OD600nm)
Time (hours)

Fig. 18.2

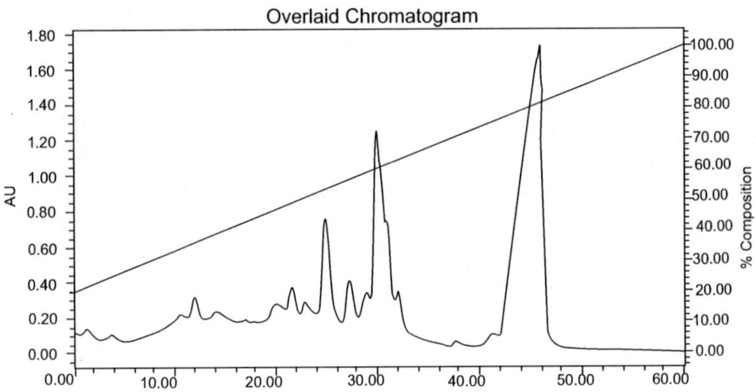
Overlaid Chromatogram
AU
% Composition

A

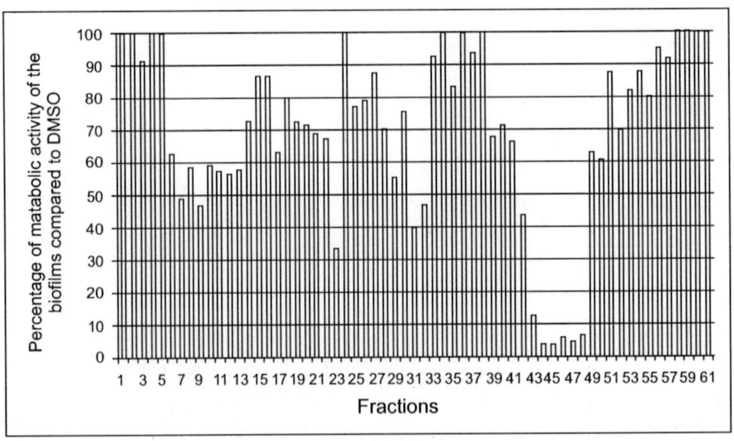
Percentage of matabolic activity of the biofilms compared to DMSO
Fractions

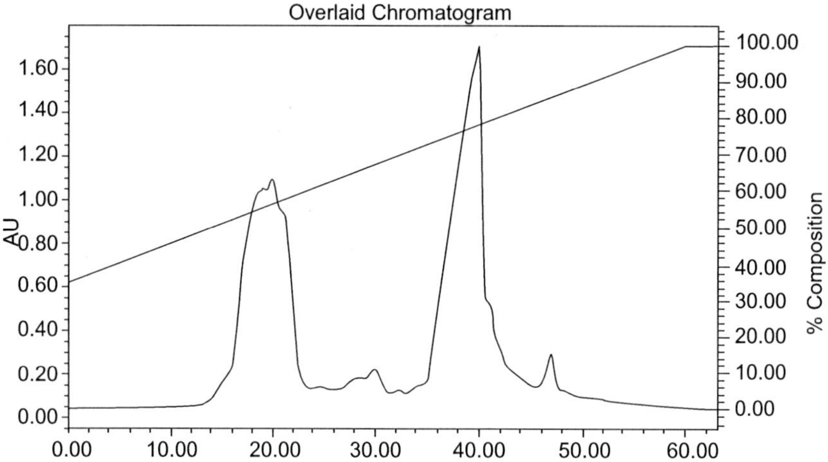
Overlaid Chromatogram
AU
% Composition
1.60
1.40
1.20
1.00
0.80
0.60
0.40
0.20
0.00
100.00
90.00
80.00
70.00
60.00
50.00
40.00
30.00
20.00
10.00
0.00
0.00
10.00
20.00
30.00
40.00
50.00
60.00

B

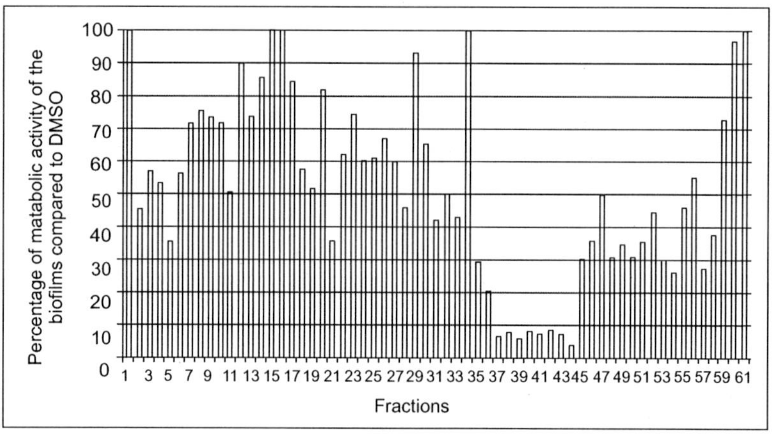
Percentage of matabolic activity of the biofilms compared to DMSO
Fractions
100
90
80
70
60
50
40
30
20
10
0
1 3 5 7 9 11 13 15 17 19 21 23 25 27 29 31 33 35 37 39 41 43 45 47 49 51 53 55 57 59 61

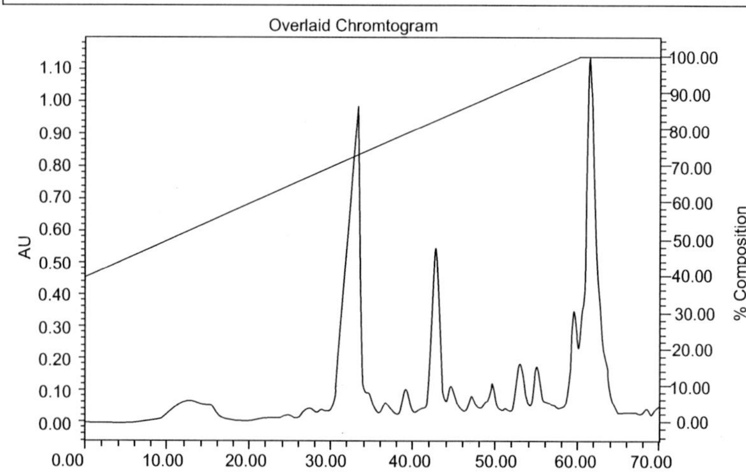
Overlaid Chromtogram
AU
% Composition
1.10
1.00
0.90
0.80
0.70
0.60
0.50
0.40
0.30
0.20
0.10
0.00
100.00
90.00
80.00
70.00
60.00
50.00
40.00
30.00
20.00
10.00
0.00
0.00
10.00
20.00
30.00
40.00
50.00
60.00
70.00

C

Fig. 18.3

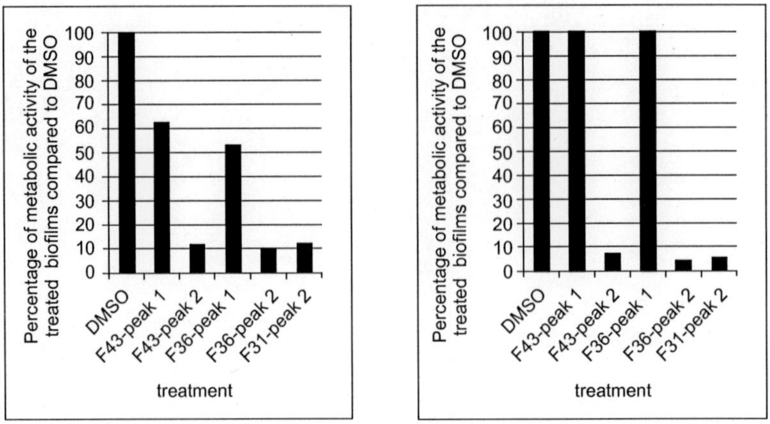
Percentage of metabolic activity of the treated biofilms compared to DMSO
100
90
80
70
60
50
40
30
20
10
0
DMSO
F43-peak 1
F43-peak 2
F36-peak 1
F36-peak 2
F31-peak 2
treatment

A

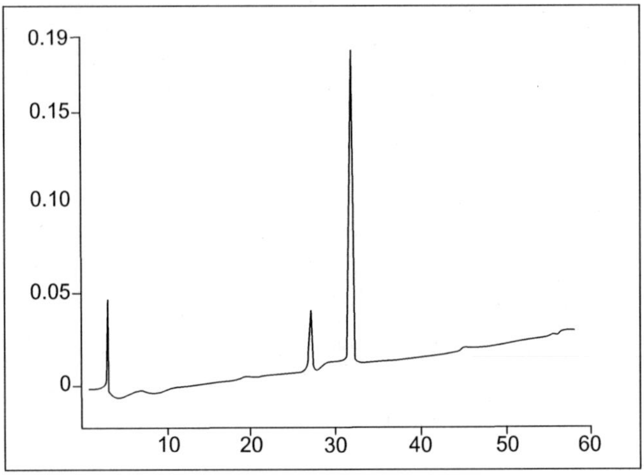
0.19
0.15
0.10
0.05
0
10
20
30
40
50
60

B

Fig. 18.4

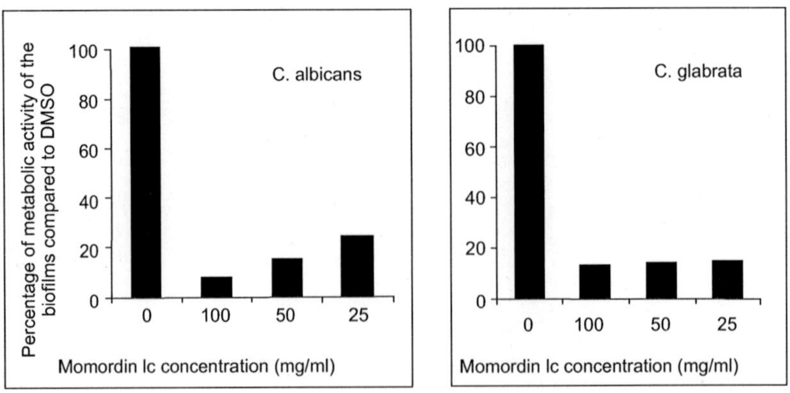
Percentage of metabolic activity of the biofilms compared to DMSO
100
80
60
40
20
0
C. albicans
C. glabrata
0
100
50
25
Momordin Ic concentration (mg/ml)

A

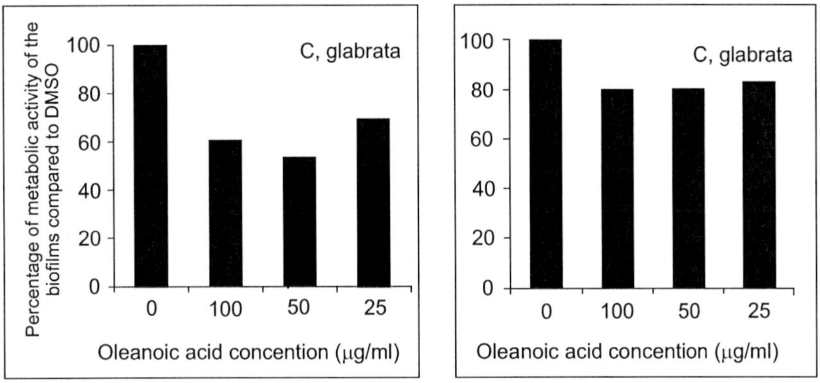

B

Fig. 18.5

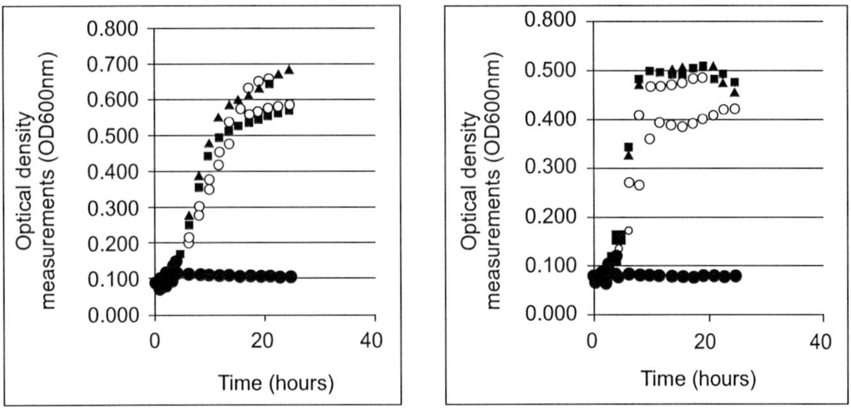

Fig. 18.6

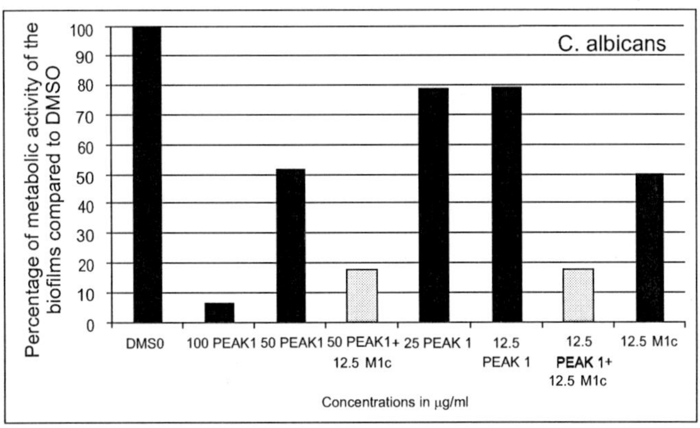

A

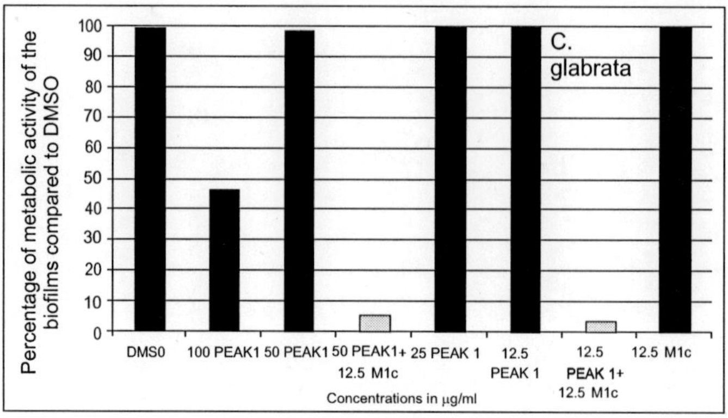

B

Fig. 18.7

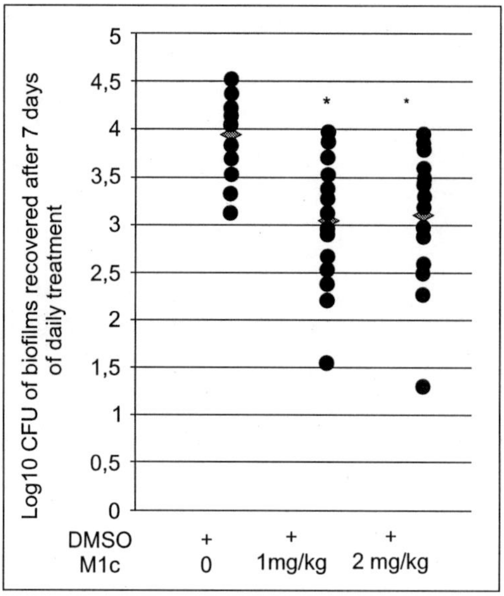

Fig. 18.8

Detailed Description of the Invention

The invention will now be described in detail in connection with certain preferred and optional embodiments, so that various aspects thereof may be more fully understood and appreciated.

Accordingly in a preferred embodiment, the invention describes antifungal composition, which effectively combats fungal infections in human or an animal. In one preferred embodiment, the fungal infection is candidiasis.

Thus the present invention is directed towards development of biologically effective extract of Lawsonia species specifically *Lawsonia inermis* (Henna) extract, which possesses antifungal activity. According to the present invention, ethyl acetate extract of *Lawsonia inermis* was found to have effective anti-candidal activity. Extract has been profiled and identified to have marker compounds including pigments (lawsone), tannins and other flavonoids and purified Lawsone has been further investigated as one of the active compound responsible for the anti-candidal activity and confirmed to possess significant anti-candidal activity. Accordingly, in an embodiment, the present invention provides the extract of *Lawsonia inermis* with unique mechanism of action which include germ tube inhibitory activity and inhibition of virulent (proteases and phospholipases) and constitutive (aspartate dehydrogenases, lumazine synthase and N Myristoyil transferases) enzymes. This mechanism of action is different from other marketed anti-fungal agents such as azoles, which inhibit the synthesis of ergosterol (the main fungal sterol); polyenes, which interact with fungal membrane sterols physicochemically; and 5-fluorocytosine, which inhibits macromolecular synthesis.

According to preferred embodiment, the invention provides a herbal pharmaceutical composition/dietary supplement which comprises biologically effective standardized ethyl acetate extract of *Lawsonia inermis*, wherein the standardized ethyl acetate extract comprises total Phenolic content which includes lawsoniaside in an amount ranging from 0.00001 to 30%; total Flavonoid content which includes luteoline ranging from 0.00001 to 40%; and Lawsone content ranging from 0.00001 to 99%, together with one or more pharmaceutical excipients, for the management of fungal infections.

According to one preferred embodiment, the invention provides a herbal composition comprising biologically effective extract of *Lawsonia inermis*, said biologically effective extract comprises 0.01 % to 99% of at least one compound selected from the group consisting of Lawsone & lawsoniaside and luteoline together with one or more pharmaceutical excipients, for the management of fungal infections. The biologically effective extract is ethyl acetate extract of *Lawsonia inermis*.

In yet another embodiment, the invention provides herbal composition comprising biologically effective extract of *Lawsonia inermis* standardized to comprise at least one of Lawsone & lawsoniaside and luteoline along with tannins.

In a further embodiment, the invention provides a composition comprising Lawsone together with one or more pharmaceutical excipients.

In yet another embodiment, the invention provides herbal composition comprising ethyl acetate extract of *Lawsonia inermis* containing bioactive compounds naphthoquinones (Lawsone, lawsoniaside), tannis and flavonoids (luteoline) for use in the treatment of systemic and localized fungal infections, more specifically, oral and vaginal candidiasis.

In yet another embodiment, the invention describes an *Lawsonia inermis* extract with novel and unique mode of action against candidiasis, which include germ tube inhibitory activity and inhibition of virulent (proteases and phospholipases) and constitutive (aspartate dehydrogenases, lumazine synthase and N Myristoyiltransferases) enzymes.

In an alternate embodiment, the invention provides use of extract containing lawsone and other signature compounds) in combination with known drugs such as azoles (fluconazole, ketaconazole, clotrimazole, corbimazole, ravuconazole and posacconazole); Amphotericins and/or echinocandins (Echinocandin, caspofungin, micafungin, anidulafungin and cilofungin) for the management of local and systemic fungal infections.

In yet another embodiment, the invention provides herbal composition comprising *Lawsonia inermis* extract formulated in the form of liquid, semisolid or solid dosage forms using one or more pharmaceutical excipients/carriers/ diluents. The pharmaceutical excipients/carriers/diluents are selected from the group consisting of polymers, diluents, binders, fillers, disintegrants, lubricants, colors, flavors and the like.

The invention also provides the *Lawsonia inermis* extract for preparation of medicament for use in oral, topical, ocular, vaginal, otic, dermal application. The pharmaceutical carriers/excipients used for the preparation of medicaments may be selected from the conventional excipients known to a person skilled in the art. The methods of formulating the composition suitable for oral, topical, ocular, vaginal, otic, dermal application may be selected from the conventional methods known to a person skilled in the art.

The anti-candidal composition according to the invention can also be used in feminine hygiene products, including maxi pads, ultra-thin pads, and feminine wipes. Further, the anti-candidial composition according to the invention can also be prepared as a suppository; tooth paste; mouth wash; as an adjunct to female and male contraceptive devices; as an adjunct to vaginal contraceptives and lubricants. In yet another embodiment, the invention encompasses pharmaceutical compositions comprising lawsone, Lawsonisides and Luteoline either alone or in combination in an amount of 0.0001% to 99.99% in association with one or more pharmaceutical excipients, for the management of fungal infections.

In yet another embodiment, the invention provides *Lawsonia inermis* extract for the preparation of various therapeutic, preventative and general health supplements in animals and human beings.

In yet another embodiment, the invention describes a *Lawsonia inermis* extract for use as Pharmaceutical, dietary supplements or nutraceuticals/health supplements/general supplements/OTC products.

Therefore, the invention includes within its scope, the compositions and the use of compounds in the biologically active extract of *Lawsonia inermis,* including compounds, Lawsone & lawsoniaside and luteoline having antifungal and anti-candidal activity; the synthetic forms of such compounds and, such compounds prepared by appropriate synthesis.

In yet another embodiment, the invention provides process for preparation of ethyl acetate extract of *Lawsonia inermis*. According to this process the dried green leaves are converted preferably into a powder by crushing or grinding prior to being treated with ethyl acetate solvent to extract there from the active ingredients. Preferably, powder of fine particles is used and the powder is macerated with the ethyl acetate solvent to obtain a dark green colored solution which has the desired concentration of dissolved biologically active extract. Accordingly, the process for preparation of biologically effective standardised ethyl acetate extract of *Lawsonia inermis*, which comprises;

(*a*) soaking the crushed powder of green leaves of *Lawsonia inermis* with ethylacetate in a ratio of 10: 1 to 1 : 10 overnight in air tight container followed by pulverization;

(*b*) extracting the pulverised crushed leaves with aqueous solvent at a temperature below 60° C for a period of time sufficient to produce a dark green colored solution which has the desired concentration of dissolved biologically active extract; and

(*c*) recovering the biologically active extract after evaporating the solvent. In yet another embodiment, the invention provides evaluation of biological activity of the extract of *Lawsonia inermis* against various fungal species such as C. albicans and C. glabrataand the zone of inhibition at various concentrations. In yet another embodiment, the Anticandidal Activity of Lawsone is evaluated and the zone of inhibition at various concentrations. According to the above studies, the Lawsone in ethylacetate extract of *Lawsonia inermis* is responsible for the Anticandidal activity, (cf. Table 18.1 and 18.2). Thus the invention further provides compositions comprising Lawsone together with one or more pharmaceutical excipients.

The following examples, which include preferred embodiments, will serve to illustrate the practice of this invention, it being understood that the particulars shown are by way of example and for purpose of illustrative discussion of preferred embodiments of the invention.

Example 1. Extract Preparation.

A source of the biologically active extract of the present invention comprises *Lawsonia inermis* plant leaf extract.

A preferred source of the biologically active material for use in the composition of the present invention is a part of the Indian *Lawsonia inermis* plant tree.

The preferred *Lawsonia inermis* tree parts for use in the present invention is shade dried green leaves. The dried green leaves are converted preferably into a powder by crushing or grinding prior to being treated with ethyl acetate solvent to extract there from the active ingredients. Preferably, a powder of fine particles is used and the powder is macerated with the ethyl acetate solvent. Any suitable method involving the use of the ethyl acetate solvent of the present invention can be used to extract the biologically active ingredients from the green leaves of the aforementioned *Lawsonia inermis*.

Ratio of Ethyl acetate to dry henna leaves for extract preparation shall be in the range of 1 : 10 to 10: 1, while the most optimum ratio shall be 1 :3. The ethyl acetate solvent for use in the extraction is used in the ratio of 1 :3 of the powdered dry leaves. The powdered leaves are soaked in the solvent for overnight in air tight container and then pulverized to fine powder using suitable external aids (mortar and pestle). The extraction should be conducted under temperature conditions which reduce the tendency of the biologically active ingredients comprising the extract to decompose. It is preferable that the temperature of the aqueous solvent be no greater than about 60° C. and preferably in the range of about 4° C. to about 20° C. When the solvent has a temperature other than ambient or room temperature (about 23° C), refrigerating or heating equipment can be used to lower or raise the temperature of the solvent to the desired operating temperature. The extracting conditions which involve the ethyl acetate solvent at the desired temperature should be carried out for a period of time sufficient to produce a dark green colored solution which has the desired concentration of dissolved biologically active extract; the extract in a dark brownish green paste form can be recovered from the solution by evaporating the liquid solvent. Prior to evaporation. The; isolution can be filtered, as may be needed, to remove therefrom solid impurities.

The ethyl acetate extract is characterised for the presence of phytoconstituents, tannins, Lawsone & lawsoniaside and luteoline and its concentrations. The total phenolic content which includes lawsoniaside; total flavonoid content which includes luteoline and lawsone content are shown in Table 18.7. According to -this phytochemical analysis, the standardised ethyl acetate extract comprises total Phenolic content in an "amount ranging from 0.00001 to 30%; total Flavonoid content ranging from 0.00001 to 40%; and Lawsone content ranging from 0.00001 to 99%. In addition to this presence of tannins, coumarines and quinines have also been confirmed.

The invention includes within its scope the use of compounds comprising the biologically active extract, including compounds comprising the anti-candidal fraction of the extract, and synthetic forms of such compounds, that is, such compounds prepared by appropriate synthesis.

Example 2. Evaluation of anti-candidal activity of *Lawsonia inermis* Extract:

Following in vitro study showed effective dose dependent anti-candidal activity for extract as well as for Lawsone treatment. Antifungal activity by modified Kerby-Bauer method.

Susceptibility disks (5 mm in diameter) were impregnated with 0.5 mg of desired compound(s)/extract dissolved in DMSO, and placed on Sabouraud dextrose agar plates separately inoculated with the C. albicans and C. glabrata. After 48 hrs of incubation at 37 °C, plates were observed for zone of inhibition. Disc containing only DMSO was used as a negative control.

> Anticandidal activity against Candida species:

Dose dependent anti-candidal activity was observed upon treatment using Lawsoniainermisextract against tested C. albicansand C. glabrata (Table 18.1).

Table 18.1: Anti-candidal Activity of Extract Against *C. albicansand C. glabrata*.

Sl.No.	Concentration of Extract	Zone of Inhibition (mm)	
		C. albicans	***C. glabrata***
1.	0 mg (Control)	NIL	NIL
2.	0.25 mg	9	7
3.	0.5 mg	13	9
4.	0.75 mg	15	11
5.	1 mg	17	14

Anticandidal Activity of Lawsone

Complete inhibition of candidal growth was found in C. albicans upon lawsone treatment in all three concentrations (50, 100 and 200 μg ml) tested as shown in Figure 18.1 and Table 18.2.

Table 18.2: Anti-candidal Activity of Lawsone against C. albicans.

Sl. No.	Concentration of Zone of Inhibition (mm)
Extract C. albicans	
1. 50 μ_d	14
2. 100 μ	16
3. 200 $\mu_§$	17 Germ tube inhibitory activity:

Dried plant extract was taken at 50(μg concentration in a test tube and resuspended in 10 μĩ of DMSO. 990 μĩ of bovine serum was added and loop full of mid log phase (105 to 107 cells/ml) Candida culture was inoculated in the serum and incubated for three hours at 37°C. Growth of germ tube was observed under the microscope (restchmar et al., 1999) (Figure 18.2).

Germ tube formation is a key aspect for virulence in dimorphic fungi. Germ tube inhibitory activity in Candida albicans was found upon Henna ethyl acetate extract treatment. Hence this extract can be used to control invasive candidiasis.

In Silico

Docking studies against following Candida sp. targets using Lawsone, lawsoniaside and luteoline

- Proteases
- Phospholipases
- Lumazine synthase
- N Myristoyltransferase&
- Aspartate semi-aldehyde dehydrogenase

Among the compounds screened, lupeoline, lawsone, aesculetin and lowsoniaside, were found to have good affinity towards screened Candida targets (Table 18.3). Lupeoline has multi-target potency with binding affinity towards 4 out of 6 Candida targets screened. Aesculetin and lawsone showed binding affinity towards 3 Candida targets. Lawsoniaside is the only compound to have affinity to 2H6T among the compounds screened. In addition to this Lawsoniaside has good affinity to 2JFB. Based on the docking score and docking energy it can be inferred that lawsone and lupeoline has moderate Candida myristoyltransferase, lumazine synthase and phospholipase inhibitory activity. Very low glide energy and docking score indicates that solamargine and lawsoniaside has very good inhibitory activity against asparatate semi aldehydede hydrogense and lumazine synthase. Lawsoniaside is the only enzyme to have very good binding energy and docking score to Candida enzyme SAP3. Table 18.3: Insilico Extra Precision (GLIDE-Schrodinger) Docking Study Results of Ligands from Henna plant leaves against Candida sp. Targets.

Table 18.3: Insilico Extra Precision (GLIDE-Schrodinger) Docking Study Results of Ligands from Henna Plant Leaves against *Candida* sp. Targets

Sl.No.	Target (PDB ID)	Phyto-chemical ligand	Plant source	Docking score	Glide energy
1.	1-Myristoyl-transferase (1NMT)	lupeoline	*L. inermis*	–3.342687	–31.735758
		lawsone	*L. inermis*	–2.603266	–24.143367
		aesculetin	*L. inermis*	–2.408067	–23.024805
2.	Aspartate semialdehyde dehydrogenase (3HSK)	lupeoline	*L. inermis*	–5.860507	–37.422997
		aesculetin	*L. inermis*	–5.246416	–24.084277
3.	Secreted Aspartic Proteinase 3 (2H6T)	Lawsoniaside	*L. inermis*	–10.120195	–58.117896
4.	Lumazine Synthase (2JFB)	lowsoniaside	*L. inermis*	–6.48773	–46.796851
		lawsone	*L. inermis*	–3.385353	–34.573629
		lupeoline	*L. inermis*	*–2.885515*	*–32.834679*
5.	Phospholipase C	lupeoline	*L. inermis*	–4.743477	–33.189219
		lawsome	*L. inermis*	–4.147062	–24.900805
		Aesculetin	*L. inermis*	–3.257346	–26.639446

In Silico Induced Fit Docking Studies - Candida Targets

Induced fit docking study inferred that lawsone can be a very good inhibitor of all three Candida targets (myristyltransferase, phospholipases and lumazine synthase) as indicated by the GLIDE energy and GLIDE score. Lawsone individually formed 4 hydrogen bonds with all three Candida targets. The site of interaction and bond distance for hydrogen bonding with respective targets were described in Table 18.4. With less GLIDE energy and more number of hydrogen bonds lawsone shall be considered to be an effective inhibitor of all three Candida targets. Table 18.4: Insilico Induced Fit (GLIDE-Schrodinger) Docking Study Results of Lawsone from Henna plant leaves against Candida sp. Targets.

Table 18.4: Insilico Induced Fit (GLIDE-Schrodinger) Docking Study Results of Lawsone from Henna Plant Leaves against *Candida* sp. Targets.

Sl.No.	Targer	Interactions	H-Bond (Å)	Docking Score	GLIDE Energy (KCAL/Mol)
1.	N-myristyl-transferase (1NMT)	TYR 335 (OH...O)	2.81	−7.18	−38.87
		(OH...O) LEU 451	2.85	—	—
		TYR 119 (OH...O)	2.74	—	—
		TYR 107 (OH...O)	2.89	—	—
2.	Phospholipase	(OH...N) HIS 76	2.96	−7.47	−33.35
		GLN 39 (NH...O)	3.18	—	—
		(OH...O) SER 37	2.84	—	—
		(OH...O) ASN 243	2.84	—	—
3.	Lumazinesynthase (2JEP)	(OH...O) VAL 90	2.96	−7.00	−32.58
		(OH...O) TRP 27	3.33	—	—
		SER 61 (OH...O)	2.91	—	—
		SER 61 (NH...O)	2.89	—	—

Phytochemical Analysis of Extract

Extract has been characterized to identify active compound(s) using chromatographic techniques such as TLC (Thin layer chromatography) and HPLC (High Performance liquid Chromatography).

TLC

TLC has been performed using different combinations and concentrations of extract to check the presence of Lawsone, one of major bioactive compound identified to have enzyme inhibitory activity, as described earlier in the in silico docking studies. Different combinations and proportions of mobile phase has been tried to separate and identify the presence of Lawsone. Different solvents used for optimizing mobile phase includes, chloroform, ethyl acetate, acetic acid, toluene, ethanol, petroleum ether, hexane and benzene. Mobile phase has been optimized to Toluene-Ethyl acetate-Acetic acid (5:4:1). Lawsone sigma standard has been used as marker to track the presence of active lawsone in the Henna extract. As described in Figure 18.3, an yellowish-orange colored band with similar Rf as that of standard Lawsone was found to be present in the TLC plate. This indicates the presence of Lawsone in the tested ethyl acetate extract of henna leaves.

HPLC analysis of Henna Extract

HPLC analysis of extract and standard lawsone was performed under the HPLC conditions described below:

Column: Luna 5u RP-C18 (Phenomenex)

Mobile Phase: Methanol -Water acidified with 0.06% of trifluro acetic acid (48:52, v/v) Flow rate: 1 ml/min

Wavelength: 248 nm

20 µĩ of extract and standard was injected into a Luna 5u RP-C 18 (250 * 4.6 mm) HPLC column containing 5 µĩ wide pore (100 A) beads and was fractionated with a mixture of Methanol-Water (48:52, v/v) acidified with 0.06% trifluoro acetic acid as mobile phase. The separation was performed using isocratic elution (0-20 mins) with a flow rate of 1 ml min^{-1}. The elution was monitored using a Shimadzu Diode-Array Detector SPD-10A VP operating at a fixed wavelength 248 nm. The lawsone standard was purchased from Sigma chemical Co., USA.

Standard lawsone peak was found at Rt 8.6 mins (Figure 18.4). Extract showed several peaks and an identical peak similar to Lawsone standard was also found at similar Rt (8.41 mins) (Figure 18.5). This indicates the presence of lawsone in the extract. The concentration of Lawsone in the extract was found to be 4 to 7µg/ml of extract.

Following in vitro study details are conducted on the extract and Lawsome:

> Protease inhibitory activity study

Stationary phase culture of C. albicans was used for SAP inhibition assay. SD broth consisting 100 µl of C. albicans, different concentration of extracts ranging from 0.5 mg/ml - 2 mg/ml and the total volume is made up into one ml by SD broth. The test tubes were incubated at 37°C for 6 hours with 140 rpm. After exposure of compounds the tubes were centrifuged at 5000 rpm for 5 min. The supernatant was discarded and the obtained pellet was washed thrice with PBS (pH 7.2). Pellet was again mixed with 100 µl of SD broth and placed in SAP induction medium (23.4% Yeast Carbon Base, 2% Yeast extract and 4% BSA, pH 5.0) containing sterile filter paper discs. The plates were incubated at 37°C for 3 - 5 days for proteolysis, after incubation the plates were flooded with 20% TCA (10 min), stained with 1.25% amido black dissolved in MeOH containing 10%

acetic acid (10 min) and destained with 15% acetic acid (10 min) and observed clear zone around the colonies. Pz (zone of proteolysis) ratio was measured between the control and compound treated colonies (GirishKumar et al, 2006).

C. albicans protease enzyme inhibitory potential of Lawsoniainermis extract was tested at two different concentrations 500 μg/ml and 750 μg/ml. Extract treatment resulted in dose depended inhibition of protease enzyme. When compared to control, extract treatment resulted in 27% and 33% protease inhibition, at tested concentrations 500 μg/ml and 750 μg/ml respectively (Table 18.5).

Table 18.5: Protease Inhibitory Activity of *Lawsonia inermis* Extracts against *C. albicans*

Sl.No.	Organism	Zone of Inhibition	
		500 μg/ml (% Inhibition)	750 μg/ml (% Inhibition)
1.	*C. albicans*	6.0 mm (27)	6.5 mm (33)

Protease Inhibitory Activity - Native Gel Electrophoresis

Detection of proteinase inhibitory activity of extract and Lawsone in C. albicans was determined using Zymogram method described by Schmidt et al., with minor modification. C. albicans NCIM 3074 culture was grown in Sabouraud broth at 37°C for 12 h. The culture was centrifuged at 7000 rpm for 5 min to pellet the cells. The cell pellet was washed twice with normal saline and centrifuged to collect the pellets. 100 μĩ. of Candida albicans cell suspension was added to proteinase induction medium containing 1% glucose, 3% yeast carbon base and 1% BSA (Bovine Serum Albumin). 500 μg mL-1 ethyl acetate extract of henna leaves and 100 μg mL-1 Lawsone separately dissolved in dimethyl sulfoxide. This was added to respective test tubes immediately after the inoculation of culture. The mixture was incubated for 24-48 h at 37°C in a shaker at 150 rpm. Culture broth was centrifuged at 7000 rpm for 15 min to remove cells. Cells were lysed and cell lysis was used for zymographic studies after protein estimation. Zymogram was performed with 1% casein incorporated in the acrylamide gel to detect the proteinase inhibition activity. The proteinase inhibitory activity was indicated by no cleavage of casein (no band formation) and it can be compared to complete cleavage of casein by proteinases (white band formation) in control groups.

As in Figure 18.6, Zymogram results show complete degradation of casein (thick White band formation) in control samples and intact Casein (no band/less intense band formation) in treated samples (Extract and Lawsone treatment). This indicates protease inhibitory activity of activity of extract and Lawsone.

> Phospholipase inhibitory activity - Spectrophotometric Analysis:

> Phospholipase activity of C. albicans of control and drug treated experiments was carried out using the protocols of Leidich et al. Briefly assay mixture consists of 1 ml of sample, 1 ml of 60% perchloric acid and heated in a sand bath at 200 C until the solution turns colourless. Subsequently, 1 ml

of 60% perchloric acid was added and the final volume was made to 9.1 ml using distilled water to this 0.5 ml of molybdate II reagent and 0.4 ml ANSA reagent mixture was added. The tubes were shaken well and heated in a boiling water bath for 8 min. exactly. The blue color developed was read using spectrophotometer at 680 nm.

Table 18.6: Protease Inhibitory Activity of *Lawsonia inermis* Extracts Against *C. albicans*

Sl.No.	Organism	% Inhibition of Phospholipase Enzyme Activity (O.D.)	
		Henna Extract (500 µg/ml)	Lawsone (100 µg/ml)
1.	*C. albicans*	44.45% (0.05)	77.78% (0.02)

Spectroscopic analysis of change in phospholipase activity of C. albicans after treatment with lawsone and extract respectively has been tabulated in table 6. Both henna extract and lawsone showed phospholipase inhibitory activity. Percentage inhibition of phospholipase activity when compared to Control was found to be 44.5% for henna extract (500 µ /çé1 treatment) and 77.78% for Lawsone (100 µg/ml treatment).

> Aspartate semi-aldehyde dehydrogenase inhibitory activity study

Lawsoniainermis extract was found to completely inhibit aspartate semialehyde dehydrogenase (ASADH) activity in C. albicans. Untreated control and DMSO control C. albicans group showed two distinct bands at Rm 0.422 and 0.672, with a later prominent band. Surprisingly Lawsoniainermis (500 µg/ml) treatment completely inhibited ASADH expression in C. albicans (Figure 18.7).

Example 3. In addition to this presence of tannins, coumarines and quinines have been confirmed. Example 4.

Table 18.7: Phytochemical Composition of Ethyl Acetate Extract of *Lawsonia inermis*

Sl.No.	Extract Components/ml	Assay method	Result concentration
1.	Total Phenolic content which includes lawsoniaside	Folin Ciocalteu method	16.55 µg/ml
2.	Total Flavonoid content which includes luteoline	Aluminimum chloride colorimetric assay	392 µg/ml
3.	Lawsone	HPLC analysis	24.32 mg/ml

Anticandida Oral and Vaginal Gel Composition

(a) Oral Gel Composition

PROCEDURE - MANUFACTURING (Oral Gel)

Step 1: The required quantities of all the ingredients like disodium EDTA, Sodium saccharin, Mixed fruit flavour, Sodium methyl paraben, HPMC 90SH- 100000, Carbopol 974P, Sodium hydroxide, Purified water are weighed accurately.

Step 2:

1. Collected required quantity of fresh purified water, in a container & boiled it. Added accurately weighed quantities of the Disodium EDTA, Sodium Saccharin, Sodium methyl paraben & Sodium hydroxide to the boiled water in container followed by stiring until completely dissolved (Solution 2).
2. Transferred the solution 2 from the container in to Planetory mixer.
3. Added weighed quantity of HPMC followed by carbopol 974P in to planetary mixer slowly and at constant speed while mixing at optimal rpm until gel base is formed.
4. Added weighed quantities of Flavour in to the mixing vessel of planetary mix containing gel base.
5. Adjusted the pH between 6 and 7.

Step 3:

1. Weighed the required quantity of gel base in planetory mixer.
2. Weighed the required quantity of Actives (henna extract/lawsone) dissolved in surfactant(s).
3. Mixed the Actives dissolved in surfactants with the gel base until uniformly dispersed fine gel was formed.

   (b) Vagina] Gel Composition

   Procedure - Manufacturing (vaginal Gel)

Step 1:

Weighed accurately the required quantities of all the ingredients like disodium EDTA, Sodium methyl paraben, HPMC 90SH-100000, Carbopol 974P, Sodium hydroxide, Purified water.

Step 2:

1. Collected fresh purified water of required quantity in a container & boiled it.

   Added accurately the weighed quantities of Disodium EDTA, Sodium methyl paraben & Sodium hydroxide to the boiled water in container followed by stirring until to achieve completely dissolved Solution.
2. Transferred the solution from the container in to Planetary mixer.
3. Added weighed quantity of HPMC followed by carbopol 974P in to planetary mixer slowly and at constant speed while mixing at optimal rpm until gel base is formed.

4\. Adjusted the pH of gel base between 4 and 6

Step 3:

5. Weighed the required quantity of gel base in planetary mixer.
6. Weighed the required quantity of Actives (henna extract/lawsone) dissolved in surfactant(s).
7. Mixed the Actives dissolved in surfactants to the gel base until uniformly dispersed fine gel was formed.

19

The Effect of Aqueous Leaves Extract of Henna

Many higher plants produce important organic compounds such as resins, tannins, flavonoids, pesticides and other pharmacological compounds; however, most of the plants have not been scientifically evaluated for their toxicity, efficiency and constitute as well. Henna (*Lawsonia inermis*) is extensively grown in the Middle East and Africa. It has an astringent taste and tea like odor. When the dried leaves are soaked in water and applied to the skin, hair or nails, auburn to red color develops, hence it is worldwide recognized as cosmetic agent used for ornamental values.

Carbon tetrachloride also known as tetra chloromethane is known to have hepatotoxic effects. Carbon tetrachloride is a synthetic chemical compound formally widely used in fire extinguishers but largely abandoned now due to its toxicity. At room temperature and pressure it is a colorless liquid with a "sweet" smell that can be detected at low levels. Exposure to higher concerntration of this compound can affect the central nervous system including the brain. When exposed, the liver is inflamed and hepatocytes will be destroyed. The objective of this study therefore is to evaluate the hepato-protective effect of L. inermis in carbon tetrachloride induced liver damage.

MATERIALS AND METHODS

Plant Collection

Fresh leaves of *Lawsonia inermis* were obtained from Gashua town of Barde Local Government Area of Yobe state Nigeria. The plant was identified by a toxonomist in the department of Biological Sciences, University of Maiduguri, Nigeria.

Experimental Animals

Thirty Swiss Albino mice weighing between 20-40g were used. They were kept in plastic cages in the laboratory for one week before the commencement of the experiment to acclimatize. They were fed commercial chick mash (Vital feeds Nig. Ltd) and given water ad libitum.

Preparation of Plant Aqueous Extract

The leaves of *Lawsonia inermis* (Henna) were washed with distilled water. The leaves were sun dried and grounded into powder using pestle and mortar. Fifty (50) grams of the powdered leaves were mixed with five hundred Milles

(500 ml) of water in a flat bottom flask and boiled for 30 minutes. It was allowed to cool and then filtered using a Whatman no. 1 filter paper size 0.1μm (micrometer). The filterate was stored at 4°C. The plant aqueous extract was prepared according to the method of Mittal and Aguwa,.

Extract Administration

The mice were divided into six groups of five mice each.

Group A mice were administrated Carbon tetrachloride at a dose rate of 4mg/kg body weight subcutaneously.

Group B mice were administered the extract at dose rate of 100 mg/kg body weight orally daily for seven consecutive days, and 24 hours after the last dose of extract. Carbon tetrachloride was administered subcutaneously at dose rate of 4 mg/kg.

Group C mice were administered the extract at dose rate of 150 mg/kg body weight orally daily for seven consecutive days, and 24 hours after the last dose of extract. Carbon tetrachloride was administered subcutaneously at the dose rate of 4 mg/kg.

Group D mice were administered the extract alone at dose rate of 100 mg/kg body weight orally daily for seven consecutive days.

Group E mice were administered the extract alone at dose rate of 150 mg/kg body weight orally daily for seven consecutive days.

Collection of Blood and Liver Sample

All the mice from each group were sacrificed 24 hours after administration of carbon tetrachloride and the blood collected in a plane sample bottle via the jugular vein. The blood was allowed to clot and centrifuge at 1500rpm and the serum collected for determination of Alanine aminotransferase and Aspartate aminotransferase concentration.

Determination Alanineaminotransferase (ALAT) and Aspartate Aminotransferase (ASAT)

The in vitro determination of Alanine aminotransferase and Aspartate aminotransferase was carried out by the method described by Reitman and Frankel, and Schmidt and Schmidt,.

Statistical Analysis

The Graphpad Instat 3.0 computer software was used to analyse the data generated. A significant level of P – 0.05 was considered.

RESULTS

The result of the experiment showing the effect of aqueous leaves extract of Henna (*Lawsonia inermis*) on carbon tetrachloride induced liver damage is presented in Table 19.1.

Table 19.1: The Effect of Aqueous Leaves Extract of Henna (*Lawsonia Inermis*) on Liver Enzymes of Swiss Albino Mice Treated with Carbon Tetrachloride.

Group	Liver Enzymes	
	Alanine Amino Transferase (ALAT)	Amino Transferase (ALAT)
A (CCl_4 4 mg/kg)	130.2 ± 6.87	217.8 ± 10.66
B (100 mg/kg of extract and 4 mg/kg of CCl_4)	101.8 ± 17.12*	185.4 ± 9.55*
C (150 mg/kg of extract and 4 mg/kg of CCl_4)	106.8 ± 10.28*	187.0 ± 9.72*
D (100 mg/kg of extract alone)	18.8 ± 3.49*[a]	90.8 ± 9.91*
E (150 mg/kg of extract alone)	13.4 ± 2.97*[a]	65.2 ± 5.63*
F (distilled water)	22.2 ± 3.11a	113.5 ± 11.12

[a]Significant (P – 0.05) decrease compared with distilled water
*Significant (P – 0.05) decrease compared with carbon tetrachloride

All the mice administered the extract showed a significant (P – 0.05) decrease in both ALAT and ASAT level when compared with group treated with carbon tetrachloride (4 mg/kg body weight) alone. However those treated with the extract alone showed higher decreased level of the enzymes then those administered the extract after CCl4 treatment.

The groups treated with 100 mg/kg body weight and 150 mg/kg body weight of the extract alone recorded significant decrease in the level of ALAT only when compared with the group given distilled water alone. However, the group treated with carbon tetrachloride (4 mg/kg body weight) alone and those treated with 100 mg/kg body weight and 150 mg/kg body weight of the extract before carbon tetrachloride administration recorded a significant increase in both ALAT and ASAT level when compared with group treated with distilled water alone.

DISCUSSION AND CONCLUSSION

The result of the study showed that the aqueous leave extract of *Lawsonia inermis* administered at the dosage used for the experiment suppressed the activity of the liver enzymes in treated animals compared with the control and the group treated with carbon tetrachloride alone.

The extract was found to contain flavonoids, tannins, coumarin, mannitol. Flavonoids are reported to exhibit antioxidant activity and are effective scavengers of superoxide anions. Beneficial effect of flavonoids has been described for successful treatment of many health conditions, including cancer and liver diseases. They can also bind to enzymes and DNA to chelate heavy metals. The extract may have exhibited hepato-protective activity due to its antioxidant property attributable to the flavonoids, since antioxidants are found to protect liver cells against damaging effects of the reactive oxygen species such as singlet oxygen, superoxide, peroxynitrite, peroxyl and hydroxyl radicals.

Antioxidants prevent the oxidative stress which comes up as a result of reactive oxygen that is known for their cellular damaging effect.

In conclusion, the aqueous extract of L. inermis has been observed to suppress the liver enzymes therefore has possible hepato-protective activity in the mice because of the presence of flavonoids.

20

Study of Henna (*Lawsonia inermis*) as Natural Corrosion Inhibitor for Aluminum Alloy in Seawater

At present, aluminum alloys are widely used in shipbuilding because they are strong and light in weight. These enable the aluminum ships to move faster, load more cargoes and travel further while maintaining stability and fuel consumed efficiency. However, aluminum is typically a reactive metal in the galvanic series. When it is in contact with other metals, it will act as the anode and may begin to corrode.

Although aluminum alloys have high corrosion resistance but it will react very actively once exposed to the saline environment especially seawater which contained mostly sodium chloride that destabilizes the protective oxide film, leading the localized attack, or pitting. Hence, alternative way is to be discovered in order to reduce the corrosion especially on aluminum alloy. Nowadays, anti-corrosion paint is introduced for the ship to reduce the rate of corrosion. However, most of the anti-corrosion paints are found to consist of high amount of chromate which is extremely toxic and harmful to environment.

The increasing concern about the toxicity of corrosion inhibitors in the industries has replaced with more environmental friendly organic inhibitors. Thus, plant extracts are becoming important as an environmentally acceptable, readily available and renewable source for wide range of inhibitors. They are the rich sources of ingredients which have very high inhibition efficiency. The corrosion inhibition activity in many plant extracts could be due to the presence of heterocyclic constituents like alkaloid and flavonoid. The presence of tannin, cellulose and polycyclic compound could enhance the film formation over the metal surface, thus aiding corrosion.

The previous study had found that henna has four main constituents which are lawsone, gallic acid, a-D-Glucose and tannic acid. These constituents have great inhibition ability which could combined with the metal cations and adsorbed on the metal surface as a formation of insoluble complex compounds to protect the metal from corrosion attack.

Therefore, the aim of this research was to investigate the feasibility use of henna (*Lawsonia inermis*) as natural corrosion inhibitor for aluminum alloy in seawater. The components of henna were determined by using Fourier Transfrom Infrared Spectroscopy while its corrosion inhibition ability was tested through immersion method in seawater and the corrosion inhibition efficiency was analyzed by electrochemical measurement.

Experiment Procedures and Method

Sample preparation

Aluminum alloy (5083) were purchased in standard size of 25 mm × 25 mm × 3 mm as test coupons. It was alloyed by 0.40% Si, 0.40% Fe, 0.10% Cu, 0.40-1.0% Mn, 4.0-4.9% Mg, 0.05-0.25% Cr, 0.25% Zn, 0.15% Ti, and the remainder are aluminum. The coupons were cleaned and polished by sandpaper following grit of 400, 600, 800, 1000 and 1200 grit. Then, they were rinsed and cleaned with distilled water, degreased with acetone and dried in the desiccators before the experiment started. The commercial henna powder made in India was prepared and the components were analyzed through Fourier Transfrom Infrared Spectroscopy (FTIR). Then it was dissolved in seawater with various concentration of 100 ppm, 300 ppm, and 500 ppm.

Weight loss measurement

Before the coupons were cleaned with acetone, the coupons were weighed for the original weight by using Sartorius Cole-Polmer analytical balance (readability: 0.0001g) and hung in the aquarium containing seawater for 60 days. One sample was taken out from the aquarium in 10 days interval for 6 weeks. Before weighing, the sample was cleaned with distilled water and dried. Then the sample was immersed in nitric acid (HNO_3) to remove the corrosion products. Finally, the sample was washed with distilled water, dried and weighed in order to obtain the final weight.

Fourier transform infrared spectroscopy (FTIR)

The commercial henna powder was placed and exposed under range of infrared ray beams. The transmittance and reflectance of the infrared rays at different frequencies was translated into an IR absorption plot consisting of reverse peaks. The spectral pattern was analyzed and matched according to IR absorption table to identify the functional group contained in the henna powder.

Immersion test

Aquariums were prepared with specific amount seawater where one as control medium while the rest of the solutions were dissolved with commercial henna powder in different concentration such as 100 ppm, 300 ppm and 500 ppm. It was carried out for duration of 60 days in enclosed condition without any disturbance. The coupons were taken out for each 10 days for further weight loss measurement, polarization test, corrosion rate analysis and inhibition efficiency calculation.

Electrochemical impedance spectroscopy (EIS)

For EIS measurements, the test was conducted by using AC signal of impedance measurements by the use of Autolab PGSTAT302N and run at the corrosion potential. All the potentials referred were relative to SCE. The impedance measurements were conducted over a frequency range of 1 MHz down to 10 mHz. The results were analyzed using the fit program FRA. The inhibition efficiency, *IE* (%) was calculated by using the Equation 1 where *R2* and *R1* are the polarization resistance in the presence and absence of inhibitors :

RESULT AND DISCUSSION

Fourier transform infrared spectroscopy (FTIR)

Figure 20.1 shows the functional group of henna. The presence of hydroxyl group appeared at 3299 cm^{-1}. There are two α,β-unsaturated carbonyl bands at 1735.2 cm^{-1} and 1625.1 cm^{-1} (C=O chelated with an α-hydroxyl) signify the presence of two carbonyl groups conjugated with a double bond (α,β-unsaturated carbonyls) and thus endorsing the possibility of having a 1,4-naphthoquinone. It was found that henna consists of a major component which is Lawsone. This compound has molecular formula of $C_{10}H_6O_3$ with molecular mass of 174.153. The phenol group of lawsone would donate electron to the metal to achieve its noble state of orbit, while the metal would receive the electron to become more stable. This indirectly retard further redox reaction and could resist metal from corrosion attack.

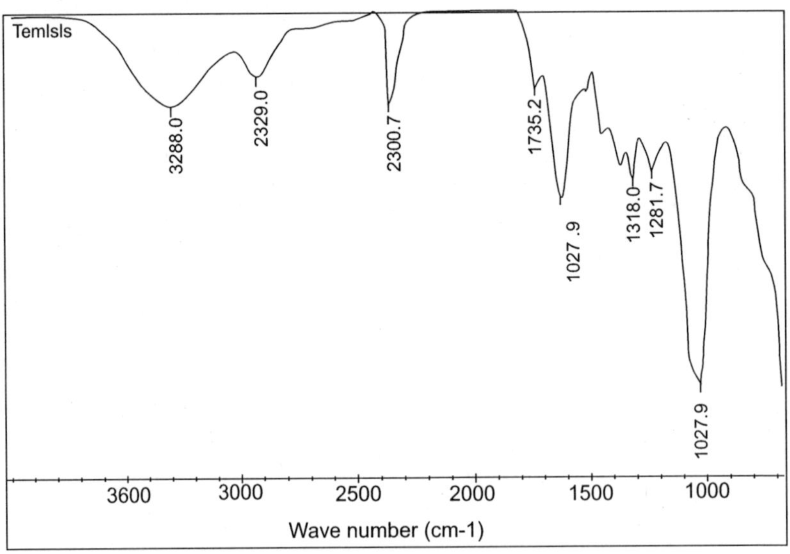

Fig. 20.1: Functional group in commercial henna powder analyzed by FTIR

Henna constituents have antioxidant characteristic especially by the naphthoquinones. The possible mechanism for chemisorptions can be attributed to the complex formation between lawsone and metal cations. The main cathodic reaction in the surface is hydrogen evolution. In this case, oxygen reduction does not play a significant role in total cathodic reaction. Therefore, the oxygen scavenging characteristic of henna is not the main responsible mechanism for the observed inhibition of henna extract yet is the chemisorption of inhibitor molecules on the surface. So, it is concluded that the chemisorption of inhibitor molecules on steel surface is the main inhibition mechanism while the inhibitive action is slightly enhanced via oxygen scavenging.

Electrochemical impedance spectroscopy (EIS)

EIS test was conducted to obtain interfacial information or working electrodes in electrolyte. The Nyquist plot for AA5083 immersed in seawater with henna as inhibitor is presented in Figure 20.2. As seen from the figure, the plot of impedance shows single capacitive semicircle which indicates the process was controlled by charge transfer and could be assigned to the oxide layer of AA5083. It was found that the addition of the inhibitor could increase the corrosion resistance of the coating formed on metal surface. Upon incresasing of inhibitor concentration, the value of polarization resistace was also increased indicating that there are gradual formation of passive film on the sample surface.

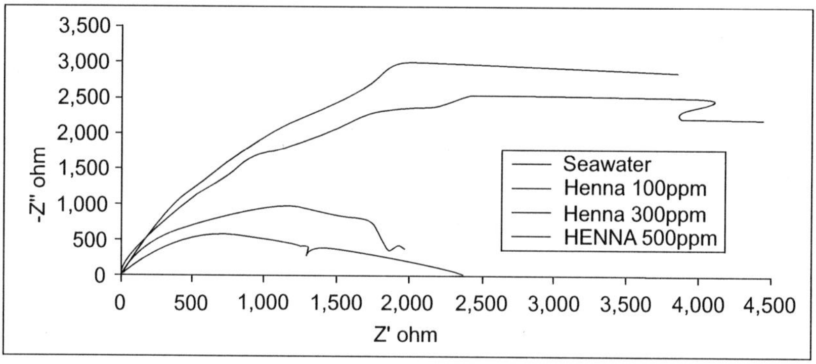

Fig. 20.2: Graph Z' ohm against Z" ohm for immersion of 30 days

The semi-circle curves represented that the henna had absorbed on the aluminum surface and produced a coating to separate the metal from the seawater. In this case, there were no direct exposure of the metal to the saline environment. On the other hand, the aluminum alloy without inhibitor had indicated that the aluminum alloy had reacted with oxygen to form aluminum oxide, Al_2O_3 and these become the film to protect the metal from further redox reaction or corrosion attack. The diameter of semicircle represented that the corrosion resistance of aluminum oxide layer formed was not good enough compared to inhibitor coating by henna. AC impedance results showed that the decrease in *Cdl* value, as shown in Table 20.1, was a result of the formation of a protective layer by the adsorption of inhibitor molecules on the AA5083 surface. The adsorption is influenced from the molecule's chemical structure, the solution's chemical composition, the nature of the metal surface, the temperature and the electrochemical potential at the metal/solution interface. The changes in *Cdl* phenomenon is influenced from the molecule's structure, the solution's chemical composition, the nature of the metal surface, the temperature and the electrochemical potential at the metal/solution interface.

Table 20.1: Impedance Parameter for AA5083 Immersed in Seawater

Concentration	R_s (Ω)	R_p (Ω)	C_{dl} (F)
0 ppm	4.5374	1233.99	2.50E–0.5
100 ppm	2.3220	2522.04	4.46E–05
300 ppm	2.3025	6762.92	3.50E–05
500 ppm	2.1887	9883.31	5.07E–05

Table 20.2: Inhibition Efficiency Gained from Impedance Paramet

Inhibitor	Inhibition Efficiency (%)
0 ppm	–
100 ppm	51
300 ppm	82
500 ppm	88

Weight Loss Measurement

The weight loss measurement is a classical way to determine the corrosion rate of aluminium alloy. The result for the weight loss measurement was summarized in Figure 20.3. The graph shown in Figure 20.3 reveals that there was an increasing in weight loss with respect to immersion time. The weight loss of coupons immersed in seawater in the presence of henna was lower compared in absence of henna which indicates that henna has retarded the corrosion process of AA5083. As the concentration increases, the weight loss decreases due to rises in surface area covered by adsorbed molecules of henna during the increment of concentration. The existences of various compounds like oxygen (polyphenols) as well as nitrogen and sulphur (glucosinate), it is hard to

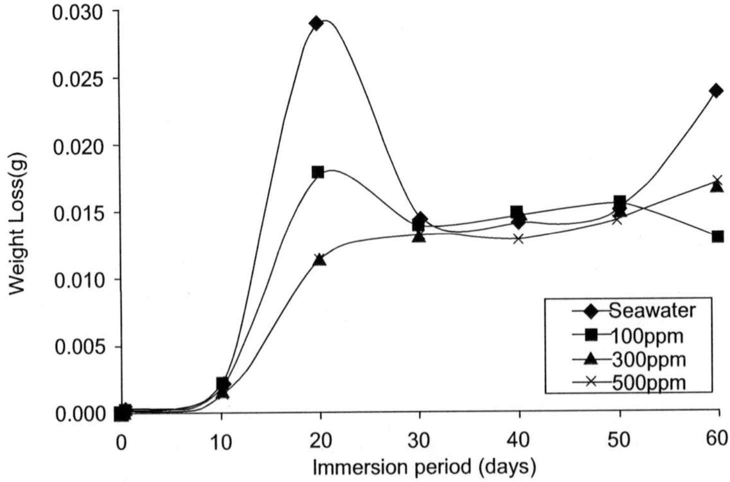

Fig. 20.3. Graph weight loss (g) against immersion period (days)

determine which components inhibit the metal from corrosion. It may be one or all of them involve in synergism action. There was considerable reduction in weight loss and hence reduces the corrosion rate with the introduction of inhibitor in corrosive media. Higher concentration of henna was effectively inhibiting the corrosion compares to lower concentration of henna.

Adsorption isotherm

Graph inhibitor concentration (C) against C/θ plotted in Figure 20.4 was illustrated by mere straight lines which indicated that the adsorption of henna on aluminum alloy 5083 follows the Langmuir adsorption isotherm. The observed inhibitive action of henna could be due to the adsorption of its molecules on the aluminum alloy surface which produce a layer or a barrier for the charge and mass transfer between the metal and the surrounding. As the concentration increased the fraction of metal surface covered by the adsorbed molecules (θ) increased and lead to higher inhibition efficiency.

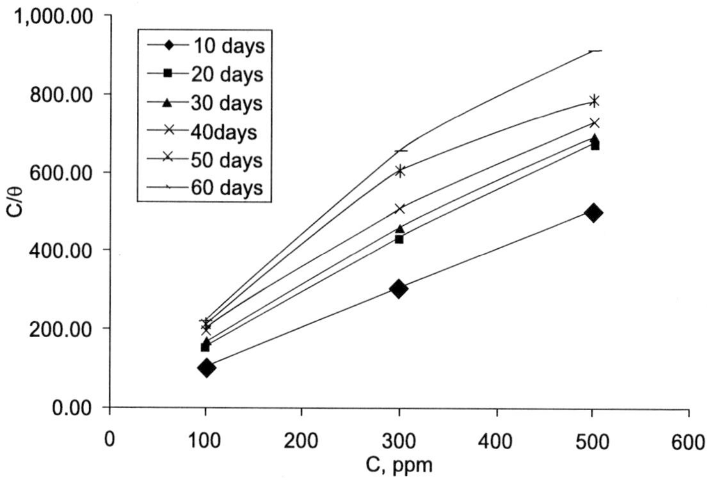

Fig. 20.4: Adsorption isotherm of various inhibitor concentration on aluminum alloy surface for immersion duration of 60 days

CONCLUSION

Henna (*Lawsonia inermis*) contain major constituents of lawsone which contributed to the chemisorptions or adsorption process by forming an isolation layers on the aluminum alloy surface which obey the Langmuir adsorption isotherm. However, the protection layer attached on metal was not permenant when exposed to saline environment and precipitation occurred as the time increased. The inhibition efficiency is proportional to its concentration dissolved. It reached the highest 88% at concentration of 500ppm. The inhibition efficiency gained from EIS measurement is still in acceptable aggrement. This research found that henna is an excellent natural inhibitor for aluminum alloy in seawater.

21 Diuretic Activity of Aqueous and Ethanolic Extracts of *Lawsonia inermis* Leaves

Since the time immemorial our traditional system of medicine and folklore claiming that medicinal plants as a whole or their parts are being used in all types of diseases successfully. About 65% of world populations have access to local medicinal plant knowledge system. Traditional systems of medicine are popular in developing countries and upto 80% of population relies on traditional medicines or folk remedies for their primary health care needs. India has about 45000 plant species and among them, several thousands have been claimed to posses medicinal properties. Diuretics are drugs that increase the rate of urine flow, sodium excretion and are used to adjust the volume and composition of body fluids in a variety of clinical situations. Drug induced diuresis is beneficial in many life threatening disease conditions such as congestive heart failure, nephritic syndrome, cirrhosis, renal failure, hypertension and pregnancy toxaemia. Most diuretic drugs have the adverse effects on quality of life including impotence, fatigue and weakness. Herbal medicines are in great demand in the developed as well as developing countries for primary health care because of their wide biological and medicinal activities, higher safety margins and lesser costs. Indian ayurvedic system is rich in treating renal problems. *Lawsonia inermis* (Lythraceae) is a perennial plant commonly called as henna, having different vernacular names in India viz., mehendi in Hindi, mendika in Sanskrit, mailanchi in Malayalam, muruthani in tamil, benjati in oriya, mayilanchi in kannada and mehendi in Bengali. It is native to North Africa and South East Asia and often cultivated as an ornamental plant throughout India, Persia and along the African coast of the Mediterranean sea. *Lawsonia inermis* is a glabrous branched shrub or small tree (2 to 6 m in height).

Leaves are small, opposite, entire margin elliptical to broadly lanceolate, sub-sessile, about 1.5 to 5 cm long, 0.5 to 2 cm wide, greenish brown to dull green, petiole short and glabrous acute or obtuse apex with tapering base. The ethnomedical uses include the use of leaves as expectorant, anti-inflammatory, depurative, liver tonic, haematinic, styptic and febrifuge. Literature review also indicated that diuretic activity of this species has not been clinically evaluated so far. So the present study aimed to evaluate the diuretic activity of aqueous and ethanolic extracts of *Lawsonia inermis* leaves in rats.

MATERIALS AND METHODS

Plant Material

The fresh leaves of *Lawsonia inermis* belonging to the family Lythraceae were collected in January 2011 at the local areas of Anantapur district, Andhra Pradesh, India. The plant material was identified and authenticated by Dr. J. Raveendra Reddy, M.Pharm, Ph.D, Department of Pharmacognosy, Raghavendra Institute of Pharmaceutical Education and Research, Anantapur and voucher specimen riper-11/11 is preserved in department of pharmacology, Raghavendra institute of pharmaceutical education and research, Anantapur.

Processing of Sample

The fresh leaves of *Lawsonia inermis* plant were dried under shade for 20-25 days. The dried leaves were pulverized into fine powder and used for extraction.

PREPARATION OF EXTRACTS

Preparation of Ethanolic Extract of *Lawsonia inermis* Leaves

The powdered drug of leaves was loaded into the soxhlet extractor and subjected to extraction with ethanol. After extraction, the solvent was distilled off and the extracts were concentrated to dryness at room temperature. The percentage yield of ethanolic extract of *Lawsonia inermis* was found to be 12% (Table 21.1).

Table 21.1: % Yield, Texture and Colour of Aqueous and Ethanolic Extract of Leaves of *Lawsonia inermis*.

Plant part	Type of Extract	% Yield	Texture	Colour
Leaves of *Lawsonia inermis*	Aqueous extract	10	Gummy	Greenish black
	Ethanolic extract	12	Gummy	Greenish black

Preparation of Qqueous Extract of *Lawsonia inermis* Leaves

The powdered crude drug of leaves was subjected for extraction process by maceration with water at room temperature for 48 hours. The extract was filtered and concentrated to dryness at room temperature. The percentage yield of aqueous extract of *Lawsonia inermis* was found to be 10% (Table 21.1).

Phytochemical Analysis

The aqueous and ethanolic extracts of *Lawsonia inermis* leaves were subjected to preliminary phytochemical screening.

Drugs and Chemicals

Deionised water, methanol (Merck specialities pvt. Ltd.), furosemide (Aventis pharma Ltd).

Experimental Animals

Male wistar rats of 200-300 gm were used to carry out the diuretic activity. The animals had free access to standard commercial diet and water *ad libitum* and were housed in cages under standard laboratory conditions i.e., 12:12 hour light/dark cycle at 25 ± 20C. The Institutional Animal Ethics Committee (878/ac/05/CPCSEA/012/2011) has approved the experimental protocol at post graduate department of pharmacology, Raghavendra institute of Pharmacuetical education research, Anantapur, Andhra Pradesh, India.

Acute Toxicity Studies

Acute toxicity studies for aqueous and ethanolic extracts of *Lawsonia inermis* was carried out in rats at different doses (500–3000 mg/kg, orally), showed no gross evidence of any abnormalities in the rats up to the end of 72 hr of the observation period. This indicates the safety of extract. Acute toxicity study was done as per OECD, 2006 Guidelines. Hence we selected 250 mg/kg and 500 mg/kg as low and high doses.

Diuretic Activity

The method of Lipschitz et al was employed for the assessment of diuretic activity. According to this method, the animal should be deprived of food and water for 18 hours prior to the experiment, and were randomly divided into six groups of six animals each as follows:

Group 1 (Control) - received saline 25 ml/kg p.o.

Group 2 (Standard) - received furosemide 20 mg/kg p.o.

Group 3 (Test) - received aqueous extract of *Lawsonia inermis* 250 mg/kg p.o.

Group 4 (Test) - received aqueous extract of *Lawsonia inermis* 500 mg/kg p.o.

Group 5 (Test) - received ethanolic extract of *Lawsonia inermis* 250 mg/kg p.o.

Group 6 (Test) - received ethanolic extract of *Lawsonia inermis* 500 mg/kg p.o.

Immediately after administration, animals were placed in metabolic cages specially designed to separate urine faecal matter. During the period of study no food, water was made available to the animals. The total volume of urine was collected and measured from control, standard and extract treated groups up to 5 hours of administration. The parameters monitored for the each individual rat were total urine volume and urine concentration of Na^+, K^+ and Cl^-. Concentration of Na+ and K+ were determined using flame photometer while Cl^- concentration was estimated titrimetrically using 0.02N $AgNO_3$ with 5% potassium chromate as an indicator. Appearance of brick red precipitate was taken as the end point.

Statistical Analysis

The results were expressed as a mean ± S.E.M. The differences were compared using One Way Analysis of Variance (ANOVA) and subsequently followed by Bonferroni's test.

RESULTS

Phytochemical Analysis

Both aqueous and ethanolic extracts of *Lawsonia inermis* revealed the presence of alkaloids, tannins, flavonoids, phenolic compounds and triterpenoids (Table 21.2).

Table 21.2: Phytochemical Analysis of Aqueous and Ethanolic Extracts of *Lawsonia inermis*

Chemical constituents	Lawsonia inermis	
	Aqueous extract	Ethanolic extract
Alkaloids	+	+
Tannins	+	+
Flavonoids	+	+
Phenolic compounds	+	+
Triterpenoids	+	+

+ = Present

Effect of Aqueous and Ethanolic Extracts on Urine Output in Rats

Urine volume in rats treated with aqueous extract of *Lawsonia inermis* at low and high doses were 4.6 ml and 6.1 ml respectively. Urine volume in rats treated with ethanolic extract of *Lawsonia inermis* at low and high dose were 7.3 ml and 9.0 ml respectively.

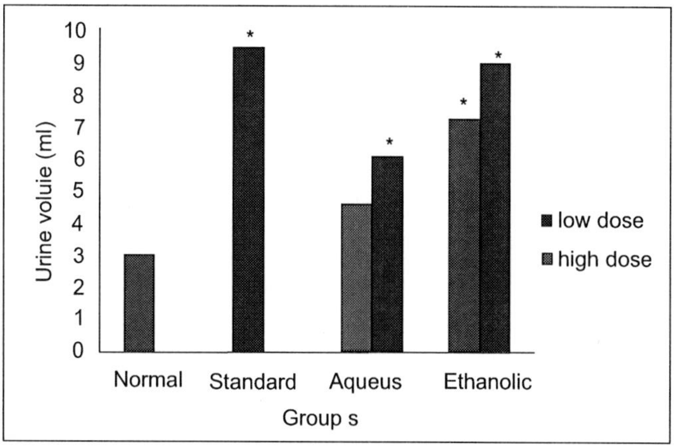

Fig. 21.1: Effect of aqueous and ethanolic extracts on urine output in rats

Effect of Aqueous and Ethanolic Extracts on Electrolyte Excretion in Rats

The concentrations of Na^+, K^+ and Cl^- in rats treated with aqueous extracts of *Lawsonia inermis at* low dose and high dose were 113.8 mEq/L, 66.60 mEq/L, 127.3 mEq/L and 127.8 mEq/L, 73.60 mEq/L and 155.6 mEq/L respectively. The concentrations of Na^+, K^+ and Cl^- in rats treated with ethanolic extracts of *Lawsonia inermis* at low dose and high dose were 120.5 mEq/L, 71.20 mEq/L, 147.5mEq/L and 136.2 mEq/L, 89.13 mEq/L and 170.5 mEq/L respectively.

Table 21.3: Effect of Aqueous and Ethanolic Extracts on Electrolyte Excretion in Rats

Treatment	Dose & Route	Electrolyte levels		
		Sodium (m. Eq/L)	Potassium (m.Eq/L)	Chloride (m.Eq/L)
Control	25 ml/kg p.o	85.10 ± 2.892	59.03 ± 1.302	97.83 ± 1.26
Furosemide	20 ml/kg p.o	145.2 ± 2.470**	87.67 ± 1.782**	174.3 ± 2.634**
Aqueous extract	250 ml/kg p.o	113.8 ± 2.042**	66.60 ± 0.6429*	127.3 ± 1.868**
Aqueous extract	500 ml/kg p.o	127.8 ± 0.9849**	73.60 ± 0.5196**	155.6 ± 2.218**
Ethanolic extract	250 ml/kg p.o	120.5 ± 0.5196**	71.20 ± 0.5033**	147.5 ± 1.637**
Ethanolic extract	500 ml/kg p.o	136.2 ± 1.222**	89.13 ± 0.2906**	170.5 ± 1.947**

*$p<0.05$, **$p<0.001$ when compared to normal

DISCUSSION

The phytochemical tests revealed the presence of alkaloids, tannins, flavonoids, phenolic compounds and triterpenoids in both ethanolic and aqueous extracts. In acute toxicity studies no mortality was found upto 3000 mg/kg. Both the aqueous and ethanolic extracts showed a dosedependent increase in urine excretion. Relatively ethanolic extract produced significant dieresis than aqueous extract. Thus the diuretic effects of both extracts are indicated by increase in both water and excretion of sodium, potassium and chloride. The active principles responsible for the diuretic effect of the extracts of *Lawsonia inermis* have not been elucidated but preliminary phytochemical analysis revealed the presence of polar compounds such as flavonoids. It may be suggested that these substances might be responsible, at least in part, for the observed diuretic activity. The effect may be produced by stimulation of regional blood flow or inhibition of vasopressin or by producing inhibition of tubular reabsorption of water and anions, the result in all cases being diuresis. From the above results it was concluded that both the extracts of *Lawsonia inermis* leaves showed significant diuretic activity relatively ethanolic extract showed more activity than aqueous extract. However, further investigations are needed to explore the exact active constituents and mechanisms responsible for the diuretic activity.

CONCLUSION

Aqueous and ethanolic extracts of *Lawsonia inermis* leaves have showed dose dependent increase in urine and electrolyte excretion. Relatively ethanolic extract showed more activity when compared to aqueous extract.

22

Phytotoxicity Effects of *Lawsonia inermis* L. on the Seed Germination and Growth Performance of Selected Pulses

A variety of plant species are being used by individuals and communities for the treatment of diseases. It is now clear that the medicinal values of these plants lie in the bioactive phytochemical constituents that produce physiological effects on human body. The most important of these bioactive constituents of plants are alkaloids, tannins, flavonoids and some other phenolic compounds. The effects of these chemicals are not limited to animals and human body alone, but also on other plants. Many plants including medicinal plants were reported to interact chemically with other plant species. Such chemical interaction is known as allelopathy.

Allelopathy is believed to be involved in many natural and manipulated ecosystems and it plays an important role in the evolution of plant communities, exotic plants invasion and replant failure. Many plant species including medicinal plants are able to produce and release bioactive compounds which are secondary metabolites into the environment and are capable of suppressing the growth of other plants. Such chemicals include tannins, phenolic acids, lignins, alkaloids, flavonoids, coumarins and terpenoids. They are present in all plant tissues including leaves, stems, roots, rhizomes, flowers, fruits and seeds, and even in pollen grains. Allelochemicals when released to the soil, inhibit germination, shoot and root growth of other plants, affect nutrients uptake or naturally occurring symbiotic relationship, thereby destroying the plant's usable source of nutrients. The manifestation of these is usually in the form of inhibited or retarded germination rate, reduced root or radicle and shoot or coleoptile extension, lack of root hairs, swelling or necrosis of root tips, discolouration, reduced dry weight accumulation and lower reproductive capacity.

According to Muller, the term allelopathy refers to the overall influence of one plant on another due to the chemical compounds being added to the environment. Allelochemicals are commonly called as secondary metabolic plant products. These are the waste products of the main metabolic pathway or primary metabolic processes of plants. These allelochemicals are accumulated in the soil and affect the growth of plants. Allelopathic research has been focused on the effect of interaction between weed species. The naturally occurring allelopathic substances are renewable and easily degradable. So, the allelochemicals are used because of their eco-friendly nature with the environment. The decomposition of plant residues potentially provides the largest quantity of allelochemicals that may be added to the rhizosphere. The aim of the present investigation is to study the allelopathic effect of medicinal plant *Lawsonia inermis L.* on the seed germination and growth performance of pulse crops *viz Vigna radiata (L),* Hepper., *Vigna mungo (L)* Hepper and *Arachis hypogaea L.*

MATERIALS AND METHODS

The seeds of *Vigna radiata (L),* Hepper, *Vigna mungo (L)* Hepper and *Arachis hypogaea L.* were procured from regional oil seed research station, TNAU, Tindivanam, Villupuram District, Tamil Nadu. Healthy uniform colour and size were taken in to account for the selection of seeds for the present study. The fully matured leaves of *Lawsonia inermis L.* were collected from five year old tree for present study.

Preparation of Fresh Plant Extract and Dried Plant Extracts

The preparation of fresh plant extracts and germination studies were followed as per the method of Padhy et al., and Bhatt and Chauhan.

Fresh Leaf Extracts

Hundred grams of fresh leaves of *Lawsonia inermis L* were collected for the preparation of extracts. These were washed thoroughly with tap water followed by the distilled water and air dried, and then they were ground to fine paste and filtered in water by muslin cloth. The extracts were again filtered and filtrates were considered as 100% concentration. From these leachates (100%) further dilutions of 5, 10, 15 and 20% were prepared with distilled water.

Germination Study

The selected seeds of *Vigna radiata, Vigna mungo and Arachis hypogaea* were surface sterilized with 0.03% formalin solution for 20 min and then washed thoroughly with distilled water. For germination study 25 seeds were placed sterilized pertri plates lined with two layers of filter paper. On the first day 10 ml of fresh extract /distilled water was added per treatments on the pertriplates. Distilled water served as control. Thereafter to keep the filter paper moist 10 ml leaves extract/distilled water was added per plate 6,9,12 and 15 days after soaking. After wards the seeds were allowed to germinate in the growth chamber and kept in light intensity of 2±0.4 K.Lux and at 30±2°C till 15 days after seed soaking. Each treatment including control was replicated five times. The number of seeds germinated in each treatment was counted daily up to 10th day after sowing and germination percentage was calculated. The emergence of radicle was taken as criteria for germination. The morphological parameters were studied on the root and shoots of 10 day old seedling of *Vigna radiata, Vigna mungo and Arachis hypogaea* were studied. Five seedlings from each replicate was selected for recording the morphological parameters such as length of shoot and root, fresh and dry weight on 10th day after sowing.

Dry Matter Production

The seedlings were separated in to root and shoot and their fresh weight were recorded. The samples were kept in hot air oven at 80°C for 48 hours. The dry weight were recorded by using an electrical single pan balance.

Germination Percentage

Germination refers to the initial appearance of the radical by visual observation. It was calculated by using following formula.

It was calculated by the formula given by Carley and Watson.

RESULT AND DISCUSSION

In the present investigation an attempt has been made to determine the allelopathic potential of *Lawsonia inermis* L. on germination, growth performance of green gram (*Vigna radiata*), black gram (*Vigna mungo*) and ground nut (*Arachis hypogaea*). The following results were obtained from the present study are shown in Table 22.1, 22.2 and 22.3.

Table 22.1: Results of Aqueous Plant Extract of *Lawsonia inermis* L on Germination Percentage of Green Gram, Black Gram and Groundnut.

Extract concentration (%)	Green gram	Black gram	Groundnut
Control	98	96	96
5	94 (-4.08)	94(-2.08)	95 (-1.04)
10	91 (-7.14)	92 (-2.08)	93 (-3.12)
15	86 (-12.24)	89 (-7.29)	90 (-10.42)
20	72 (-26.53)	84 (-12.5)	86 (-10.42)
25	61(-37.75)	70 (-27.08)	73 (-23.95)

All values are % average of six indidual observations over control plants.

Table 22.2: Results of Aqueous Plant Extract of *Lawsonia inermis* L on Seedling Length(cm/plant) of Green Gram, Black Gram and Groundnut

Extract concentration (%)	Green Gram		Black Gram		Groundnut	
	Fresh weight	Dry weight	Fresh weight	Dry weight	Fresh weight	Dry weight
Control	1.97	0.218	2.1	0.220	2.98	0.314
5	1.75 (-11.16)	0.210 (-3.66)	1.95 (-7.14)	0.215 (-2.27)	2.70 (-9.39)	0.281 (10.50)
10	1.45 (-26.39)	0.16 (-26.60)	1.65 (-21.42)	0.17 (-22.72)	2.45 (-17.78)	0.260 (-19.70)
15	1.10 (-44.16	0.12 (-44.95)	1.37 (-34.76)	0.13 (-40.9)	2.20 (-26.17)	0.243 (-22.16)
20	1.0 (-49.29)	0.09 (-58.71)	1.15 (-45.23)	0.09 (-59.0)	2.10 (-29.53)	0.221 (-29.61)
25	0.85 (-56.86)	0.074 (-66.05)	1.00 (-52.38)	0.075 (-65.9)	2.07 (-30.53)	0.201 (-35.98)

All values are % average of six indidual observations over control plants.

Table 22.3: Results of Aqueous Plant Extract of *Lawsonia inermis* L on Fresh and Dry Weight (mg/plant) of Green Gram, Black Gram and Groundnut

Extract concentration (%)	Green Gram		Black Gram		Groundnut	
	Root Length	Shoot Length	Root Length	Shoot Length	Root Length	Shoot Length
Control	11.4	15.2	10.6	14.3	7.10	12.20
5	11.0 (–3.5)	14.4 (–5.26)	10.2 (–3 .78)	14.1 (1.41)	6.69 (–5.78)	11.65 (–4.5)
10	10.3 (–9.65)	13.7 (–9.86)	9.2 (–7.78)	13.5 (–5.59)	6.32 (–9.5)	10.9 (–10.65)
15	8.26 (–24.56)	12.4 (–18.42)	9.2 (–13.20)	12.6 (–11.88)	6.11 (13.94)	10.1 (–17.2)
20	7.9 (–30.70)	9.4 (–38.15)	8.4 (–20.75)	11.3 (–20.9)	5.36 (–24.50)	9.3 (–23.77)
25	6.2 (–45.56)	8.9 (–41.44)	7.2 (–32.07)	9.6 (32.86)	5.12 (–27.88)	8.50 (–32.7)

All values are % average of six indidual observations over control plants.

Germination Study

The germination of green gram, black gram and groundnut seeds was adversely affected by the various concentrations of the extract of *Lawsonia inermis* L. When increasing the concentrations of leaf extract from 5 to 25% there was an increasing the inhibitory effect on germination of all the three test plants (Table 22.1). The maximum inhibition was observed in all the three plants at 25% extract treatments when compared with control set of seedlings. The seeds of green gram severely affected by the extract treatments then the black gram and groundnut seedlings. In the green gram, nearly 40% of the seeds were not germinated at 25% of the weed extract treatment. But in the black gram and groundnut the inhibitory effect was 30% and 27% respectively.

Seedling Growth

The shoot length and root length of green gram, black gram and groundnut seedlings showed a decreasing trend with increasing the extract concentrations (Table 22.2). The maximum reduction on seedling growth was observed in the green gram seedling at 25% of plant extract followed by black gram and groundnut. In the green gram the reduction of shoot length and root length was respectively for 45% and 41% and in the black gram; 32% and 25.87% respectively for shoot and root length whereas the reduction was 27% and 30% in the groundnut respectively for shoot and root length.

Fresh Weight

The fresh weight and dry weight of green gram, black gram and groundnut seedlings were given in Table 22.3 and under the treatments of various concentrations of *Lawsonia inermis* L extract. The maximum fresh weight decreases was observed at 25% of the leaf extract (43% green gram 42% of black gram and 40% of groundnut seedlings) when compared with other concentration of extract and control set of seedlings.

Dry Weight

The maximum value of dry weight was recorded only in control set of seedlings of three test plants then the treated ones. The minimum values of dry weight were observed at 25% of plant extract in the green gram; 0.074 mg/ plant. In black gram; 0.075 mg/plant and in groundnut; 0.201 mg/plant. The lower concentrations of (5, 10 and 15%) extracts the retarding effect was in the ascending order like the fresh weight changes.

Discussion

The results of the present study shows the leaf extract of *Lawsonia inermis* L affect the seed germination and growth pattern of green gram (*Vigna radiata),*black gram (*Vigna mungo*) and ground nut *(Arachis hypogaea).* The germination of green gram, black gram and groundnut was adversely effected by the various concentrations (5, 10, 15, 20 and 25%) *Lawsonia inermis* L extract treatments. The germination of all three plant seeds was affected maximum at 25% concentration of leaf extracts. The inhibitory effect was concentration dependent. The similar results were reported by Prasad and Priyadarshani, Bhakat et al. and Jeasrinivas *et al.,* in various crop plants by the application different weed extracts. The result of Prasad and Priyadarshani revealed that aqueous leaf and flower extracts of *Lawsonia inermis* L cause gradual decrease in seed germination seedling survival cotyledonary area, leaves/plants, branches/plant, plant height, root weight, days to flower, fertilization values, chromocentres, nucleus and pollen viability of turnip. At higher concentration (20 and 25%) of *Lawsonia inermis L* extract showed maximum adverse effect of germination of green gram, black gram and groundnut seeds. The inhibition on seed germination may be due to the presence of high amount of allelochemicals in 25% extract concentration of *Lawsonia inermis L.*The seedling growth i.e. root length and shoot length of green gram, blackgram and groundnut were reduced by the treatment of various concentration of leaf extract. At 25% concentration, the maximum inhibitory effect was observed in the green gram seedlings then that of black gram and groundnut. In the study of Gupta reported that the extract of *Lawsonia inermis* L retarded the seed germination and seedling growth of cluster bean,ladyfinger.Mandal et al. reported the leaf extract of *Populus deltoids* adversity inhibited seed germination seedling growth and reproduction, these findings favors the present study. The plant extracts of *Lawsonia inermis L* strongly affected the seed germination, seedling growth, fresh and dry weight because of the presence of allelochemicals in the plant extract.

23 Commercial Production of Different Dyes

Natural dyes have become a part of human life since time of immemorial. The Alchemy of colours started its use from an early time. Use of natural dyes in colouration of textile materials and other purpose is just one of the consequences of increased environmental awareness. Natural dyes exhibit better biodegradability and generally have a better compatibility with the environment. Also they possess lower toxicity and allergic reactions than synthetic dyes.

Today, in the world of growing environmental consciousness, natural colourants have attracted the attention of everyone. Natural dyes used in food are screened for safety but the information is not known for most of the natural dyes used in craft dyeing and with potentially wider use. There is a tendency to assume that consumable natural products are safer and better than synthetic product because they came naturally. The safety of natural dyes needs to be proved if they are used more widely and in commercial process. Indigo, a blue dye was extracted from the leaves of leguminous plant and turmeric (Curcuma longa), a yellow dye, was extracted from the ground root of Indian saffron plants. Turmeric was the only yellow dye that did not require a mordant to fix it on cotton or silk but is sensitive to light, soap and alkali which reduce its value considerably.

Logwood is the most important in black and blue dyeing. It was used on cotton, silk and wood with various mordents for a wide range of colours, but its fastness to light was generally rather poor. Henna (*Lawsonia inermis*) leaves is an ancient dye, evidence being the Egyptian mummies found in the tombs who had their nails dyed with henna. In the present times, it is used in many countries for dyeing hair, eyebrows and fingernails. During religion festivals and marriages etc. the use of henna for dyeing the palms and fingernails is an auspicious ritual in most Bangladeshi state. For use a colouring material, henna powder is pasted with water and applied to the part to be dyed. For dyeing hair, it is applied as a pack, it acts as a substantive dye for keratin and imparts an orange red colour. It is harmless and causes no irrigation of skin. In our country this plant is used to gardening and dyeing the part of bodies hair and also used in Ayurvedic medicine. The natural dye from turmeric, kapila, and onion coat is applied to silk and wool fabrics dyeing. This three plant gives natural yellow dyes.

Hair Dyes and Hair Treatments

Hair has no vital function in the human body but provides an outward sign of health and social communication. The history of hair coloring dates from ancient dynasties of Egypt and China where mineral and plant dyes were widely available to cosmeticians. Through the ages, women in particular have dyed their hair to hide grayness and to improve their appearance.

General Features of Hair

In all mammals, hair develops as an epidermal structure from papillae deep in the skin and acquires characteristic patterns on the scalp, eyebrows, eyelashes, and elsewhere on the body. In humans, hair growth is continuous throughout life (declining with advancing age), occurs in cyclic patterns, and is influenced by androgens, thyroid hormones, and dietary factors. Human hair is composed largely of keratin and consists of a narrow central medulla surrounded by a thick envelope (cortex) of elongate cells, which contain numerous melanin granules that determine the natural color. The hair is ensheathed in a multilayered cuticle of overlapping cells that become progressively imbricated (having edges overlapping in a regular arrangement) with continued growth. These cuticular cells are rich in cystine (disulfide bonds) and become rough or show a weathered appearance through exposure to environmental exposure or poor health.

Chemically, human hair contains approximately 85 percent protein, 7 percent water, 3 percent lipid, 4.7 percent protein-bound sulfur (as cystine), and low concentrations of trace minerals (e.g., iron, zinc, copper). The phosphorus content is approximately 80 milligrams per 100 grams (0.003 ounces per 3.5 ounces) of hair. Hair is normally associated with sebum and exocrine secretions from skin glands that confer greasiness but influence its water content and mechanical and physical properties.

Hair follicles are determined prenatally; about 100,000 hairs are found on the scalp region of most adults. Hair density, color, and condition vary according to age, race, and genetic background. Natural hair colors vary from albino or white to blond, red, or intense black and reflect ethnic origin (Caucasoid, Negroid, etc.), age, diet, and health. While hair color is closely related to the density of melanin granules, impairment in a person's health or substances in the diet that influence the availability of trace minerals are potential causes of changes in hair color or condition.

The configuration of the hair shaft (i.e., straight, wavy, spiral, or peppercorn) is attributable to the number and distribution of disulfide bonds. Hair straightening requires reduction of these disulfide bonds and fiber cross-linkages. Hair serves to eliminate toxic materials (e.g., lead) and metabolites from the body, and may be used to monitor environmental contamination.

For example, copper deficiency is a cause of Menke's "kinky" hair syndrome; protein deficiency leads to hair loss and discoloration. Hair keratin carries a strong negative charge and binds inorganic materials; it becomes prone to discoloration through exposure to environmental chemicals (e.g., cobalt, tar in cigarettes, picric acid, trinitrotoluene, etc.). Prolonged exposure to copper in diet, tap water, or swimming pools is a cause of green hair.

Natural Hair Color and Its Control

Melanin granules are secreted by melanocytes in the hair papilla and distributed to keratin in the hair cortex and inner layers of the hair sheath during normal development. Melanogenesis is subject to hormonal control and has been the focus of intensive genetic studies. Two main forms of melanin exist in human skin—eumelanin and phaeomelanin, both of which are derived from tyrosine through the action of tyrosinase (a cupro-enzyme) and possibly other key enzymes (with nickel, chromium, iron, and manganese as cofactors). Tyrosine is converted to dihydroxyphenylalanine and, via a series of intermediate steps, to indole-5,6-quinone, which polymerizes to eumelanin. Phaeomelanins are produced by a similar mechanism but with the incorporation of sulfur (as cysteine) by a nonenzymatic step in the oxidation process.

Hair color is a balance between these two melanins. Albino or white-haired individuals have latent melanocytes, but possibly show defects in tyrosinasemediated events. Graying of the hair is age-related and possibly results from declining melanocytic function or retarded hair growth resulting from atrophy or degenerative changes in hair papillae. Hair melanin absorbs insufficient ultraviolet (UV) light energy to afford protection for most individuals against sunburn.

Hair Dyes and Cosmetic Coloring

A wide variety of dyes, dressings, and conditioners are available to men and women to enhance the color of hair or to alter its condition, providing the "feel good" factor. Natural hair dyes such as henna and mineral salts are still used, but hair dyeing increasingly involves careful chemical manipulation of the chemistry of hair fibers through bleaching or enhancement of natural colors. Additionally, social and cultural customs have led to the increasing demand for exotic colors (reds, greens, blues, yellows, etc.). Hair coloring is a well-defined science with intense study of the interaction between hair keratin and highly reactive organic dyes, oxidizing agents, and conditioners.

Available Hair Dyes Include

Minerals such as lead acetate (<1% aqueous), lead sulfide (kohl); silver nitrate; salts of bismuth, copper, and cobalt (commonly called "gradual" colorants)

- Vegetable materials such as henna (flowers and leaves of *Lawsonia inermis* that contain acidic naphthoquinone, chamomile, and indigo).

- Synthetic dyes including a large number of organic dyes to provide permanent, semipermanent, temporary, or progressive color changes or to enhance natural colors.

The dyeing process provides for temporary, semipermanent (direct dyes), and oxidation-type reactions (semipermanent or permanent colors). It may involve absorption or adsorption (electrostatic) of the colorant into/to the hair structure, bleaching or otherwise masking the natural melanin colors, or alteration of the structure of the hair shaft, allowing deep penetration of the colorant. The hair cuticle provides a barrier to the absorption of hair dyes, particularly those of high molecular weight, but damaged fibers exhibiting higher negative charges and reduced phospholipid content are more porous. Dye uptake is determined by the partition coefficient between the hair and the dye carrier (water, alcohol, etc.), pH, and chemical charge (dye-fiber interaction). Thickeners and surfactants can also influence dye uptake.

Table 23.1: Color Indexed Dyes Used As Temporary Colors in Hair Cosmetics

CI Acid Yellow 1	
CI Acid Yellow 3	(D & C Yellow No.10)*
CI Acid Orange 7	(D & C Orange No. 4)
CI Acid Orange 87	
CI Acid Red 3	(D & C Red No. 33)
CI Acid Red 211	
CI Acid Violet 43	(D & C Violet No. 2)
CI Acid Violet 73	
CI Acid Blue 9	(FD & C Blue No. 1)
CI Acid Blue 168	
CI Acid Green 25	(D & C Green No. 5)
CI Acid Brown 19	
CI Acid Brown 45	
CI Acid Black 107	
CI Basic Yellow 57	(Arianor™ Straw Yellow)
CI Basic Red 76	(Arianor™ Madder Red)
CI Basic Blue 99	(Arianor™ Steel Blue
CI Basic Brown 16	(Arianor™ Mahogany)
CI Basic Brown 17	(Arianor™Sienna Brown)
Sunset Yellow	(FD & C Yellow No. 6)
Ponceau Red	(FD & C Red No. 4)
CI Solvent Brown 44	

*F - food color, D - drug additive, C- cosmetic coloring

The vast array of natural dyestuffs, metallic salts, and synthetic organic chemicals available to cosmeticians are regulated in the United States (by the Food and Drug Administration [FDA]), the European Union, and many other countries, and regulatory toxicity information is documented.

Henna

Henna is the oldest and most widely used vegetable dye utilized in hair coloring. A temporary chestnut color is produced in blond or auburn hair by applying a paste of henna flowers and leaves ground in hot water immediately before use. (The dye is unstable in aqueous solution.) The addition of indigo achieves darker blue-black shades; extracts of walnut shell or logwood enhance brown coloration.

Mineral Dyes

Of the mineral dyes, only lead acetate is commercially available. In the United States, the FDA permits maximal concentrations of 0.6 Hair dyes and other hair treatments have been popular for centuries, but in recent years have been more chemically sophisticated, taking into account the chemical makeup of hair.

Table 23.2: Natural Dyes from Plants Used as Hair Colorants

Plant	Hair Colorant
Henna (*Lawsonia inermis*)	2-hydroxy-1,4-naphthaquinone
Chamomile	42,5,7trihydroxyflavone
Indigo (Indogofera sp.)	CI Pigment Blue 66 - $C_{16}H_{10}N_2O_2$
Logwood - haematein	$C_{16}H_{12}O_6$

Percent; in the United Kingdom, less than 1 percent is allowed. (Kohl or "suma," an eyelash and eyelid cosmetic used in Asian countries, contains up to 80 percent lead and is a known cause of anemia.) In contact with hair, the lead salt is poorly absorbed but interacts with keratin to deposit lead sulfide (at permitted levels [<0.5%] lead is absorbed into the skin without toxic implications). Silver nitrate has been used to color hair brown-black without significant absorption of metal into the circulation; silver is deposited in the hair cortex as silver sulfide. Metallic hair dyes tend to be long-lasting and are lost as hair grows and is shed naturally. Hair coloration is achieved as a gradual process through repeated application of rinses or pastes over several days.

Temporary dyes. Temporary dyes are frequently acidic and provide short-term coloration (i.e., wash out after one shampoo). They are of low penetration and do not involve melanin bleaching or structural changes in the hair fiber. They are commonly identified with a color index (CI) number or as U.S. Certified Colors; they are water-soluble, high-molecular-weight pigments. Temporary dyes are employed in water-thin color rinses, colored hair-setting lotions, colored styling gels, lotions, and shampoos. Hair dyeing is improved when the colors are applied under moderate heat. Hair dyeing and color balance is difficult to control with temporary methods because of the inconsistency of dye delivery systems and instability of the dye-keratin "bonding."

Essential Ingredients of Oxidative Permanent and Semipermanent Dyeing Systems

- Surfactant
- Solvent
- Alkalizing Agent
- Oxidant
- Dye

Semipermanent dyes. Semipermanent dyeing systems are designed to last for several weeks. They impart darker colors without the use of oxidizing agents or structural changes in the hair shaft or papillae. Melanin may be partly masked but is not bleached. These dyes diffuse more readily into and out of the hair (aided by solvents and surfactants) and are progressively lost with hair shampooing and normal growth. The method employs dyes that are already colored, and in general is without the toxic risks associated with semipermanent or permanent methods, which involve de novo color production and strong oxidizing agents. When the dye is lost through shampooing, the hair resumes its natural color.

Table 23.3: Colors Produced in Oxidative Dyeing Systems Using Some Common Primary Intermediates and Couplers

	***p*-aminophenol**	***p*-phenylenediamine**	**N,N- *bis* -(2-hydroxyethy)-*p* – phenylenediamine**
m -aminophenol	Warm brown	Red-brown	Medium violet
Resourcinol	Yellow green	Greenish brown	Yellow-gray
2-methylresourcinol	Ash brown	Yellow brown	Gray-violet
m -phenylenediamine	Orange-yellow	Blue	Greenish-blue
5-amino-o-cresol	Orange	Purple-red	Purple
a- *naphthol*	Red-orange	Violet	Blue

Oxidative dyes. Oxidative hair dyeing systems involve the use of more toxic reagents. They are multistep processes leading to semipermanent or permanent coloration, according to the extent of bleaching involved. Surfactants and solvents influence the penetration of the active constituents; alkalizing agents determine pH. The resulting hair colorations are more stable against normal wearing processes than semi permanent preparations and involve an initial oxidation reaction, a coupling reaction, and production of a color reaction with dyeing of the hair fiber. The process requires a primary intermediate, a *m* -coupler or secondary intermediate (color modifiers), and hydrogen peroxide.

Hydrogen peroxide is commonly used as the oxidizing agent; it has the capacity to bleach melanin but it initiates the first coupling reaction and the ultimate development of the color. Initial oxidation of primary intermediates (e.g., *p*-aminophenol, *p*-phenylenediamine) by hydrogen peroxide is followed by coupling with an agent like resourcinol, phenols, *m*-aminophenols, or *m*-phenylenediamines. Further oxidation of this secondary intermediate leads to the formation of colored indamines, indolanilines, and indophenols. As a general rule, the higher the electron-donating capacity of the coupling agent (especially unsubstituted carbocyclic *m*-couplers), the higher the absorbance maximum of the indo-dye formed. In the presence of couplers, diand monoimines react to produce indo-dyes.

Many of the organic aromatic amines used in hair dyes are strong sensitizers and oxidative dyes should be used with extreme caution. *P*-phenylenediamine and its derivatives, commonly employed in permanent or semipermanent hair colorings, are strong sensitizing agents and may damage the hair. Although a large number of possible combinations of primary intermediates and couplers leading to the production of exotic hair colors is possible, the cost of conducting regulatory toxicological evaluation is prohibitive in developing many interesting colors.

Bleaches

Lightening or removal of hair color without structurally damaging the hair shaft is a difficult process. Oxidizing agents, including hydrogen peroxide, can be extremely harmful to hair and will oxidize some cystine to cysteic acid, rendering the fibers less cohesive and susceptible to hydration and swelling under alkaline conditions. Bleached hair shows a loss of melanin granules at the periphery of the hair. Hair color is lost (platinum blond appearance) and the fibers become dry and fragile. Bleaching is inhibited by shampoos or acid rinses.

Hair Conditioners

Hair conditioning includes permanent waving, straightening, and setting. In each case, sequential chemical treatments lead to modifications of the hair shaft with temporary or prolonged changes in disulfide bond distribution and behavioral characteristics. Softening, reshaping, and hardening are integral to permanent waving and involve an initial reduction in disulfide bonds and adhesiveness of adjacent hairs using heat or steam, thioglycollates, or ammonium hydroxide; styling with heated rollers; and setting or neutralizing the reaction. This last event is a reversal of the earlier reduction process with reconstitution of disulfide bonds from adjacent cystine moieties using hydrogen peroxide or a similar oxidizer. Hair straightening is a similar process, but may involve the additional use of hair dressings like gels, sprays, and creams (pomades) to hold the hair in place. Hot comb techniques may be used to disrupt the disulfide bonds followed by application of oils, petroleum jelly, or liquid paraffin.

Mousses are designed for hair styling and setting hair in position. Commonly, formulations are based on cationic conditioning polymers with quaternary ammonium salts, alcohols, perfumes, colorants, water, and preservatives. They may be in propellant, foam, or jelly form for direct application to hair after shampoo or cutting.

Composition of Typical Styling Mousse

- Polyoxyethylated fatty alcohol
- Deionized water
- Polyquaternium compound chloride
- Vinyl caprolactam/polyvinylpyrolidone/dimethylaminoethyl methacrylate copolymer
- Ethanol
- Amodimethicone—tallow trimonium
- Additives (perfumes, preservatives, etc.)

Hair dye is one of the oldest known beauty preparations, and was used by ancient cultures in many parts of the world. Records of ancient Egyptians, Greeks, Hebrews, Persians, Chinese, and early Hindu peoples all mention the use of hair colorings. Early hair dyes were made from plants, metallic compounds, or a mixture of the two. Rock alum, quicklime, and wood ash were used for bleaching hair in Roman times, and herbal preparations included mullein, birch bark, saffron, myrrh, and turmeric. Henna was known in many parts of the world; it produces a reddish dye.

Many different plant extracts were used for hair dye in Europe and Asia before the advent of modern dyes. Indigo, known primarily as a fabric dye, could be combined with henna to make light brown to black shades of hair dye. An extract of the flowers of the chamomile plant was long used to lighten hair, and this is still used in many modern hair preparations. The bark, leaves, or nutshells of many trees were used for hair dyes. Wood from the brazilwood tree yielded brown hair dyes, and another hair dye known in antiquity as *fustic* was derived from a tree similar to the mulberry. Other dyes were produced from walnut leaves or nut husks, and from the galls, a species of oak trees. Some of these plant-derived dyes were mixed with metals such as copper and iron, to produce more lasting or richer shades.

The golden red hair captured by many Renaissance painters was artificially produced by some women. The Italian recipe was to comb a solution of rock alum, black sulfur, and honey through the hair and then let the hair dry in sunlight. Other hair dyes, dating from the sixteenth century, were preparations of lead, quicklime, and salt, or silver nitrate in rose water. Another early method of coloring hair was to apply powder. Pure white powder for hair or wigs was the mark of aristocratic dress in Europe during the seventeenth and eighteenth centuries. White powder was made of wheat starch or potato starch, sometimes mixed with plaster of paris, flour, chalk, or burnt alabaster. Similarly colored powders were sometimes used as well. These were made by adding natural pigments such as burnt sienna or umber to white powder to make brown, and India ink was sometimes used to make black powder. In Biblical times, people used powdered gold on their hair. The use of powdered gold and silver returned briefly as a fad in Europe among the wealthy in the mid-nineteenth century. Other hair colorants were blocks similar to crayons made with wax, soap, and pigments. These could be wetted and rubbed on the hair, or applied with a wet brush.

Preparations such as these were the only hair dyes available until the late nineteenth century. Hydrogen peroxide was discovered in 1818, but it was not until 1867 that it was exhibited at the Paris Exposition as an effective hair lightener. A London chemist and a Parisian hairdresser began marketing a 3% hydrogen peroxide formula at the Exposition as *eau de fontaine de jouvence golden* (golden fountain of youth water), and this was the first modern chemical hair colorant. Advances in chemistry led to the production of more hair dyes in the late nineteenth century. The first synthetic organic hair dye developed was pyrogallol, a substance that occurs naturally in walnut shells. Beginning in 1845, pyrogallol was used to dye hair brown, and it was often used in combination with henna. So-called amino dyes were developed and marketed in Europe in the 1880s. The earliest was p-phenylenediamine, patented in Germany by E. Erdmann in 1888 as a dye for fur, hair, and feathers. To dye hair with p-phenylenediamine and related dyes, a weak solution of the chemical, mixed with caustic soda, sodium carbonate, or ammonia, was applied to the hair. Then hydrogen peroxide was applied, which brought out the color. The amino dyes produced a more natural-looking black than previous dyes, and could make shades of red and brown as well.

A French hairdresser, Gaston Boudou, first marketed a standardized range of hair dyes in 1910. Whereas earlier hair colors had been mixed on the spot by hair dressers, and the colors produced were variable, Boudou's dyes produced a predictable color. Sold in a range of 18 colors, from black to light blond, these became very popular both in Europe and in the United States. The amino dyes, however, caused allergic reactions in a significant portion of users. Researchers in the United States are credited with creating a modified, less toxic amino-based hair dye, for standardizing the method of applying the dye, and for establishing strict specifications for the purity and strength of the raw materials. Further advances in hair dye chemistry were made by the makers of Clairol. Clairol produced the first one-step hair dye in 1950. This eliminated the time-consuming preliminary shampoo and pre-lightening that was the established hair-dying protocol. With intensive marketing of this easy-to-use product, the percentage of women in the United States who dyed their hair grew from approximately 8% to almost 50% by 1973.

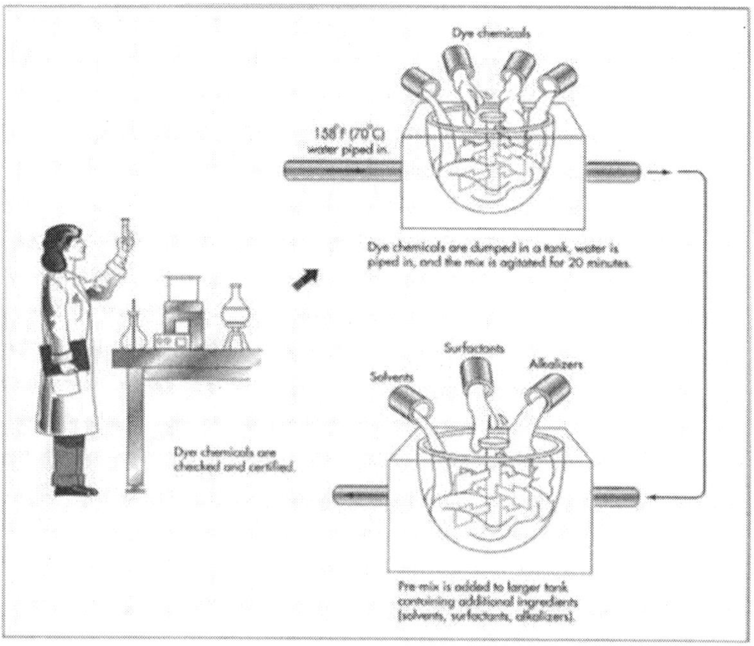

Raw Materials

Most commercial hair dye formulas are complex, with dozens of ingredients, and the formulas differ considerably from manufacturer to manufacturer. In general, hair dyes include dyes, modifiers, antioxidents, alkalizers, soaps, ammonia, wetting agents, fragrance, and a variety of other chemicals used in small amounts that impart special qualities to hair (such as softening the texture) or give a desired action to the dye (such as making it more or less permanent). The dye chemicals are usually amino compounds, and show up on hair dye ingredient lists with such names as 4-amino-2-hydroxytoluene and m-Aminophenol. Metal oxides, such as titanium dioxide and iron oxide, are often used as pigments as well.

Other chemicals used in hair dyes act as modifiers, which stabilize the dye pigments or otherwise act to modify the shade. The modifiers may bring out color tones, such as green or purple, which complement the dye pigment. One commonly used modifier is resorcinol, though there are many others. Antioxidants protect the dye from oxidizing with air. Most commonly used is sodium sulfite. Alkalizers are added to change the pH of the dye formula, because the dyes work best in a highly alkaline composition. Ammonium hydroxide is a common alkalizer. Beyond these basic chemicals, many different chemicals are used to impart special qualities to a manufacturer's formula. They may be shampoos, fragrances, chemicals that make the formula creamy, foamy, or thick, or contribute to the overall action of the formula.

Hair dyes are usually packaged with a developer, which is in a separate bottle. The developer is most often based on hydrogen peroxide, with the addition of small amounts of other chemicals depending on the manufacturer.

B.I.S. Specifications

BIS IS 11142:1984 (R2005) Specification For Henna Powder

IS 7159 (1984): Methods of test for henna powder

For more Information contact at:

Headquarters:

Manak Bhavan, 9 Bahadur Shah Zafar Marg,
New Delhi-110 002
91 11 23238821,23233375,23239402
91 23238821, 23239399 (Fax)
sales@bis.org.intandards Institution.

Sr.No.	Sales Outlets Address	Telephone No/Fax/e-mail
01.	**Director (Sales)** Manak Bhawan,9, Bahadur Shah Zafar MargNew Delhi-110 002	91-11-23238821,23233375,2323940291-23238821, 23239399(Fax)
02.	**Western Regional Office**Manakalaya,Plot No. E-9, MIDC, Road No. 8, Behind Telephone Exchange, Andheri (East), Mumbai-400 093	Phone 022-28329295Fax 28374231Email: saleswro@bis.org.in
03.	**Eastern Regional Office**5, Chowringhee ApproachP.O. Princep Street,Kolkata-700 012	033-23205324391-33-23377459(Fax) ero@bis.org.in
04.	**Northern Regional Office**SCO 335-336, Sector 34-AChandigarh-160 022	91-0172 266551291-0172 2602025 (Fax)910172-2609285, 2664750,2624136(PBX)nro@bis.org.in
05.	**Southern Regional Office**C.I.T. Campus, IV Cross RoadChennai-600 013	91-044-22542315, 22541584,2254147091-044-22541087 (Fax)sro@bis.org.in

Note: The use of the ISI Certification Mark is governed by the provisions of the Indian Standards Institution (Certification Marks) Act and the Rules and Regulations made thereunder. The ISI Mark on products covered by an Indian Standard conveys the assurance that they have been produced to comply with the requirements of that standard under a well-defined system of inspection, testing and quality control which is devised and supervised by ISI and operated by the producer. ISI marked products are also continuously checked by ISI for conformity to that standard as a further safeguard. Details of conditions under which a licence for the use of the ISI Certification Mark may be granted to manufacturers or processors, may be obtained from the Indian Standards Institution.

APPLICATION OF EXTRACTS OF HENNA

A dye can generally be described as a coloured substance that has an affinity to the substrate to which it is being applied. The dye is generally applied in an aqueous solution, and may require a mordant to improve the fastness of the dye on the fibre. Dyes appear to be coloured because they absorb some wavelengths of light preferentially, and are obtained from animal and vegetable sources. Until the middle of the nineteenth century, all dyes available to man came from natural sources, mainly vegetable extracts and a few from animal products. The range of colours was. limited as was the utility of dyes. The Gram's staining method is based on the ability of a cell to retain the crystal violet dye during solvent treatment, and on the difference in the microbial cell wall that is amplified. The cell walls for Gram-negative microorganisms have higher lipid content than Gram-positive cells. Henna, Lawsonia inarmis produces a red orange dye molecule, "lawsone", also known as hennotannic acid. This molecule has an affinity for bonding with protein and has been used to dye skin, fingernails, hair, leather, silk and wool. The leaves are also used as prophylactic against boils, burns, bruises, skin inflammations and as a gurgle against sore throat. The roots of this plant are useful in burning sensation, leprosy, strangury, premature grey of hair and tuberculostatic activity. The major phytochemical constituents of Henna Lawson, is found to possess significant anti inflammatory, analgesic and antipyretic activities. Recently, this compound has been reported to have a growth inhibitory effect against human colon carcinoma, HCT-15 cells. Henna (L. inermis) is a plant, which grows wild in abandoned areas and commonly known as 'Lalle' in Nigerian major languages with slight difference in pronunciation. This plant is a worldwide known cosmetic agent used to colour hair, skin and nails.

The first human-made (synthetic) organic dye, mauveine, was discovered by William Henry Perkin in 1856. Many thousands of synthetic dyes have since been prepared. Synthetic dyes quickly replaced the traditional natural dyes. They cost less, offer a vast range of new colours, and impart better properties upon the dyed materials. Despite the biotechnological advance in medical science today, biological stains are vital in laboratory diagnosis and the Gram's staining method remains an important simple diagnostic tool in diagnostic and research laboratories. The commonly used counter stain in Gram's staining reaction is safranine. Safranin is also used as counter stain in endospore and capsule staining.

Acid fast staining used in identifying all bacteria in the Genus Mycobacterium including the two important disease producers Mycobacterium tuberculosi and Mycobacterium leprae uses carbol fuchsin as primary stain and methyl blue as counter stain. Today dyes are synthetically prepared from aromatic compounds like coal tars the derivative of natural dyes Henna, (L. inarmis) that are available and can easily be processed. Despite the benefits of Henna, L. inarmis, it has not been reported as a biological stain. In this study, we report the use of Henna, L. inarmis extracts as a natural counter stain in Gram's staining reaction.

MARKET SURVEY

Henna (*Lawsonia inermis* L.), popularly known as Mehndi, has long been used in India and the Middle East countries for colouring palms of hands, soles of feet and finger nails. It is also used for dying of hairs, beard and eye brows, for personal adornment. Tails and manes of horses are also sometimes dyed with henna. It is also used for colouring leathers and skins. Recently, there has been an increase in its use as a hair dye in the Western Europe and North America. In 1955, India produced 2800 tonnes of henna and Punjab and Gujarat were the major henna-producing states while Rajasthan had only 5 per cent share in the total production. In 2012-13, the production of henna in Rajasthan was of 67,540 tonnes, with 90 per cent share in the total henna production of the country. The trade of dried henna leaves in the Sojat city regulated market (the only regulated market of henna in the country) increased from 30,264 tonnes to 64,744 tonnes, at an annual compound growth rate (ACGR) of 9 per cent during the period 2000-2013. As per the FAO report, India exported 9500 tonnes to 18600 tonnes of henna per annum during the period 2000-13. In the year 2013-14, the estimated export of henna, in all forms, was around 60,500 tonnes with a value of around Rs. 590 crores.

Henna is a perennial plantation crop with economic life-span of 25 years. It is a highly capital intensive crop as it requires about Rs 30,800 per ha for establishment. On an average, it provides a net return of about Rs. 8,300 per ha with BCR more than one, positive NPV and IRR higher than the opportunity cost of capital. Thus henna cultivation has been found profitable and economically viable and provides a sustainable income to the farmers of arid fringes of Rajasthan. The economic viability parameters for henna plantations have been found more sensitive to changes in price than cost. Introduction of some improved implements or automatic machines for hoeing, weeding and harvesting, etc. can bring down the labour cost and consequently will provide higher returns to farmers.

The global Henna dyes market is projected to grow at a CAGR of 3.6% from 2015 to 2020 and reach 11 million metric tons by 2022. Asia-Pacific, with its thriving economies and rapidly expanding manufacturing bases, is expected to experience highest consumption during the next five years.Other natural based dye cannot compete with Henna Dye due to its special properties.

The major driving factors of colorants market are growth in end user industries, rising demand for high performance pigments (HPP), and rising preference towards environment-friendly products.Henna Dyes have a large number of applications ranging from hair dye,cosmetics, and textile. The cosmetic industry is recording significant growth due to growing infrastructure.

According to the industry estimates, the global demand for different dyes are anticipated to grow at a CAGR of 5.4% during the next five years. The demand for printing ink based on Henna Dye is driven by various factors such as technological developments and increasing demand for digital inks.

The factors restraining the growth of colorants market are raw material price volatility, its global over capacity, and environmental concerns. Some of the trends witnessed in dyes market are shifting of the manufacturing facilities from U.S. and Europe to India, China, and Taiwan and the rising preference towards eco-friendly products.

In the dye market, Asia-Pacific accounts for the largest share. This region is one of the key markets for dyes production. In the Asia-Pacific, India and China are the important countries contributing towards the growth of dye market.

The dye market has also been segmented on the basis of product types - dyes of different shades.

We have used various secondary sources such as Company's Annual Reports, Organizational Websites, and Databases to identify and collect information useful for this extensive commercial study of Henna dyes. The primary sources – selected experts from related industries and selected suppliers - have been interviewed to obtain and verify critical information as well as to assess the future prospects of dyes.

So it will be advisable to invest in production and plantation of Henna Dye Industry.

BLACK COLOUR DYE

The henna-based hair coloring and/or hair conditioning compositions of this method comprise from about 75 to about 95 weight percent of henna powder, from about 1.5 to about 5 weight percent of a non-ionic surface active agent, from about 2.5 to about 15 weight percent of a water soluble polymer and from about 0.5 to about 5 weight percent of a quaternary salt. In addition, the compositions can include, for example, titanium dioxide and additional conditioning agents. Titanium dioxide serves to lighten and improve the appearance of the composition and also takes up excess oil from oily hair. A suitable range of proportions for titanium dioxide is from about 2.5 to about 8 weight percent.

The henna powder used in the compositions of this method can be either the color-imparting henna powder or, if only conditioning is desired, the non-color imparting henna powder. In the practice of this method, the henna composition is mixed with hot tap water, preferably at a temperature of at least 120°-130° F., in a ratio of 1 part powder to about 31/2 to 41/2 parts of water.

The powder and water are mixed to a smooth consistency and applied to freshly shampooed hair. After the application of the henna paste, the hair is covered with a plastic cap to prevent drying and allowed to process for about 1 hours at room temperature, or for a shorter period when heat is added, as by a hair dryer. The paste is then rinsed or shampooed from the hair. It is preferred, in the practice of the method aspect of this method to additionally rinse the hair with an acid rinse, preferably with a citric acid containing rinse having the pH of from about 2.0 to about 3.5.

The non-ionic surface active agent used in the practice of this method is preferably one that can be utilized in powder form and can be selected from materials which are available in any form suitable for conversion to powder form. The preferred surface active agents are non-ionic polyethylene oxide-propylene oxide block polymers such as Pluronic F-77. The incorporation of the surface active agent eliminates the lumpy consistency encountered with the commercial henna preparations and assists in removing the henna composition from the hair after treatment.

Anionic surface active agents cannot be used in the practice of this method because they would react with and neutralize the cationic quaternary salt.

The water soluble polymers employed in the practice of this method are preferably high molecular weight water soluble polymers having amide type linkages similar to the amide linkages of protein, such as polyvinylpyrrolidone K-30 or K-90. It is preferred that the water soluble polymers have a molecular weight of at least 30,000 and more preferably have a molecular weight of at least 300,000. The incorporation of a high molecular weight water soluble polymer having an amide type linkage similar to the amide linkages of protein improves the wet combing properties of henna treated hair and imparts additional body and luster to the hair.

The selection of the quaternary salt employed in the practice of this method is preferably limited to those compounds which are commonly available as powders and possess anti-static properties. The preferred quaternary salts which meet the criteria include, for example, lauryl pyridinium chloride, and cetyl pyridinium chloride, and the corresponding bromides.

Illustrative henna powders useful in the practice of this method include Henna Natural, green henna leaves and brown henna leaves. The neutral or natural colors do not produce any color and thus can be used as conditioning agents alone.

The henna powders are preferably sterilized before being mixed with the other constituents of the compositions of this method. Sterilization by contact with ethylene oxide gas is preferred.

The following examples further illustrate the compositions.

Example 1: A henna composition for normal hair is prepared having the following formulation:

Ingredient	Weight Percent
Henna powder	90
Polyvinylpyrrolidone K-90	5
Pluronic F-77	3
Lauryl pyridinium chloride	2
Fragrance	q.s.

The fragrance is incorporated into the powder, formulation by preparing a 10% slurry of the perfume in henna powder, adding the appropriate amount to the bulk of the formulation and blending thoroughly.

BURGUNDY COLOUR DYE

Metal complex dyes are pre-metalised dyes, in which one or two dye molecules are co-ordinated with a metal ion. Mordanting of dyes in this way can work in a way wherein the positively charged metal ions are capable of interacting quite strongly with the hair, This is especially true for copper and more so in damaged hair which has a higher negative charge than undamaged hair. The metal ions can then interact with the (i.e. form complexes with) the aromatic plant hair dye molecules, thus locking them to the hair.. Whether this effect occurs at the hair surface or within the hair depends to some extent on the size of the dye molecule and the strength of the hair/metal ion/dye interaction. The stronger the interaction the more likely the dye complex is to be held close to the surface of the hair.

If the metal ion/dye complex is particularly strong then a water insoluble complex is formed to be fixed just prior to use. The coloured insoluble complex is then precipitated on and around the surface of the hair.

The present method provides for a hair colour composition/ kit for dyeing keratin fibers comprising selectively atleast one or more dye, plant dye, concentrated plant dye in combination with atleast one or more inorganic metal salt based mordanting agent for generating dye/ plant dye/concentrated plant dye-metal complex free of pH controlling agents and oxidizing agents, with safe modified base colour and/ or base colour of the dye/ concentrated plant dye thereby displaying superior colour delivery and colour variance under ambient temperature conditions. Preferably, the said dye/plant dye/ concentrated plant dye based hair colour composition/ kit provides for complexed dye/plant dye/ concentrated plant dyes with inorganic metal salt basedmordants wherein the dyes/ plant dyes favour generation of the modified and/ or base colour of the said dye/plant dye when present in their selective levels. The said dye/ plant dye/ concentrated plant dye molecules include anyone or more flavonoids, terpenoids polyphenols or its derivatives, as the basic molecular skeleton of the said dye/ plant dye and preferably comprises anthocyanins (such as Haematoxylin), Tanins, Benzoquinones, Naphthoquinones (such as Henna,

Walnut), Anthroquinones (such as Alizarin), & carotenoids including selective additional monoazo, hydroxyl, carboxyl or amino groups, which are capable of forming strong co-ordination complexes with transition metal ions such as chromium, cobalt, nickel, copper and the like.

The experiment protocol is based on conventional methodology for the generation of modified base colour and/ or base colour shades of the dyes involving dye/ plant dye/ concentrated plant dye combination with at least one or more inorganic metal salt based mordanting agent.

Black Shades

1 Haematoxylin + 3% Ferrous chloride Brownish Black shade

2 Haematoxylin + 3% Ferrous sulphate Natural black

Violet Shades

3 Haematoxylin + 3% zinc sulphate Violet shade

4 Haematoxylin + 3% zinc chloride Violet shade

5 Haematoxylin + 3% zinc nitrate Violet shade

6 Haematoxylin + 3% zinc oxide Dark violet shade

7 Alizarin + 3% Magnesium oxide Dark violet shade

8 Alizarin + 3% Magnesium carbonate Dark violet shade

9 Alizarin + 3 % Sodium carbonate Dark violet shade

10 Haematoxylin + 3% potassium tellurate Violet shade

11 Alizarin + 3% potassium tellurate Dark violet shade

Brown Shades

12 Haematoxylin + 3% copper sulphate Brown

13 Haematoxylin + 3% cupric nitrate Metallic brown

14 Haematoxylin + 3% cupric chloride Very shine metallic brown

15 Haematoxylin + 3% cupric acetate brown

Burgundy Shades

16 Alizarin + 3% zinc sulphate Dark burgundy

17 Alizarin + 3% zinc chloride burgundy

18 Alizarin + 3% zinc nitrate burgundy

19 Alizarin + 3% zinc oxide burgundy

Yellow Shades

20 Quercetin + 3% zinc chloride Dark yellow

21 Quercetin + 3% zinc nitrate Dark yellow

2 Quercetin + 3% Magnesium sulphate Yellow

3 Quercetin + 3% Magnesium chloride Yellow

4 Quercetin + 3% Magnesium nitrate Yellow

5 Quercetin + 3% Magnesium oxide Yellow

Hence it is concluded from the above table, that the dye haematoxylin which originally has an ash shade, also generates different modified colour shades simply upon selective combination with specific inorganic metal salt based mordanting agents in the absence of any pH controlling agent or oxidizing agent.

It is further observed from the above table that Iron salts reacted with Haematoxylin produce the black/ brown shade, Zinc salts react with alizarin to generate burgundy shade, copper salts react with haematoxylin to yield the brown shade, salts of magnesium reacted with Quercetin to yield yellow shades, Zinc salts reacted with haematoxylin to generate violet shades, Potassium tellurate reacted with haematoxylin to yield violet shade and also reacted with alizarin to generate dark violet shade, magnesium salts and sodium salts also reacted with alizarin to result in dark violet/ violet shades thus displaying a broad colour variance in the absence of any pH controlling agent and oxidizing agent.

Safety Instructions Of Burgundy Henna Hair Dye

Color should be kept away from direct sunlight & preferably in a dark place

The packet of Color should be opened only when ready to use

The color should be mixed only in a plastic or glass bowl and not metal bowl

The paste should be applied with the application brush

Paste should be used immediately after preparation, (within 4-5 minutes) otherwise it may not be effective

Take proper care to ensure that color solution does not go into your eyes

The preparation should not be used for dying eyebrows or eyelashes as severe inflammation of eye may result. In case the paste gets into eyes, the same should be rinsed immediately

MAHOGONY SHADE

It is known to dye keratinous fibers, and in particular human hair with dyeing compositions containing oxidation dye precursors, generally called oxidation bases, such as ortho- or para-phenylenediamines, ortho- or para-aminophenols and heterocyclic compounds. These oxidation bases are generally combined with couplers. These bases and these couplers are colorless or weakly colored compounds which, combined with oxidizing substances, may give rise, via a oxidative condensation process, to colored compounds.

This type of coloring by oxidation makes it possible to obtain permanent colorings but it leads to a degradation of the keratinous fibers via the use of oxidizing agents.

Furthermore, it is known to dye keratinous fibers, and in particular human hair, with dyeing compositions containing direct dyes. The conventional dyes which are used are, in particular, dyes of the nitrobenzene, anthraquinone, nitropyridine, azo, azo, xanthene, acridine, azine or triarylmethane type, or natural dyes. These dyes may be non-ionic, anionic, cationic or amphoteric.

These dyes which are colored and coloring molecules have an affinity for the keratinous fibers.

These compositions containing one or more direct dyes are applied to the keratinous fibers for a time necessary to obtain the desired coloring, then rinsed.

The colorings which result therefrom are particularly chromatic colorings which are, however, temporary or semi-permanent due to the nature of the interactions which bond the direct dyes to the keratinous fiber, and their desorption from the surface and/or from the core of the fiber are responsible for their low dyeing power and for their poor resistance to washing or perspiration.

The object of the present method is to provide novel compositions for dyeing human hair which respect the nature of the hair and have strong, not very selective and resistant dyes, capable of generating novel strong dyes which may give various shades.

This objective is achieved with the present method, one subject of which is a composition for coloring keratin fibers, especially the hair, which comprises one or more natural dyes, and one or more organic solvents chosen from alcohols, ethers or esters having a δH value of the Hansen solubility parameter δH less than or equal to 15 MPa1/2.

Another subject of the method is a kit comprising a first anhydrous composition comprising one or more natural dyes and a second aqueous composition, the first and/or the second composition comprising one or more organic solvents chosen from alcohols, ethers or esters having a value of the Hansen solubility parameter δH less than or equal to 15 MPa1/2.

The expression "natural dyes" is understood to mean any dye or dye precursor that is naturally occurring and is produced either by extraction (and optionally purification) from a plant matrix optionally in the presence of natural compounds such as ash or ammonia, or by chemical synthesis.

As natural dyes, mention may be made of quinone dyes (lawsone, juglone, etc.), alizarin, orceins and cochineal carmine. It is also possible to use extracts or decoctions containing these natural dyes and in particular henna-based extracts.

According to one particular embodiment, the composition of the method comprises henna. According to one variant, the composition comprises one or more additional natural dyes chosen from curcumin, chlorophyllin, isatin, sorghum and cochineal carmine.

Lawsone are dyes obtained from an extract of henna leaves, and are optionally chemically modified to act in the reaction.

The Following Dyeing Composition was Prepared

Henna Powder	65
Curcumin	4
Isatin	4
Orcein	2
Propylene carbonate	10
Ethanol	10
Hydroxyethyl cellulose (MW 1 300 000)	1.5
Citric acid	qs for pH 3
Demineralized water	qs for 100

This composition was applied, on the one hand, to locks of natural gray hair having 90% of white hair and, on the other hand, to locks of permed gray hair, having 90% of white hair, for 30 minutes at ambient temperature.

At the end of the waiting time, the locks were rinsed, shampooed then rinsed and dried. They were dyed a sparingly selective mahogany shade.

CHESTNUT BROWN SHADE

It has now surprisingly been found that the required coloring effect and covering of grey hair can be obtained without any adverse effect on the hair structure by colorants based on oxidation dye precursors providing the colorants also contain a substantive plant dye or the plant product henna natural.

Although the products according to the method are particularly suitable for coloring hair, they may also be used in principle for other coloring applications, for example for coloring textile fibers or wool.

The hair colorants according to the method are present in powder or granular form. They contain an oxidation dye precursor as a first compulsory component.

In one embodiment of the method, the hair colorants according to the invention contain only one oxidation dye precursor of the primary intermediate type.

Examples of primary intermediates suitable for in accordance with the method are primary aromatic or heteroaromatic amines containing another functional group in the p-position. According to the method, other compounds of the type mentioned additionally containing one or more functional groups, such as OH groups, NH2 groups, NHR groups or NRIR2 groups, where R, R1 and R2 independently of one another represent optionally substituted C1-4 alkyl groups, are also suitable.

However, the colorants according to the method preferably also contain at least one secondary intermediate. According to the method, colorants containing more than one primary intermediate and more than one secondary intermediate may also be preferred.

According to the invention, preferred secondary intermediates are α-naphthol, resorcinol, 4-chlororesorcinol, 2-methyl resorcinol, m-aminophenol, m-phenylenediamine, m-toluylenediamine, 1,5- and 1,7-dihydroxynaphthalene, 5-amino-2-rnethylphenol, 6-amino-2-methylphenol or derivatives of the compounds mentioned. These secondary intermediates may be used either on their own or in combination with other secondary intermediates of the type just mentioned or in combination with other secondary intermediates known to the expert.

According to the method, primary and secondary intermediates containing amino groups may also be used in the form of their salts, particularly hydrochlorides and sulfates.

Another compulsory component of the colorants according to the method is the oxidizing agent.

Suitable oxidizing agents are addition compounds of hydrogen peroxide with urea, melamine, potassium and sodium perborate and mixtures of such hydrogen peroxide addition compounds with potassium, sodium or ammonium peroxodisulfate.

In one embodiment of the method, the hair colorants additionally contain a substantive plant dye. The substantive plant dye is normally present in the form of a powder obtainable by grinding and subsequent sieving of henna plant parts, such as stems, flowers/blossom, leaves, roots, fruit and seeds.

Particularly preferred plant dyes are the henna dyes. Red henna consists of the dried powdered leaves of the plants Lawsonia alba, Lawsonia spinosa and/or *Lawsonia inermis*. So-called henna black comes from the leaves of dyer's woad (Isatis tinctoria) and is used in mixtures with Lawsonia henna to obtain darker shades of red.

The hair colorants according to the method may also contain synthetic substantive dyes as an optional component, more particularly for nuancing the color.

According to the method, preferred synthetic substantive dyes are 4-hydroxypropylaniino-3-nitrophenol, HC Red No. 3, N,N'-bis-(2-hydroxyethyl)-2-nitro-p-phenylenediamine, HC Blue No. 2, HC Yellow No. 2, HC Yellow No. 12, HC Blue No. 12 and 2-amino-6-chloro-4-nitrophenol.

The hair colorants according to the method preferably contain the oxidation dye precursors in quantities of 1 to 10% by weight, based on the solid hair colorant as a whole.

The content of powder-form dye-containing plant parts in the hair colorants according to the method may be from 40 to 60% by weight.

If the hair colorant according to the method is present in powder form, unwanted dust emission can occur according to the nature of the individual components. This is problematical not only in regard to dosage, but also for example in regard to the working conditions in hair salons.

In one preferred embodiment, therefore, hair colorants according to the method may be subjected to a special dust-binding treatment.

This is preferably done by spraying on an inert organic compound. The compound in question may be liquid at room temperature or even solid at room temperature providing it can be liquefied by heating to moderately high temperatures. Solid compounds with melting points below 50° C. will normally be used.

To bind (Just, the inert organic substance is preferably sprayed onto the powder-form hair colorant.

Preferred dust binding agents are paraffins, vegetable, animal and synthetic oils and low-melting waxes. Other suitable components are, for example, triglycerides and fatty alcohols.

Particularly preferred dust binding agents are paraffins oils, paraffins with melting points in the range from 40° C. to 50° C., polysiloxanes, such as dimethyl polysiloxane, caprylic/capric acid triglyceride, octyl dodecanol and beeswax.

The percentage content of oils or waxes in the hair colorants according to the method may be between 1 and 30% by weight and, more particularly, is between 7 and 15% by weight, based on the overall composition of the hair colorant.

The hair colorants according to the method may additionally contain as thickeners guar flour, sodium alginate, gum arabic, guar or caruba gum, pectins, cellulose derivatives, such as methyl cellulose and hydroxymethyl cellulose, hydroxypropyl methyl cellulose and carboxymethyl cellulose, and various polymers, more particularly acrylic acid derivatives. However, inorganic thickeners, such as bentonite and/or silica, may also be used. These thickeners are present in quantities of preferably 0.1 to 5% by weight and, more preferably, 0.5 to 3% by weight, based on the total weight of the hair colorant.

The hair colorants may additionally contain cationic and amphoteric polymers, film-forming anionic and nonionic polymers and also surfactants or mixtures thereof in quantities of—in each case—0.1 to 5% by weight.

Preferred surfactants are soaps, alkyl benzenesulfonates, alkyl naphthalene sulfonates, fatty alcohol sulfates or ether sulfates or sulfonates, quaternary ammonium compounds, fatty acid diethanolamides, polyethoxylated or polyglycerized alkylphenols. The surfactants are present in the hair colorant according to the method in quantities of 0.1 to 25% by weight and preferably in quantities of 0.1 to 15% by weight, based on the total weight of the colorant.

Finally, any other additives conventionally used in hair colorants, such as in particular penetration agents, sequesterants, antioxidants, buffers and perfumes, may be added to the hair colorants according to the method.

The present method also relates to a process for the production of a hair colorant in powder or granular form, in which the oxidation dye precursor, the oxidizing agent, the plant dye and/or the henna neutral are thoroughly mixed, optionally in the presence of additives typically encountered in hair colorants, an inert organic compound optionally liquefied by heating is sprayed onto the powder mixture obtained with continuous agitation and the powder mixture is optionally converted into granular form.

A coloring paste hereinafter referred to as the application mixture is prepared from the hair colorants according to the method immediately before use by adding corresponding quantities of water.

The application mixture may be applied both to wet hair and to dry hair. According to the method, it is preferably applied to dry hair.

EXAMPLES

1. Application of Hair Colorants

An application mixture of 80 g of hair colorant according to the method and 320 ml of hot water was prepared in the form of a spreadable paste. The hair coloring paste obtained was immediately applied quickly and fully by brush to dry, previously unwashed shoulder-length hair from the roots to the ends. The fine temple hair received only a thin coating of the paste. It was important to ensure that all the hair was thoroughly coated with the hair coloring paste. The hair was then covered with a hood so that the hood closely followed the contours and was fixed in such a way that it could not slip. The paste applied was left on the hair thus covered for 30 minutes in the presence of heat (ca. 40° C.). After this contact time, the hood was removed and the hair coloring paste was thoroughly washed out with tap water (30° C.). The hair was then shampooed and rinsed until the hair and skin were completely clean.

2. Formulation Examples

0.15 kg resorcinol

0.10 kg 1-hydroxy-3-aminobenzene

0.15 kg 2-amino-3-hydroxypyridine

0.15 kg 4-hydroxypropylamino-3-nitrophenol

0.10kg HC Yellow No.12

0.30 kg 2-methyl resorcinol

1.25 kg 2,5-diaminotoluene sulfonate

1.00 kg camomile

1.50kg henna black

2.50 kg henna red

60.80 kg henna natural

20.00 kg sodium perborate

5.00 kg carboxymethyl cellulose

93.00 kg of the above mixture were stirred in a mixer (for example a Lodige mixer) and then sprayed with 7.00 kg of paraffin oil (15 mPa?s, as measured at 2° C.).

40 g of the hair colorant were thoroughly mixed with 160 g of warm water (40° C. – 50° C.) to obtain a readily spreadable application mixture. This mixture—applied with a brush—was allowed to act on 50% grey, dark blond hair for 30 minutes at 40° C. The application mixture was then rinsed off and the hair was shampooed and dried. The 50% grey, dark blond starting hair had assumed a uniform light chestnut color after the treatment.

GLODEN BROWN SHADE

Although vat dyes are widely used for dyeing cellulosic fibrous materials, they are very rarely used for animal fibers, for example wool or hair, because these fibers do not withstand the required very high pH of about 13 without undergoing drastic damage. Moreover, in most cases very aggressive reducing agents are used, for example sodium dithionite (hydrosulfite) or sodium hydrogen sulfite. For these reasons, the dyeing of animal fibers with vat dyes has thus far not been adopted in practice.

The purpose was therefore to provide a method whereby hair can be dyed with vat dyes in a simple and gentle manner.

Surprisingly, we have now found that dyeing with vat dyes (for example indanthrene dyes) can be carried out also under physiologically tolerable conditions by suitably adjusting the pH before dyeing. In this manner, uniform hair colorations are obtained while at the same time the hair is treated as sparingly as possible. Moreover, this method allows so-called brightening dyeing to be achieved with partial or complete decolorization of the natural hair pigment melamine during the final oxidation step.

Suitable reducing agents are those which in an alkaline medium form enediols (enediolates), for example monohydroxyacetone, dihydroxyacetone, acetoin, glutaroin, adipoin, glycol aldehyde, benzoin, 2,3-dihydroxyacrylaldehyde and cyclopentadiolone, among which acetoin, monohydroxyacetone and dihydroxyacetone are particularly preferred.

Suitable alkalinizing agents for the reduction step are sodium hydroxide and potassium hydroxide or the alkali metal salts of aromatic monohydroxy- and polyhydroxy compounds, for example sodium phenoxide and potassium phenoxide, as well as sodium cresolate and potassium cresolate. The pH for the reduction step is in general 10 to 13.

The reducing agents are used either in an equimolar amount or in up to a 50-fold molar excess, based on the vat dye, a 3-fold to 5-fold molar excess being particularly preferred.

Moreover, the reduction can be carried out in the presence of an organic solvent which is used at a concentration from 0.1 to 80 weight percent and preferably from 5 to 50 weight percent. The organic solvent should be able to form a homogeneous phase with water. Suitable are both protic and aprotic organic solvents, for example ethanol, n-propanol, isopropanol, n-butanol, glycols, for example ethylene glycol and propylene glycol, lactones, amides of the lower carboxylic acids, ureas, sulfones and sulfoxides. Mixtures of these solvents can also be used.

After the colorant has acted for about 1 to 60 minutes and preferably for 5 to 30 minutes at about 15 to 60° C., the coloration is developed "oxidatively". Suitable oxidants for developing the coloration are besides simple air oxidation particularly hydrogen peroxide or a compound of addition thereof to urea, melamine or sodium borate, in the form of a 1% to 12% and preferably 1.5% to 6% aqueous solution. The mixing ratio of dye to oxidant depends on the concentration of the oxidant and usually amounts to about 5:1 to 1:2 and preferably 1:1, the amount of oxidant in the resulting mixture of dye and oxidant preferably being from 0.5 to 8 weight percent and particularly from 1 to 4 weight percent. The oxidant is allowed to act until the dye is once again in its insoluble pigment form (usually for about 2 to 5 minutes) and is thus fixed on the hair in washing-resistant manner. The treatment time can, of course, be extended depending on the degree of brightening desired. If the natural pigment is to be brightened by more than two brightening degrees, it is possible also to use a persulfate or a mixture of a persulfate and hydrogen peroxide or an addition compound thereof. Alkaline persulfate/peroxide preparations are preferably used in this case.

Following the dyeing procedure, the hair is rinsed with water and dried. Optionally, the hair can additionally be washed with a shampoo and possibly post-rinsed with an acidic conditioner. The hair is then dried.

DYE MIXTURE

- 70.0 g Henna powder
- 10.0g of propylene glycol
- 1.0g of Golden Yellow RK (C.I. Vat Orange 1; C.I. 71105)

- 12.0g of sodium hydroxide (10% aqueous solution)
- 3.0g of sodium chloride
- 3.0g of acetoin
- 50.5g of water

The afore-said substances were mixed and allowed to stand for 20 min at 40° C. The pH was then adjusted to 10.0 with 2.5 g of lactic acid (90% aqueous solution). 10 g of the mixture obtained in this manner was applied to bleached natural hair. The hair was then covered with a plastic cap or plastic sheet. After a treatment time of 30 min at 40° C., 10 g of a 6% aqueous hydrogen peroxide solution was massaged in and allowed to act for 5 minutes. The hair was rinsed with water, then with an acidic conditioner and finally dried.

The hair assumed a uniform golden-brown color.

DARK BROWN SHADE

The present method relates to a composition for dyeing keratinous fibres, in particular human keratinous fibres such as hair, comprising, in an appropriate dyeing medium, at least a mixture of at least 2 cationic direct dyes of a given formula, and at least one quaternary ammonium salt mixtures of cationic dyes, compositions thereof, to processes for their preparation and to their use in the dyeing of organic material, such as keratin fibers, wool, leather, silk, cellulose or polyamides, especially keratin-containing fibres, cotton or nylon, and preferably hair, more preferably human hair.

The actual technical problem of the present method was to provide brilliant dyes that are distinguished by deep dying having good fastness properties with respect to washing, light, shampooing and rubbing, and that preferably exhibit satisfactory stability under reducing or oxidizing dyeing conditions, for the dyeing of organic material.

The multiplicity of shades of the dyes can be increased by combination with other dyes.

Therefore the hair dye compositions of the present method may be combined with dyes of the same or other classes of dyes, especially with direct dyes, oxidative dyes; disulfide dyes, pigments or mixtures thereof.

Direct dyes are of natural origin or may be prepared synthetically. They are uncharged, cationic or anionic, such as acid dyes.

Furthermore, autooxidizable compounds may be used in combination with the hair dye composition according to the present method.

Autooxidizable compounds are aromatic compounds with more than two substituents in the aromatic ring, which have a very low redox potential and will therefore be oxidized when exposed to the air. The dyeings obtained with these compounds are very stable and resistant to shampoo.

Representative cosmetic film-forming resins usefully employed in the hair setting lotions of this invention include polyvinylpyrrolidone, having a molecular weight between 40,000 and 400,000; copolymers of vinylpyrrolidone and vinyl acetate (70-30:30-70%); copolymers of vinyl acetate and an unsaturated carboxylic acid such as crotonic acid (90:10) having a molecular weight of about 20,000-50,000; copolymers resulting from the copolymerization of vinyl acetate (75-85%), crotonic acid (5-18%) and an acrylic or methacrylic ester (5-15%), copolymers resulting from the copolymerization of vinyl acetate and an alkyl vinyl ether, copolymers resulting from the copolymerization of vinyl acetate (63-88%), crotonic acid (5-15%) and a vinyl ester (5-25%) of a long carbon chain acid (10-22 carbon atoms) or an allyl or methallyl ester of a long carbon chain acid (10-22 carbon atoms), copolymers resulting from the copolymerization of 65-80% ester of an unsaturated alcohol (2-12 carbon atoms) and a short carbon chain acid (2-5 carbon atoms) or a 7-12% unsaturated short chain acid (4-20 carbon atoms) and 10-20% at least one ester of a saturated short chain alcohol (8-18 carbon atoms) and an unsaturated acid (4-20 carbon atoms) and copolymers resulting from the copolymerization of at least one unsaturated ester at at least one unsaturated acid.

The preferred cosmetic film forming resins include polyvinylpyrrolidone, copolymers of crotonic acid and vinyl acetate, copolymers of vinylpyrrolidone and vinyl acetate, copolmers of maleic anhydride and butyl vinyl ether, terpolymers of methyl methacrylate-stearyl methacrylatedimethyl methacrylate; and terpolymers of vinyl acetate-allyl stearate and allyloxy-acetic acid.

The cosmetic film forming resin is generally present in amounts of about 1-3 percent by weight of the total composition.

The alcohols conveniently employed to produce the hair setting lotions according to the present method are low molecular weight alcohols, preferably, ethanol or is opropanol, which are present in amounts generally of about 20-70 percent by weight of said composition.

The following examples are given to illustrate the method. In the examples an ethyl alcohol at 96° corresponds to 950.189 g/kg of alcohol.

Prepartion of 2-amino-5-(2'-methoxy-4'-amino anilino)-1,4-benzoquinone 0.02 mole (2.78g) of 3-amino-4-methoxy phenol is dissolved in 200 cc of water to which has been added 20 cc of ammonia (22° Be) and 50 cc of H2 O2 (20 volumes). As soon as this solution has been prepared, there is added, with agitation, a solution of 0.02 (4.27g) of methoxyparaphenylenediamine sulfate in 200 cc of water. After 4 hours of agitation, the reaction mixture is filtered and the resulting 2-amino-5-(2'-methoxy-4'-amino anilino)-1,4-benzoquinone is washed with water. The raw product is then recrystallized in a mixture of dimethyl formamide and water and dried under a vacuum with a boiling water bath for 8 hours. The product exhibits a melting point of 267° is applied for 30 minutes, at room temperature to bleached human hair, and rinsed. The result is a reddish brown /dark brown dyeing with good fastnesses.

1. Henna Powder	60 kg
2. Nitropara phenylene diamine	5 kg
3. Copolymer of Vinyl Acetate & Crotonic Acid	10 kg
4. Ethyl Alcohol	5 kg
5. Triethanol amine	10 kg
6. Surfactant	5 kg
7. Methyl paraben	2 kg
8. Hydrogen Peroxide	2 kg

LIGHT BROWN SHADE

The present compositions can also be employed as a hair rinse lotion for use in imparting to the hair a slight coloration. In this embodiment the compositions are applied to washed hair which application is not followed by any rinsing operation.

Further, the compositions of the present method can be used as a hair setting lotion to impart a slight coloration to the hair and to improve the holding power of the set. In this embodiment, the compositions comprise a hydroalcoholic solution of the dye component in combination with at least one cosmetic film-forming resin. The hair setting lotion is applied to previously washed and rinsed wet hair, followed by rolling the hair up on curlers and drying the hair.

It is known that various hair dye compositions up to now often exhibit the disadvantage of rendering the hair dull and hard. To overcome this disadvantage, that is, to restore to the hair the favorable characteristics it possessed before the dyeing operation, it has been proposed to treat the hair with cationic products, these products being applied after the dyeing operation and before a final setting of the hair. However, it has been noted that this supplemental operation also provides certain disadvantages and does not always impart with certainty good cosmetic properties to the hair.

It has now been found that it is possible to dye the hair without deleteriously interfering with the brightness or luster or the softness to the touch of the hair by employing the composition of the present method.

The method thus relates to a new composition for dyeing hair which comprises a combination of two specific formulations which are applied sequentially to the hair.

These specific formulations are a hair dye formulation comprising a conventional oxidation hair dyeing composition containing a hair dye or dye precursors in admixture with at least one cationic polymer, and a shampoo formulation to be applied immediately following the use of the said hair dye formulation and containing at least one anionic detergent. Preferably, the shampoo formulation also contains at least one cationic polymer.

It has now been found, through extensive research, that the application of the said hair dye formulation followed by the application of the said shampoo formulation provides particularly satisfying results, especially with regard to untangling of wet hair, while at the same time imparting to dry hair such interesting cosmetic properties as luster, brightness, softness to the touch, excellent untangling and remarkable ease of styling characteristics.

The hair dye formulation employed in the composition of the present method is an oxidation hair dye composition comprising in addition to a cationic polymer, an oxidation dye component and a conventional carrier.

It is known that oxidation hair dye compositions employ dyes termed "oxidation dyes" which are aromatic compounds of the diamine, amino phenol or phenol type. These aromatic compounds are dye precursors which are transformed into dye compounds by condensation in the presence of a large excess of an oxidizing agent, generally H2 O2. Among the oxidation dyes, there are on the one hand "bases" which are ortho- or para diamines or mono- or di-ortho or para amino phenols and, on the other hand, "modifiers" which are meta-diamines, meta-amino phenols or polyphenols.

The "bases" principally employed are paraphenylenediamine, para-toluylenediamine, chloroparapheny-lenediamine, para-aminodiphenylamine, ortho-phenylenediamine, ortho-toluylenediamine, 2,5-diaminoani-sole, ortho-amino phenol and para-amino phenol.

The "modifiers" principally employed are: meta-phenylenediamine, meta-toluylenediamine, 2,4-diaminoanisole, meta-amino phenol, pyrocatechol, resorcinol, hydroquinone, α-naphthol, 1,5-dihydroxy naphthalane and 2,6-diamino pyridine. The "bases" are also termed "base oxidation dyes" while the "modifiers" are also called "couplers".

The oxidation dyeing composition contains principally, besides the cationic polymer, a mixture of bases and modifiers, with a conventional carrier. Preferably, the carrier is one which provides the said composition in the form of a cream or gellable liquid. Representative carriers include, principally, fatty acids, fatty amides, alkyl sulfates, polyoxyethylenated alkyl sulfates and water, in varying amounts.

In the oxidation hair dyeing composition used in the present method, the various components thereof can be provided in the following amounts, by weight:

1. Henna Powder	60 kg
2. Cetyl Alcohol	10 kg

3. Distearyl diamine chloride 5 kg
4. Quaternium-80 5 kg
5. Citric Acid 5 kg
6. Basic yellow dye 2 kg
7. Preservatives 1 kg
8. Perfume

BLONDE SHADE

In recent years, there is an increasing demand from consumers toward dyeing their hair in a lighter color than their own haircolor (starting haircolor), and many products generally called "fashion hair dyes" are available on the market.

Hair dyes, which are used for such purposes and include hair bleaches, are each composed of a first pack containing an alkali agent and a second pack containing an oxidizing agent. The alkali agent employed in the first pack has been added to heighten bleaching or dyeing effect and to obtain a wide range of colors ranging from a light color to a deep color. In particular, when one wants to change his or her hair into a tone lighter than the tone of his or her own haircolor, sufficient bleaching power is required. When a hair dye is used for such purposes, a fully sufficient amount of an alkali is therefore required. To dye hair well with good color retention, a sufficient amount of an alkali is also required.

Conventionally, ammonia has been used as an alkali agent in general. Ammonia is, however, accompanied by drawbacks that it has an intensely irritating odor and makes consumers feel unpleasant upon dyeing.

- Henna Powder 60 kg
- Ferrous Sulphate 10 kg
- Tetra sodium ethylene diamine tetraacetate 3 kg
- Mono ethanol amine 2 kg
- Potassium Carbonate 2 kg
- Propyle Glycol 5 kg
- Oleic Acid 5 kg
- Meta amino phenol 5 kg

The hair dye compositions according to the present method do not give off an intensely irritating odor and have low irritating property, can change hair into a lighter tone in a short time or can dye hair well in a color ranging from a light color to a deep color, and moreover, assures good retention of the thus-obtained tone or color.

GENERAL METHOD OF PRODUCTION

Washing drying and pulverizing

The dried plant leaves were washed with water to remove the adhering materials. The leaves were then dried in an oven at 40 °C for 24 hours and finely powdered with the help of a grinding machine.

Extraction of dye from henna leaves dried powder (Alkalizalion process)

100 g dried leaves powder sample was taken saturated Na_2CO_3 solution for 24 hours at pH 8.5-9.2 at room temperature. The solution becomes reddish orange colour. Then percolated with Na_2CO_3 solutions until all of the colour has been removed and then filter again. The reddish orange colour was developed due to the presence of alkali.

Acidification process

The alkali reddish orange colour solution was acidified with hydrochloric acid at pH 4-5. After acidification the colour of solution change from reddish orange to yellow orange. This colour is developed by the action of acid.

Then the solution is left overnight in settling tank. Then all other ingredients are added with vigorous stirring. Then after vacuum filtration, the product is dried in Tray dryer. Then pulverization process takes place. The product was made to fine powder by grinder.Then the powder is passed through sieve to make it finer.

Extraction with chloroform by liquid-liquid extraction system

The acidified colour solution was taken into separating funnel and shaken with successive portion of chloroform (until 1ml of chloroform extract imparted no colour on shaking with 1ml of sodium carbonate solution). The chloroform extract was dried with anhydrous sodium sulfate and filtered. The chloroform extract produce a orange yellow colour, this solution kept away from light until all the chloroform were vaporized. Then cauliflower like clusters of needles with dark mahogany colour crystalline mass of about 7.05 g was obtained and is preserved for further investigation.

MANUFACTURERS/SUPPLIERS OF HENNA DYES

Henna Dyes

Ganga Prasad Puneet Kumar

Puneet Kumar (Manager)

Plot No. 65, Street No. 2, New Ahirwara

Faridabad - 121002, Haryana, India

Mobile: +(91)-9711062449, +(91)-9810520423

Telephone: +(91)-(129)-2297123

Fax: +(91)-(129)-2504879

Agarwal Herbal Products
Rajesh Agarwal (CEO)
Office No. 474, Central Facility Building No. 2,
4th Floor, Sector No. 19 C, Vashi
Navi Mumbai (India) - 400705
Mobile : +(91) - 8691030676
Phone : +(91) - (22) - 27655002
V. J. S. Pharmaceuticals Private Limited
Mannu Shukla
No. 3382, Desh Bandhu Gupta Road,
Karol Bagh, New Delhi - 110005, Delhi, India
Mobile: +(91)-9871377778, +(91)-8447654440
Impressions Cosmetics
Anju Gupta (Proprietor)
R- 7- A, 2nd Floor, Green Park Main
New Delhi (India) - 110016
Mobile : +(91) - 9212035015
Phone : +(91) - (11) - 26524413, +(91) - (11) - 30969219
Abhinav Export Corporation
No. 2, Corporation Seewage Road,
Seevaram Village, Perungudi,
Chennai-600096
Tel: + 91 44 24962788
Mobile: +91-9176652234
Email: abhinavexport@gmail.com
Kajal Dulhan Mehandi Center
Vikashji Chauhan (Proprietor)
Shop No. 1-2, Plot No.-47, Geeta Nagar,
Part - 2, Nandanvan Road, Punagam
Surat - 395010, Gujarat, India
Mobile: +(91)-9277707070, +(91)-9979266815
Natural Herbal
Nitesh Agarwal (Proprietor)
Mr.Ritesh Agarwal
Rendari Road, Near Gas Godown
Sojat - 306104, Rajasthan, India
Mobile: +(91)-9929718241, +(91)-9414121241

Telephone: +(91)-(2960)-221241, +(91)-(2960)-222153
Fax: +(91)-(2960)-220121
Jham jham trading company
Muzafar Hussain
Plot No. 4-5, Near Navegajpeer Dargh,
N.H. 14, Beawar Road
Sojat - 306104, Rajasthan, India
Mobile: +(91)-9887874399

MANUFACTURING PROCESS

Checking ingredients

- Before a batch of hair dye is made, the ingredients must be certified. That is, the chemicals must be tested to make sure they are what they are labeled, and that they are the proper potency. Certification may be done by the manufacturer in-house. In many cases, the ingredients arrive from a reputable distributor who has provided a Certificate of Analysis, and this satisfies the manufacturer's requirements.

Weighing

- Next a worker weighs out the ingredients for the batch. For some ingredients, only a small amount is necessary in the batch. But if a very large batch is being made, and several ingredients are needed in large amounts, these may be piped in from storage tanks.

Pre-mixing

- In some hair dye formulas, the dye chemicals are pre-mixed in hot water. The dye chemicals are dumped in a tank, and water which has been already heated to 158°F(70°C) is pumped in. Other ingredients or solvents may also be added to the pre-mix. The pre-mix is agitated for approximately 20 minutes.

Mixing

- The pre-mix is then added to a larger tank, containing the other ingredients of the hair dye. In a small batch, the tanks used may hold about 1,600 lbs (725 kg), and they are portable. A worker wheels the pre-mix tank to the second mix tank and pours the ingredients in. For a very large batch, the tanks may hold 10 times as much as the portable tanks, and in this case they are connected by pipes.
- In a formula in which no pre-mixing is required, after checking and weighing, the in gredients go directly to the mixing step. The ingredients are simply mixed in the tank until the proper consistency is reached.

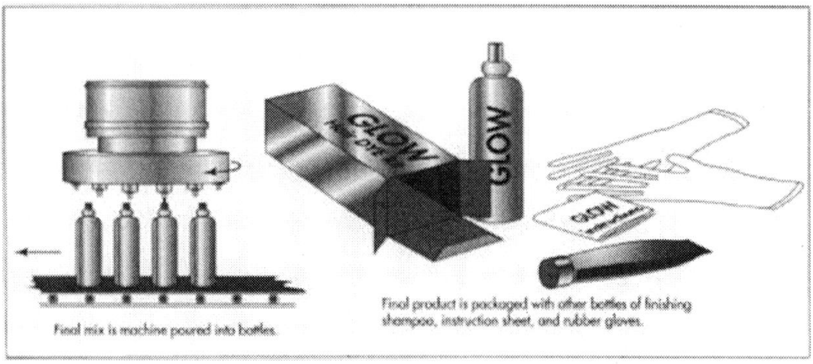

- If a heated pre-mix is used, the second mix solution must be allowed to cool. The ingredients that follow the pre-mix may be additional solvents, surfactants, and alkalizers. If the formula includes alcohol, it is no added until the mix reaches 104°F(40°C), so that it does not evaporate. Fragrances too are often added at the end of the mix.

Filling

- The finished batch of hair dye is then piped or delivered to a tank in the filling area. A nozzle from this tank lets a measured amount of hair dye into bottles, moving beneath it on a belt. The filled bottles continue on the belt to machines, which affix labels and cap them.

Packaging

- From the filling area, the bottles are taken to the packaging line. At the packaging line, the hair dye bottle is put in a box, together with any other elements such as a bottle of developer or special finishing shampoo, instruction sheet, and gloves and cap, or any other tools provided for the consumer. After the package is complete, it is put in a shipping carton. The full cartons are then taken to the warehouse to await distribution.

Quality Control

Government regulations control what ingredients may be used in hair dyes, as many of them are toxic. Industry researchers will have already tested a formula numerous times in the laboratory before it reaches the manufacturing stage, to make sure a formula is non-irritating, works well, performs consistently, etc. As part of the manufacturing process, workers check their chemicals before they go into a batch, to make sure only the correct chemicals at the correct potency are used. After the batch is mixed, samples are taken, and these are subjected to a series of standard tests. Lab technicians make sure that the batch is the required viscosity and pH balance, and they will also test the dye's action on a swatch of hair. If a hair dye formula is being made for the first time, or if a formula has been altered, technicians will also test samples of the dye after the filling stage.

The Future

Hair dye manufacturers are increasing their use of computers to control and automate the manufacturing process. Computers can be used to weigh and measure ingredients, to control reactions, and to regulate equipment such as pumps. The future may see more fully automated manufacturers and increased efficiency.

Antioxidant and Immunomodulatory Constituents of Henna Leaves

For centuries, henna leaves were renowned as the most extensively used natural hair dying and tattooing agent in many civilizations and cultures. The word henna which means "to become queen" is indicative of something highly elegant. The plant has got several vernacular names e.g. Ligusturum egypticum which is the Latinized English synonym for henna. It arises from the common name for the same plant in England, namely of the Egyptian privet. The plant extract or its purified compounds exhibit a variety of biological activities such as anticomplementary activity, dihydroorotate dehydrogenase inhibitory activity, macrophage-stimulating activity as a result of stimulation of secretion of GMCSF (granulocyte macrophage colony stimulating factor), antimicrobial activity, anti-sickling activity, hepatoprotective activity, cytotoxic activity, anti-inflammatory, antipyretic, and analgesic activities. In the light of the previous activities, we investigated the compounds responsible for the immunomodulatory effects of henna. In addition, an antioxidant-screening assay was conducted to detect whether a redox mechanism may be involved in the immunomodulatory action of henna.

Seven compounds were isolated adopting the lymphocyte transformation assay (LTA)-guided fractionation of the total methanolic extract of henna (*Lawsonia inermis* L.) leaves. Immunoactive fractions were subjected to further phytochemical investigation. Seven compounds were isolated (Figure 23.1), five from the chloroformic fraction [p-coumaric acid (1), lawsone (2), apigenin (3), luteolin (4), and 2-methoxy-3-methyl-1,4- naphthoquinone (5) as well as two compounds from the ethyl acetate fraction [cosmosiin (6) and apiin (7)].

Essential Oil Composition

The GC-MS analysis revealed that the presence of at least twenty eight of components in L. inermis Linn leaves. Nine compounds were indentified; representing 80.6% of the total oil (Table 1). The major constituents are listed in order of their elution from a HP-5MS capillary column as shown in Figure 1 and Table 1. The constituents of the oil were eugenol (17.6%), hexadecanoic acid (15.1%), Phytol (10.2%), α-terpineol (8.4%) and Etherphenylvinyl (6.7%). Of these major constituents, eugenol, hexadecanoic acid, phytol and α-terpineol are relatively common for essential oils of higher plants. In the earlier report, from the essential of α-terpineol15 and Phytol16 were reported as the major constituents. It is necessary to point out that the chemical compounds of any plant essential oil can vary greatly depending upon geographical region, the age of the plant, local climate, seasonal variations, experimental conditions and genetic difference are responsible for the changes in the types of chemical compounds.

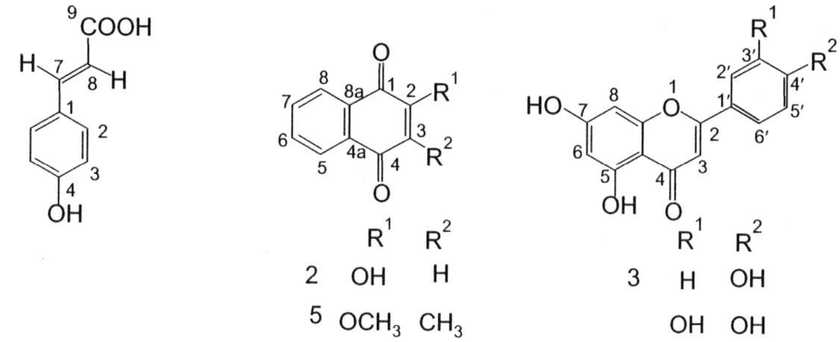

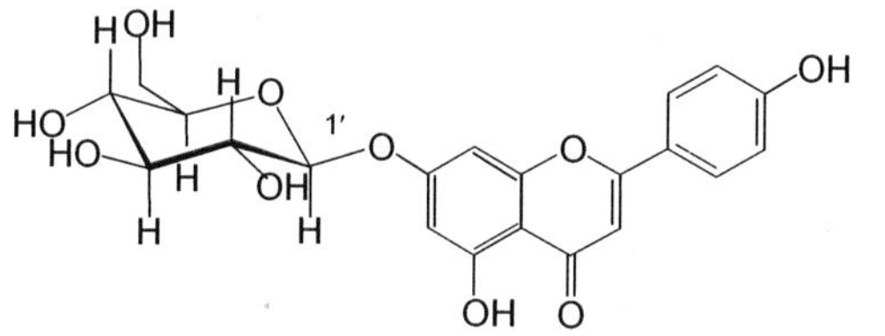

6

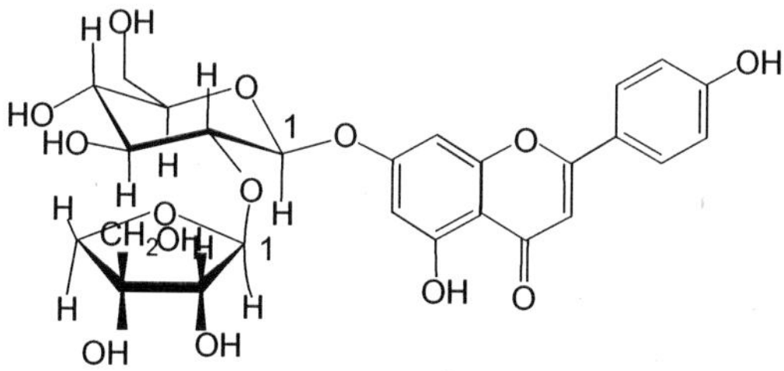

7

Fig. 23.1: Compounds isolated through bioassay-guided fractionation of henna (*Law-sonia inermis* L.) leaves; *p*-coumaric acid (1), lawsome (2), apigenin, (3) luteolin (4), 2-methoxy-3-methyl-1,4-naphthoquinone (5), cosmosiin, (6), apiin (7).

The Chemistry of Henna

The molecule in henna responsible for dying hair is lawsone, otherwise known as hennotannic acid (or 2-hydroxy-1,4-naphthoquinone by IUPAC standards). Here's a picture I snagged from Sigma Aldrich's website:

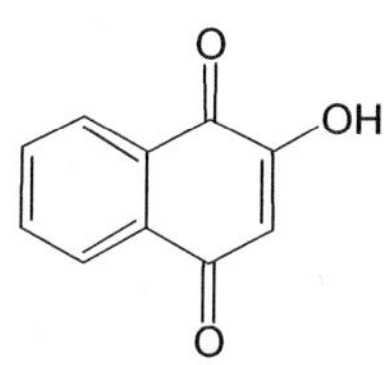

Lawsone, a.k.a. hennotannic acid

In the world of hair dye, the lawsone of henna is considered a "deposit-only" dye since it doesn't interact with the melanin of hair strands. As a naphthol molecule, it's also termed a red coupler in the cosmetics industry. Red couplers produce red pigments on the specific surface they are dying, not in the prepared mixture (a.k.a. dye precursors) itself.

Table 23.4: Chemical Composition of the Essential Oil of Leaves of *L. inermis* Linn

Retention time (min)	Compound*	Composition
7.56	Linalool^{M}	4.23
10.48	α–terpineol^{M}	8.36
11.42	Etherphenylvinyl^{A}	6.72
15.32	1,3–indandione^{A}	6.60
15.91	Eugenol^{A}	17.61
21.04	Cis–hexahydro–8a–methyl1,	
	8–[2H,8H]–naphthalenedione^{k}	5.60
29.23	Oxirane–tetradecyl^{E}	6.20
32.53	Hexadecanoic acid^{F}	15.07
35.99	Phytol^{D}	10.17

*Compounds listed in order of elution from HP–5MS column. ^{M}monoterpene, ^{D}diterpene, ^{A}aromatic, ^{E}ether, ^{F}fatty acid, ^{K}ketone.

Most melanin is found in the innermost cortex layer of hair, along with keratin. Keratin is key. Lawsone has an affinity for keratin, and interacts with it directly in a non-oxidative process (i.e. a process directed towards the retention of electrons).

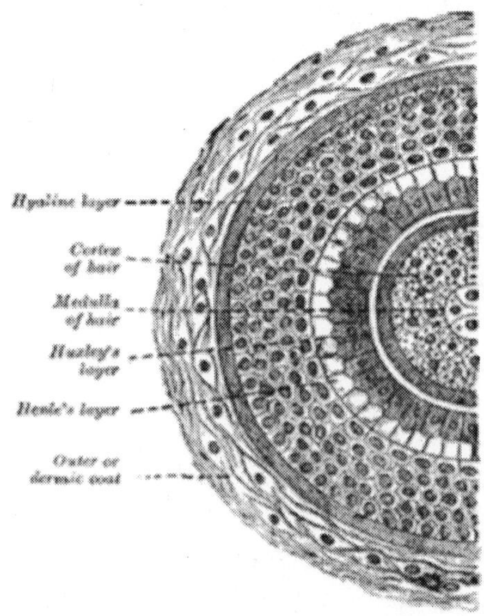

The anatomy of a hair strand. Image from Wikipedia.

The anatomy of a hair strand. Image from Wikipedia.

Lemon juice is a very acidic substance with a pH generally cited between 2 and 2.5. (For comparison, the outer albumen sac of eggs is typically cited as slightly basic, around 7.6, and the inner yolk is cited as around 6.0, slightly acidic.) However, lemon juice is not so acidic that human skin and hair cells are negatively affected. (All things being relative.)

At the heart of it, the acidic functionality of lemon juice serves to destabilize the henna plant's cellulose while allowing the lawsone molecules to remain intact. Both lawsone and lemon juice are acids, and as such follow the general rule of thumb of "like dissolves like." The lemon juice attacks the lawsone directly to create a unified acidic substance.

This unified acidic substance comes in handy later when interacting with keratin (discussed below).

When mixing henna with egg, I would predict that the mixture turns brownish, indicating that the red pigment-causing lawsone is binding to or interacting with the protein-dense eggs and basic elements of the plant. (Please correct me if I'm wrong about the color— it is only a prediction. I have not observed it firsthand). It therefore does not act like a dye precursor. When mixing henna with acidic lemon juice, however, there is no color change. The mixture remains green, indicating that the lawsone molecules have not bound to the added reagent (lemon juice instead of egg).

Henna powder does not contain much lawsone (in most peer-reviewed articles it's measured at less than 2% for pure henna) and the process of breaking down cellulose is lengthy, which is why it takes several hours. (Think of all the extra machinery ruminants need just to do it on a day-to-day basis.) Using eggs as a reagent, I would also predict it takes less time because the reagent is not targeted at degrading cellulose—instead, it is interacting with it at multiple points, creating a conditioning formula that has the ability to bind to multiple proteins within the hair strand. Some lawsone molecules may still be present to bind to keratin, but it is more likely to be inhibited and/or sterically hindered by the other molecules it has interacted with in the egg mixture. In short, eggs decrease the effectiveness of the dying agent, but perhaps not the mixture's conditioning abilities.

On a slightly related note, this is why henna and placenta conditioner exists. Similar mixture, similar outcome.

When a lemon juice-henna mixture is applied to the hair after several hours, another important reaction occurs. The solution is still hopping with hydrogen atoms after hours; it's still acidic. These abundant hydrogen molecules serve to reduce (i.e. add electrons to) the disulfide bridges of the composed keratin fibers, which breaks the bridges and "cuts" the keratin fibers up. In its reduced form, sans most bridges, keratin is more accessible. Ideally, each cystine disulfide bridge is broken into two cysteine residues.

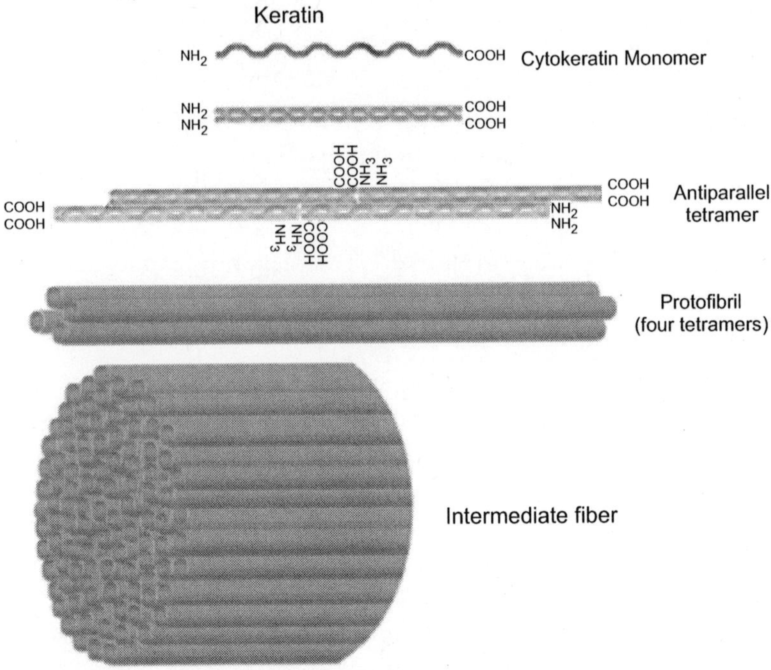

The disulfide bridges of keratin can be converted into separate cysteine residues by adding acid (lemon juice). Image from Sigma Aldrich.

Lawsone, a relatively small molecule, then migrates to the cortex of the hair strand to coat the keratin via a Michaels' reaction. You'll note this reaction happens quite quickly, making it a somewhat annoying ordeal to remove henna stains from skin, even after only a few seconds of exposure.

Lawsone's Affinity for Keratin is Intense

If you're really curious, you can get a sense of the numerous reactions by drawing out a few of the amino acids (here's an older article with a list) and lawsone. You'll note that there are many locations at which a Michaels' reaction can occur. For your reference, common attacking nucleophiles (a.k.a. Michael donors) include lithium dialkyl cuprates, enamines, ß-diketones, ß-keto esters, ß-keto nitriles, and alpha-nitro ketones, while common electrophiles (a.k.a. Michael acceptors, the alpha,ß-unsaturated carbonyl compounds) include conjugated aldehydes, conjugated ketones, conjugated esters, conjugated amides, conjugated nitriles, and nitroethylenes.

10 Tips for Formulating the Hair Color of Your Client's Dreams

Follow our Hair Color Formula Guide to create your client's best hair color yet! Knowing these tips will ensure absolute color success.

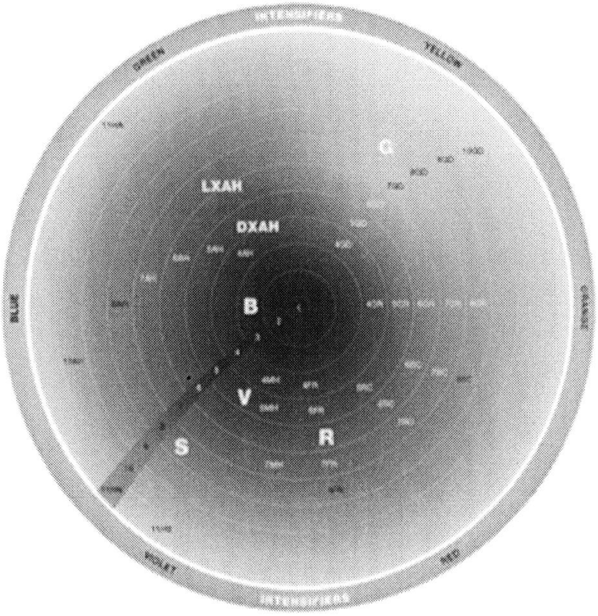

Color Theory is Cosmetology 101

(1) Know Thy Color Wheel

Understanding the relationship between colors is essential when formulating your client's ideal hair color.

The Color Wheel is comprised of 3 Primary Colors: Red, Yellow, Blue, and 3 Secondary Colors: Green, Violet, Orange. Tertiary Colors are created by combining a primary color with the secondary color beside it on the Color Wheel. Example: Yellow-Orange

Knowing which of these colors enhance and cancel out one another is vital for formulating the correct hair color. For example, if you're looking to eliminate unwanted warmth (red), selecting a cooler tone (green) will effectively neutralize the previous color.

(2) Know Predominant Tones

Every color line has various predominant tones (background pigment found in each hair color tube or bottle).

When formulating your client's perfect hair color, it's important to know the different background pigments present in your color line. For example, one line's 'N-series' or 'neutrals' could fall on the warmer side of the Color Wheel; whereas, another line could have a tonal value at the blue-violet base.

If you aren't aware of your color line's predominant pigments, then you will not be able to accurately use the Color Wheel to create your client's desired color.

(3) Determine Client's Natural Level

Hair color will range from levels 1-10. Level 1 being the darkest and Level 10 being the lightest color.

Within each of those levels are the 2 underlying color pigments: eumelanin (black-brown) and pheomelanin (red-brown), which control the shade of the hair. Dark hair (levels 1-4), contain high concentration of red pigment; whereas, blonde hair (levels 7-10) consists of mainly golden pigments. If your client's level is somewhere in the middle (levels 5-6), more orange pigments are present in the hair, a combination of red and yellow.

Whether you are lifting or depositing, knowing which tones are present in your client's natural level will help you make a better color choice.

(4) Understand Grey vs. White Hair

Grey and white hair is not the same, and should not be treated as such.

Grey hair still contains some pigment; whereas, white hair color does not. Often, not knowing the difference between white and grey hair can result in muddy color results or lack of proper pigment load.

Think about it.

White hair is completely absent of pigment. If you mix the colors white and red, what would be the result? Pink!

When dealing with white hair it necessary to add the missing anchor pigments to give the color you're depositing something to hold on to.

Grey hair is actually an optical illusion, it contains both the color of pigmented hair and white hair. Since grey hair still contains some pigment, it should be formulated differently than white hair.

In addition, knowing the ratio of white or grey hair to pigmented hair is necessary when formulating. For example, if hair is 75% grey, you may want to consider lowering your developer to color ratio – allowing for more color than developer, or dropping down a level for ample pigment weight.

(5) Consultation is Key

As a professional Hair Stylist, it's your job to direct and steer the consultation with your client.

Client's may think they are in the driver's seat, but you're the instructor with the emergency peddle – pump the breaks when necessary to avoid a hairy disaster!

For example, if your client's hair is in poor condition and would not be able to withstand a perm or extreme lightening service, then don't be afraid to speak up.

Also, be sure you and your client are on the same page when it comes to color selection.

More than likely, you and your client's idea of a 'honey blonde' or 'red-brown' will vary. We suggest having them bring in a few photos of their desired color, and having them point out what they do and do not like about each picture.

This will give great insight when formulating, and help you understand what your client expects from their color service.

You should also be inquiring if your client is currently taking any medications.

Medications for the heart and thyroid are just some of the medication types that can completely alter your color results.

PRO TIP: Use Malibu's Crytal Gel for 100% removal of build up, medications, and hard water minerals prior to your color service.

(6) Determine Hair's Porosity, Density, and Texture

The importance of determining the health of your client's hair and their hair type cannot be overstated.

Fine, medium, and coarse hair all absorb color differently.

Damaged and pre-lightened hair tends to be more porous. Porous hair tends to over accept color (especially ash tones), so depending on your desired result, your formula will have to take into consideration the hair's porosity level.

Additionally, the more porous the hair, the less amount of processing time and developer volume is needed.

If hair is overly porous or coarse and resistant (e.g., grey hair), you'll need to treat the hair prior to your color service

For instance, if hair is porous, it is lacking protein, and could use a protein treatment.

Note: Use a treatment with the proper pH; actual conditioner will close the cuticle, making it more difficult for color molecules to be absorbed into the hair.

PRO TIP: Try Powerbuild Reconstructor (80% protein, 20% moisture)

P.S. Just like Miley Cyrus and raunchy publicity stunts, protein and color molecules are attracted to each other; adding protein to the equation will help your hair color be richer and longer lasting!

If hair is coarse, the cuticle scales are tightly packed down and need to be softened. Treating the hair prior to service will allow the hair's cuticle to open and accept the color, all without using a stronger developer.

Also, different nationalities tend to yield different hair textures.

For example, Asian hair tends to be very round shaped, and African-American hair tends to be quite flat. The natural shape of the hair will affect hair's texture and consequent processing time.

(7) Know Your Developer Strengths

Understand the lifting ability of your developers!

Each color line's developers will vary in strength.

One line's 20 volume developer may give you 1-2 levels of lift, where some color lines will just deposit. The power of each developer should be known before mixing it with a color or lightening powder, so that the structural integrity of the hair is kept intact.

FRIENDLY REMINDER: Color doesn't lift color, at least not with predictability.

(8) Proper Mixing

Knowing your color to developer mixing ratio is vital to color success!

For example, most High Lift blonde series will require a larger amount of developer. Instead of mixing color to developer of 1:1, high lift blonde will need the added strength of more developer to get to a lighter lever, so use a mixing ratio of 2 (developer): 1 (color).

Also, be sure to accurately assess the amount of hair your client has. That way, you don't have to go mix more color while the applied color is processing on the hair.

(9) Proper Processing Time

A numerous amount of factors will affect your color's processing time!

Here's a few to take into consideration:

- Health of Hair
- How Many Levels of Lift
- Percentage of Grey or White Hair
- Strength of Developer Used
- Hair Texture

Also, be sure to consult your manufacturer's Technical Manual for recommended color processing times; these will vary color line to color line.

A Choice of Shades

Henné Color Henna hair colouring powders come in 7 different colours, from black to golden blond, a palette of colours to help you obtain personalised results according to your hair's natural colour and your desires. These oxidant-free hair colours do not help to lighten your hair.

Consult the colour chart and the table below to choose your colour.

Colours	Your hair colour
Golden Blonde	Light blond, Dark blond
Chestnut brown	Dark blond, Light chestnut
Copper	Dark blond, Light chestnut, dark chestnut, Brown
Mahogany	Dark blond, Light chestnut, Dark chestnut, Brown, Black
Auburn	Light chestnut, Dark chestnut, Brown, Black
Brown	Dark chestnut, Brown, Black
Black	Dark chestnut, Brown, Black

MATERIALS AND METHODS

Experimental Organisms

The clinical isolates of *Escherichia coli* ATCC25922, *Listeria monocytogenes* ATCC15313 ATCC27853 and *Staphylococcus aureus* ATCC28923 used were obtained from Molecular Biology Department.

Preparation of Crude Extracts from the Powdered Leaves of *L. inermis*

Hot aqueous extraction

Two hundred grams of the powdered leaf of *L. inermis* was soaked in 1000 ml boiled distilled water, shaken and left for 24 h. The solution was filtered using No.1 watt man filter paper. The filtrate was dried in a hot air oven at 30°C for three days to get rid of residual water. The residue was scraped grind, weighed and store in a dried air tight container. The dried powder obtained was 9.03 g (pH 4.03).

Cold aqueous extraction

This was carried out with the method above except that cold distilled water was used instead of hot. The dried powder obtained was 10.10 g with pH of 4.13.

Ethanolic extraction

200g of powdered *L. inermis* were packed into a thimble and transferred into Soxhlet extractor with 1 L of 95% ethanol for about 72 h until there was no colour change in the ethanol, indicating the end point of extraction completion. The extract was harvested and concentrated in a rotary evaporator separating the ethanol from the real extract. However, the remnant ethanol in the extract was removed by placing the extract in porcelain dishes in the oven at 80°C until the weight remained constant. The extract weighed 4.98 g (pH 2.86) and was then collected in air tight plastic container and stored in the refrigerator at 4°C ready for use.

Phytochemical screening

The extracts of *L. inermis* were screened for phytochemical constituents according to Trease and Evans.

Fourier Transform Infrared Spectroscopy (FTIR)

Figure 23.1 shows the functional group of henna. The presence of hydroxyl group appeared at 3299 cm^{-1}. There are two α,β-unsaturated carbonyl bands at 1735.2 cm^{-1} and 1625.1 cm^{-1} (C=O chelated with an α-hydroxyl) signify the presence of two carbonyl groups conjugated with a double bond (α,β -unsaturated carbonyls) and thus endorsing the possibility of having a 1,4-naphthoquinone. It was found that henna consists of a major component which is Lawsone. This compound has molecular formula of $C_{10}H_6O_3$ with molecular mass of 174.153. The phenol group of lawsone would donate electron to the metal to achieve its noble state of orbit, while the metal would receive the electron to become more stable. This indirectly retard further redox reaction and could resist metal from corrosion attack.

Fig. 23.2: Functional group in commercial henna powder analyzed by FTIR

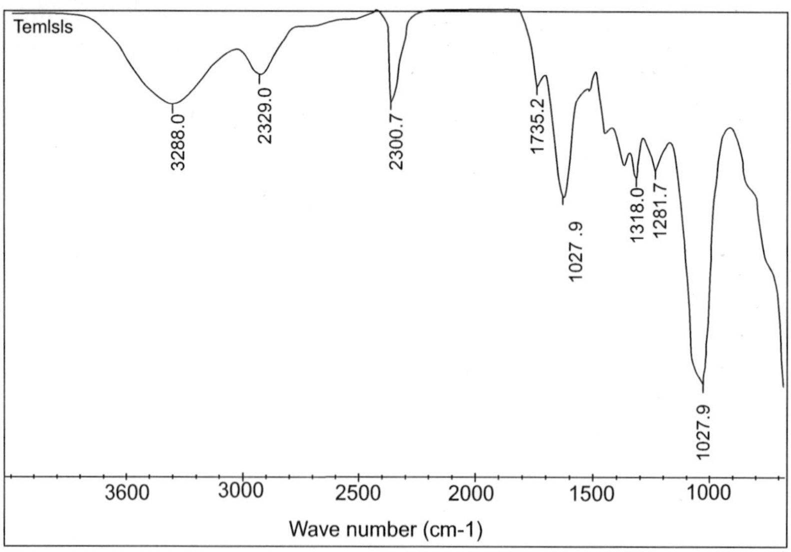

Fig. 23.3: Functional group in commercial henna powder analyzed by FTIR

Henna constituents have antioxidant characteristic especially by the naphthoquinones. The possible mechanism for chemisorptions can be attributed to the complex formation between lawsone and metal cations. The main cathodic reaction in the surface is hydrogen evolution. In this case, oxygen reduction does not play a significant role in total cathodic reaction. Therefore, the oxygen scavenging characteristic of henna is not the main responsible mechanism for the observed inhibition of henna extract yet is the chemisorption of inhibitor molecules on the surface. So, it is concluded that the chemisorption of inhibitor molecules on steel surface is the main inhibition mechanism while the inhibitive action is slightly enhanced via oxygen scavenging.

Preparation of Extract Solution of L. inermis for Gram Reaction

Aqueous Extracts

2.5 g of dried aqueous (hot and cold water extracts) was dissolved in 100 ml of distilled water in three different bottles each, one of the solution was ripened by oxidation with potassium permanganate, the other with hydrogen peroxide and the third solution was used without oxidation. Solution A and B was ripened with potassium permanganate and hydrogen peroxide, while solution C was used without oxidation. Another 2.5 g of dried extract was dissolved in 50 ml distilled water in another two different bottles (to increase the concentration by 50%). One of the solutions saturated with potassium alum, the other with ferric chloride.

Alcoholic Extract

Three different solutions of ethanol extracts were prepared by dissolving 1.25 g of the extract in 50 ml distilled water (the dissolved solution was filtered to remove some particles as it does not completely dissolve). One of the solutions was oxidised with potassium permanganate, the other with hydrogen peroxide and the third was used without oxidation. Another 2.5 g of dried extract was dissolved in 50 ml distilled water in another two different bottles (to increase the concentration by 50%). One of the solutions saturated with potassium alum, the other with ferric chloride. Hydrogen ion (pH) concentrations of various Henna extracts were determined using pH meter (Methrom Digital pH meter) and recorded. Hot aqueous extract without additional substances; 4.03, hot aqueous extract with potassium permanganate; 7.16, hot aqueous extract with hydrogen peroxide; 3.41, hot aqueous extract saturated with potassium alum; 2.72, hot aqueous extract saturated with ferric chloride 1.02, cold aqueous extract without additional substances; 4.13, cold aqueous with potassium permanganate; 7.00, cold aqueous with hydrogen peroxide; 3.40, cold aqueous extract saturated with potassium alum; 2.72, cold aqueous extract saturated with ferric chloride 1.02, ethanolic extract without additional substances; 2.86, ethanol extract with potassium permanganate 6.55 and ethanolic extract with hydrogen peroxide 2.01.

Staining Organisms with Henna Extract

Smears of the E. coli ATCC25922, L. monocytogenes ATCC15313 and S. aureus ATCC2892 were made and fixed. These smears were Gram stained with Gram's reagents and counter stained along with the different batches of Henna extracts as counter stains. In every batch one positive control (counter stained with normal counter stain) and one negative control (with no counter stain) were included, and the result was recorded.

RESULTS

Phytochemical Analysis

The extracts of L. inermis gave positive tests for alkaloids, saponin, tannin and glycosides and negative for flavonoids and resin.

Staining Reaction of Henna Extract on Experimental Bacteria

Thirteen differently constituted Henna extract stain solutions were used as counter stain in Gram staining two identified Gram positive and two identified Gram negative bacteria, out of which only two (hot and cold extracts solutions both oxidised with potassium permanganate) stain Gram negative bacterium (E. coli) better, in shade of brownish colour. However, all the stain solutions when used as a counter stain on Gram positive bacteria did not show much difference with the positive control that was Staphylococcus and L. monocytogenes counter stained with normal stain (neutral red). The Henna extracts stain solution and the conventional counter reactions on the experimental bacteria are shown on Figures 23.2 to 23.7.

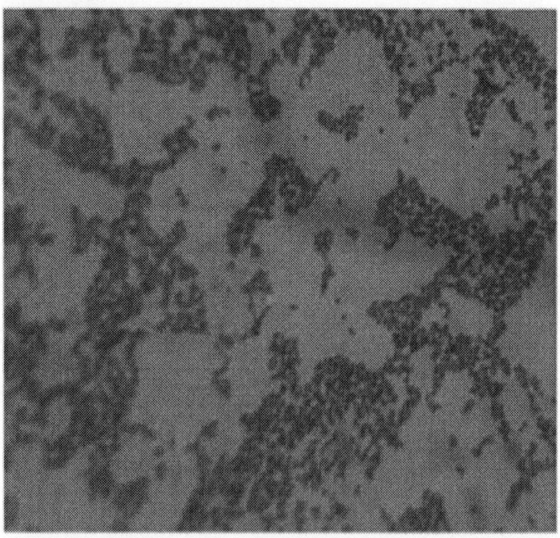

Fig. 23.4: Oxford S. *aureus* ATCC 28923, counter stained with aquesous Fenna extract × 100.

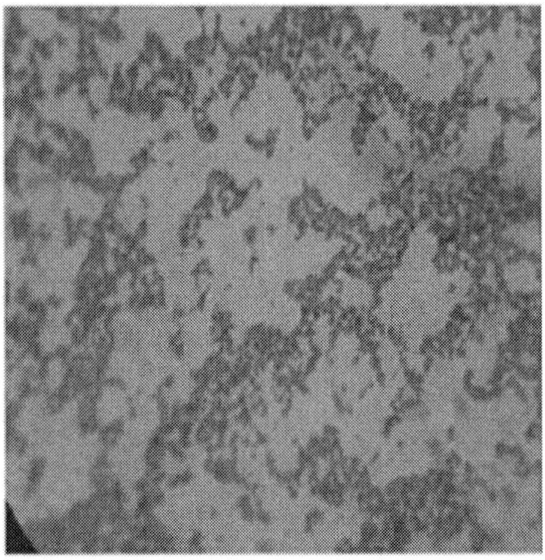

Fig. 23.5: Oxford S. *aureus* ATCC 28923, counter stained with aquesous Fenna extract × 100.

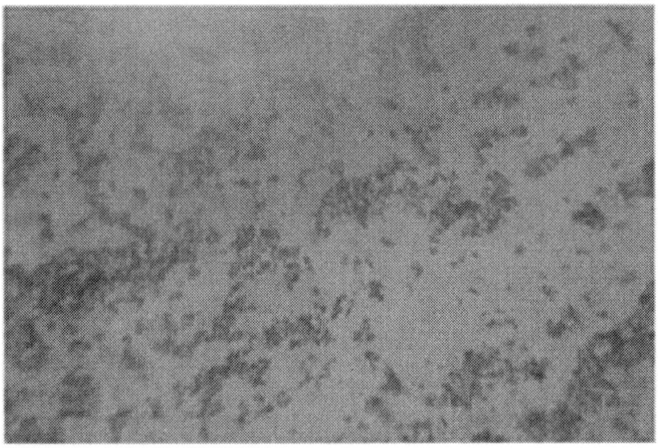

Fig. 23.6: L. *monocytogenes* ATCC 15313, counter stained with henna extract × 100.

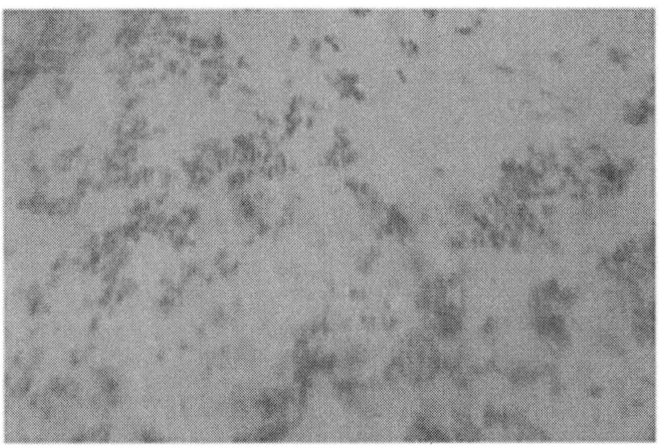

Fig. 23.7: L. *monocytogenes* ATCC 15313, counter stained with safranine × 100.

Fig. 23.8: ***E. coli*** **ATCC 25922, counter stained with henna aqueous extract × 100.**

Fig. 23.9: ***E. coli*** **ATCC 25922, counter stained with Safranine × 100.**

FLOW SHEET

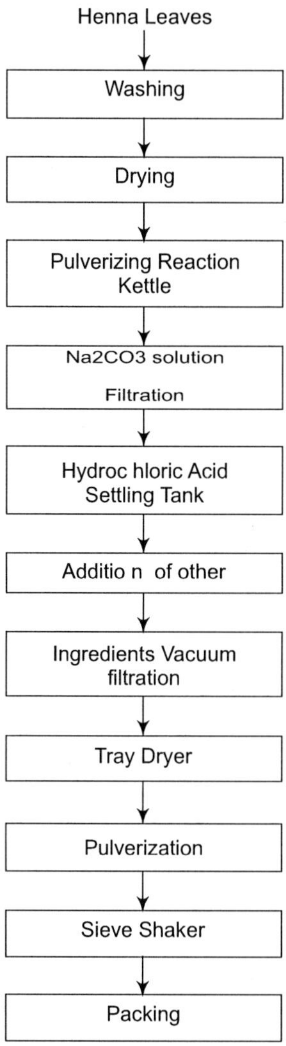

ADDITIONAL INFORMATION ON HEENA HAIR DYE

Henna

A wide array of Henna based Hair Colors as per the current trend in hair styling & coloring.

Black Henna Powder

Dark Brown Henna Powder

TBrown Henna Powder

Special Brown Henna Powder

Super Brown Henna Powder

Light Brown Henna Powder
Lemon Yellow Henna Powder
Orange Henna Powder
Mahogany Henna Powder
Wine Red Henna Powder
American Cherry Henna Powder
Royal Blue Henna Powder
Burgundy Henna Powder
Golden Brown Henna Powder
Green Henna Powder
Neutral Henna Powder
Natural Henna Powder
Herbal Henna Powder

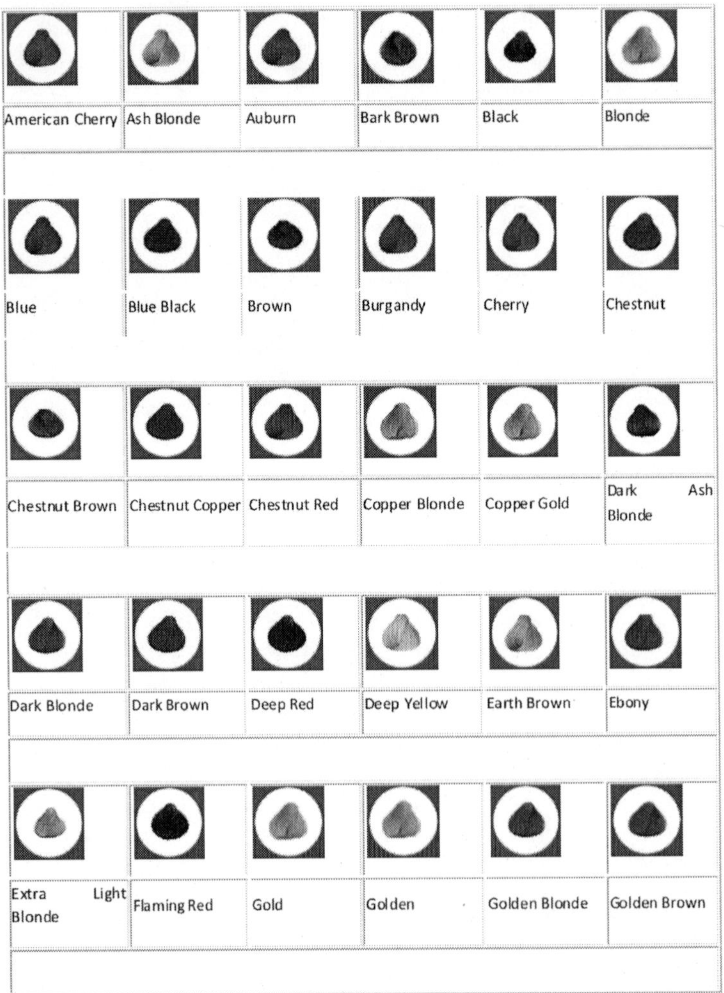

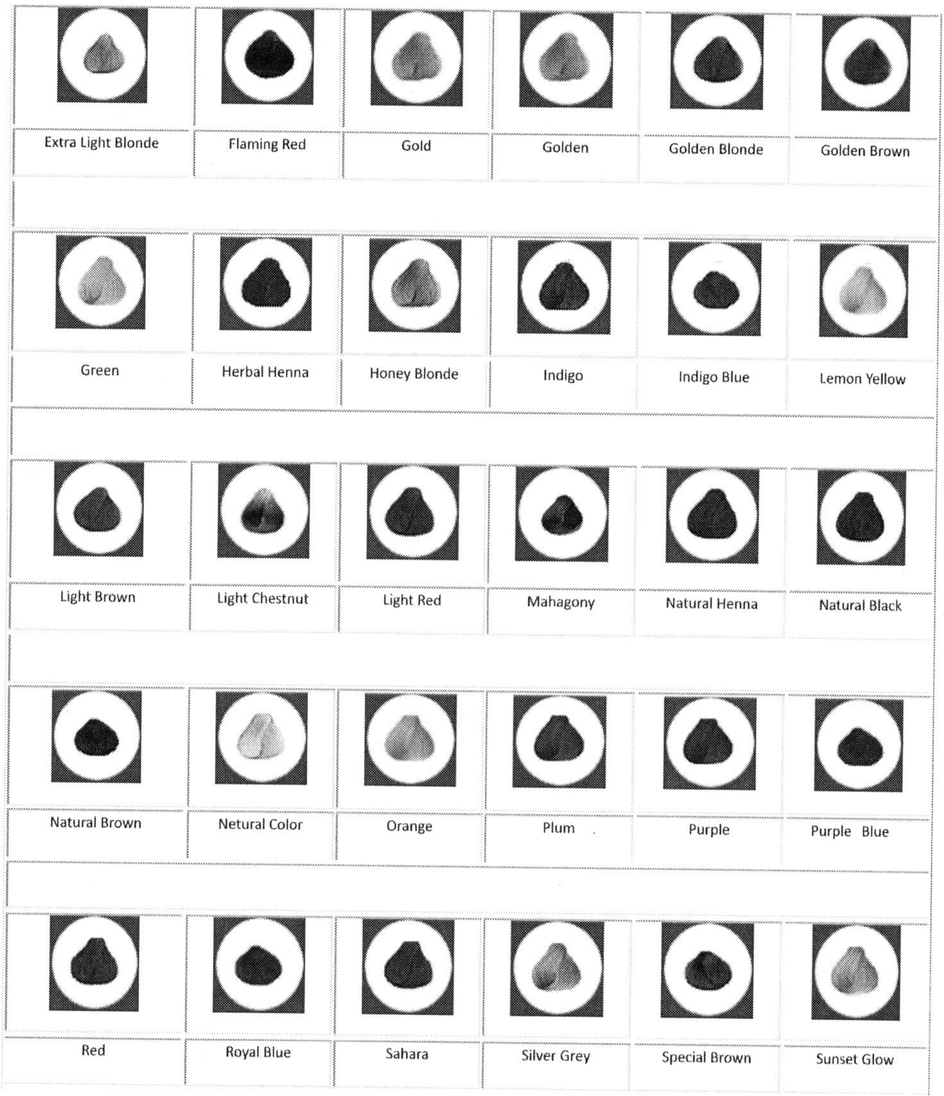

Sensitivity Test

PPD containing preparations may also cause inflamation of the skin in some cases. Hence, it is always advisable that a preliminary test is always carried out to determine whether or not special sensitivity exists. For carrying out the test, cleanse a small area of skin behind the ear or upon the inner surface of the forearm, using either soap and water or alcohol. Apply a small quantity of the hair color as prepared for use to the area and allow it to dry. After 24 hours, wash the area gently, if no irritation or inflammation is apparent, it may be assumed that no hypersensitivity to the color exists. The test should, however be carried out before each and every application.

Preparation of Paste

1. Take out the powder in a plate / bowl and add app. 3 parts water to 1 part powder to make a paste so that it can be applied on hair easily and gently.

2. Apply this paste on hair. After five minutes comb the hair so that the paste should reach as the roots of hair. If any whiten observed on hair, apply some more paste on that portion.

3. Wash the hair after 30 minutes until rinsing water becomes clear and the rinsed water is entirely colourless. Please note that while washing the hair keep the eye and mouth closed.

4. Use about 50 gms or more depends upon your hair density. Use 50 gms of depending upon the density.

Cautions

1. Henna hair colorus packet should be kept away from direct sunlight, preferably in a dark place.

2. This preparation should not be used for dyeing eyelashes or eyebrows as it can cause inflammation.

For external use only

Natural henna hair color powder can be used by all, irrespective of age factor.

BLONDE HAIR COLORS

Did you know that only 2% of people in the world are naturally blonde? Oh well, you can always go the salon and get the striking blonde hair...

There are many many shades of blonde hair color, some are bright golden ones while some come very close to brown. Selecting the right shade of blonde hair dye can totally alter your look. However, it is very important you choose the right shade to avoid a bad hair job. Your stylist will help you in choosing the right shade.

TRENDY BLONDE HAIR COLORS

Platinum Blonde Hair Color

Platinum blonde hair, which is also called towheaded, is a tint of silver, and is the lightest among the blonde hair colors. It is one of the most prominent shades of blonde, and makes you stand out in a crowd. Immortalized by none other than the legendary actress Marilyn Monroe, this is one look that's sure to stay in vogue for years to come! Just add dark smokey eye makeup and you'll be ready to flaunt your new hot look!

Ash Blonde Hair Color

This is also a light blonde color that gives an ash-like tint to the hair. If you color your hair ash blonde, then your hair may look grayish, giving an older look to your face. To avoid this, you can go for a combination of ash blonde and dark blonde tones. You can also add highlights of ash blonde to the lower part of your hair. This will result in a great multi-toned blonde look!

Yellowish Blonde Hair Color

This blonde hair color gives that sun-kissed look to your hair. With its yellow shades, it looks great on any type of hair texture. If you have fair skin, then yellowish blonde is a perfect choice for you. However, avoid using this blonde hair color if you have medium or dark skin tone.

Sandy Blonde Hair Color

This color is a shade of grayish-hazel or cream, and looks good on lighter skin tones. It is a neutral type of hair color which is neither too pale nor too dark. This hair color look best on long hair that has a good texture.

Golden Blonde Hair Color

If you want to give a dramatic look to your traces, one of the best hair colors to go for, is the golden blonde hair color. Well, you need to have a fair complexion to wear that stunning look with golden blonde hair. Those who just got a subtle tan, can add this shade to their hair and have a completely sun kissed look.

Strawberry Blonde Hair Color

One of the best blonde hair color ideas for those with a pale complexion with peach or golden undertones, or a brown complexion with pink or golden undertones, is to opt for a strawberry blonde look. Dark strawberry blonde hair color, with undertones of auburn or dark brown, looks great on curly locks.

Blonde Hair with Red Highlights

Blonde hair with red highlights looks attractive. Red streaks in golden strands emerges out as stylish and attractive. We provide you some tips on trying different shades of red on your blonde hair.

Blonde hair is simply ideal for wearing different hair colors. Nevertheless, red is the most sought after hair color when it comes to redefining your fashion statement. Red highlights in blonde hair are enamored mostly by youngsters, who love follow the latest fashion trends. The bright red streaks flashing on blonde hair look bold and gorgeous. Red highlights in dark brown hair also look ravishing.

Red Highlights: Shades

Red is indeed a tricky color and it requires proper blending for creating the perfect fashionable look. It is always advisable to get red highlights done on your blonde hair from an experienced hair stylist. Pick up shades that will suit your skin tone. When your hair color complements your hair as well as your complexion, then the difference in your appearance is evident and is for the better.

Bold Red: It is the perfect color for extremely fair-complexioned women with blonde hair.

Orange Red: This color also suits blondes with fair and olive complexion. Youngsters can try out orange-red highlights.

Plum Red: Plum red is meant for both fair and medium toned blondes.

Strawberry Red: This is the ideal color for blondes with fair complexion. Strawberry red is a brilliant contrasting hair color for dark toned blondes.

Purple Red: Purple red is the color for teens and youngsters. Opt for this tone at night parties and club hangouts.

Mahogany Red: It is the darkest shade of red, that suits blonde as well as dark brown hair. Mahogany red is the perfect highlight for medium to dark toned women.

Copper Red: Copper red is to some extent similar to mahogany red. It is extremely attractive and probably the best red highlight for dark brown hair. It also looks fabulous on blondes.

Red Gold: Red gold has a metallic sheen which adds shine and shimmer to your blonde hair. It suits every type of complexion.

Fire Red: It is the perfect color for women having blonde hair and dark complexion. Nevertheless, fair-complexioned women can also wear it without any hesitation.

Berry Red: Berry red is for blondes with fair complexion. It has the typical color of red merged with berry.

Cadmium Red: Cadmium red highlights looks good on dark brown and blonde hair. It blends well with fair undertones.

Brownish Red: Reddish brown or brownish red is a mixture of two shades which gives a fine texture to hair. It suits both blonde and dark brown hair.

Irish Red: This color complements fair and olive complexioned blondes.

Honey Red: It is similar to golden red highlights. Honey red is an ideal color for fair-complexioned blondes.

Tips for Red Highlights on Blonde Hair

Once you get red hair highlights, it is important to take care of your hair not only to retain the color but also to preserve the quality of your hair. Red color fades sooner than any other hair color as its molecules are of big size. You can mix a little amount of dark brown with red to get a long-lasting effect. Opt for color-enhancing and color-guard shampoos. Do not wash your hair everyday as this will enhance the fading effect. Keep your hair moisturized with serum and use a conditioner after rinsing.

Now that you know the variety of red highlights, you can easily pick the best one for yourself. Step into a reputed salon and choose a premium brand for your hair. I'm sure you will love to see those red flicks in your blonde hair.

Formulation and Evaluation (HENNA COLOUR BASE)

Formulation I

Henna	Mandara	Amla	Bhringraj
1.0 gm	0.5 gm	0.5 gm	1.0 gm

Table 23.3: Formulation 1

Henna	Bhringraj	Sariva	Ratanjot
F1 0.5 gm	0.5 gm	0.5 gm	0.5 gm
F2 1.0 gm	0.5 gm	0.25 gm	0.25 gm
F3 0.75 gm	0.75gm	0.25 gm	0.25 gm
F4 0.25 gm	1.0 gm	0.25 gm	0.5 gm

Table 23.4: Formulation 2

Henna	Bhringraj	Indigo
IF1 1.5 gm	1.0 gm	1.5 gm
IF2 0.5 gm	1.0 gm	2.5 gm
IF3 2.0 gm	1.0 gm	1.0 gm

Table 23.5: Formulation 3

Henna	Bhringraj	Sariva	Ratanjot	Indigo
BAF1 0.5 gm	0.5 gm	0.5 gm	0.5 gm	0.5 gm
BAF2 0.5 gm	0.5 gm	0.25 gm	0.25 gm	1.0 gm
BAF3 0.75 gm	0.5 gm	0.25 gm	0.25 gm	0.75 gm
BAF4 1.0 gm	0.25 gm	0.5 gm	0.25 gm	0.5 gm

Table 23.6: Formulation 4

Henna	Curry	Leaves	Amla	Methi Seeds
KM1	0.5 gm	0.5 gm	0.5 gm	0.5 gm
KM2	0.75 gm	0.75 gm	0.25 gm	0.25 gm
KM3	0.5 gm	0.5 gm	0.25 gm	0.75 gm
KM4	0.5 gm	0.25 gm	0.75 gm	0.5 gm

DESCRIPTION

AMLA: contains Phyllemblin,Ascorbic acid,Gallic acid,Tannins & Pectin

BHRINGRAJ: contains Wedololactone

INDIGO: contains Indoxyl

HENNA: contains Lawsone

CURRY LEAVES: Linalool,Geranyl Acetate,alpha Terpineol

RATANJYOT: contains Naphthaquinone derivatives

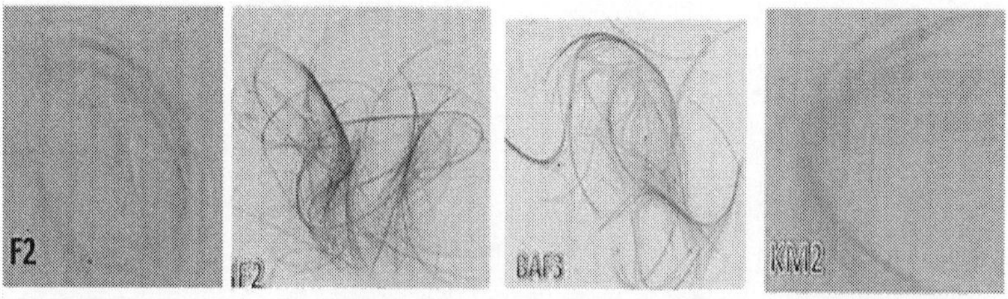

Fig. 23.1: Photographs of human hair treated with best formulation F2, IF2, BAF3 and KM2

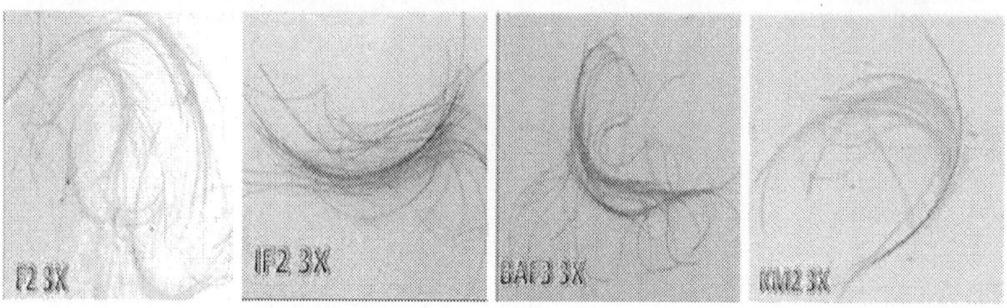

Fig. 23.10: Microscopic photos of human hair treated with IF2, F2 and BAF3 at different condition such asone time coating, three time coating, effect of sunlight after 20 days and effect of detergent after 20 days.

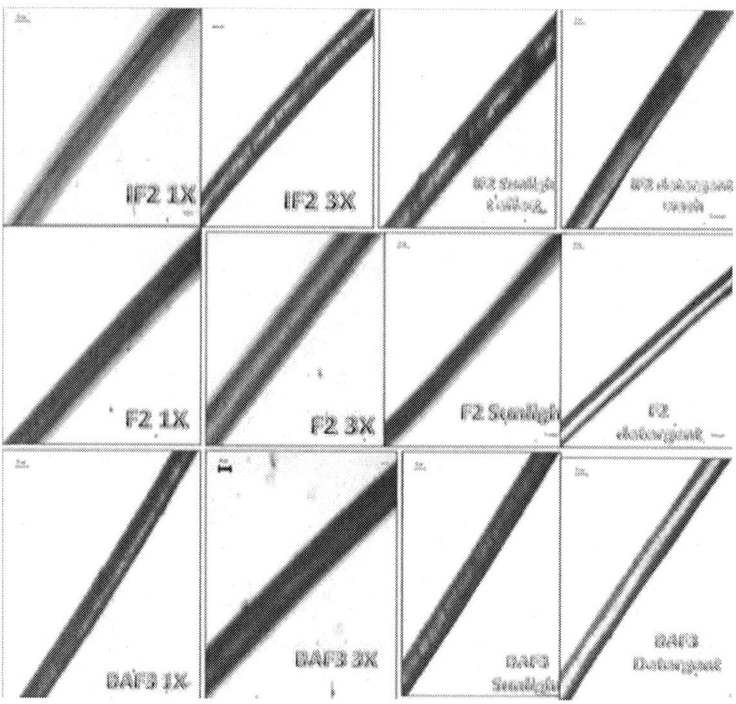

1X-one time coating, 3X-three time coating, Sunlight-effect of sunlight, detergent-effect of natural detergent wash.

Fig. 23.11: Microscopic photos of human hair treated with marketed hair dyes three times.

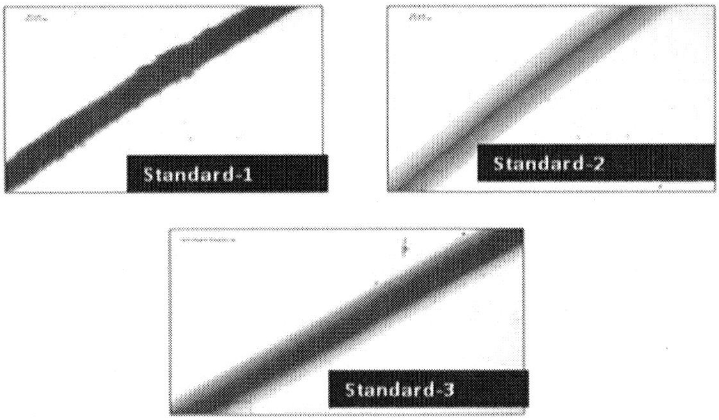

Fig. 23.12: Effect of sunlight on F2 formulation.

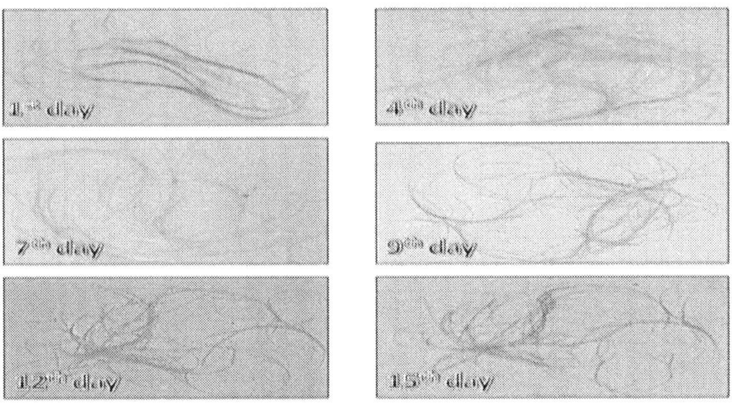

Fig. 23.13: Effect of natural detergent on human colored hair of formulation F2

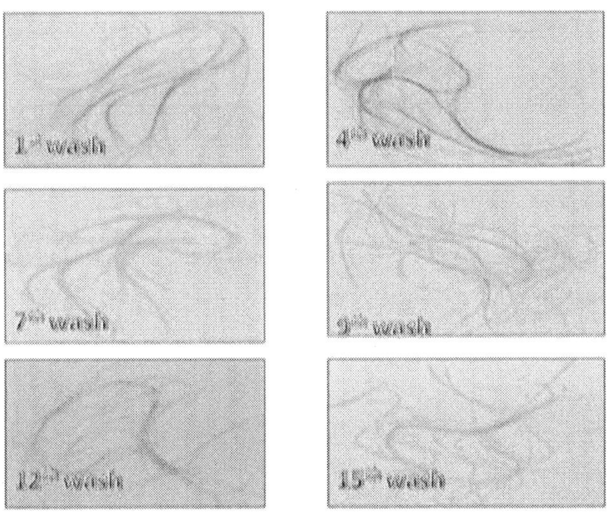

Formulation and Evaluation

(a) Sample–I

- 10%Aqueous extract of *Cymphomandra betaceae* (Fruits) containing 35% flavanoid and 10% tannins.
- 20% Aqueous extract of *Tagetes erecta* (Flower) containing 20% carotenoid.
- 40% *Aloe vera* gel Leaf) containing 0.3% polysaccharide and 98.5% water.
- 10% Henna extract
- 10% Red sandal wood extract
- 10% Sappanwood Extract

(b) Sample–II

- 20%Aqueous extract of *Cymphomandra betaceae* (Fruits) containing 35% flavanoid and 10% tannins.
- 30% Aqueous extract of *Tagetes erecta* (Flower) containing 20% carotenoid.
- 10% *Aloe vera* gel Leaf) containing 0.3% polysaccharide and 98.5% water.
- 20% Henna extract
- 10% red Sanda woodextract
- 10% Sappan Wood extract

(c) Sample–III

- 30%Aqueous extract of *Cymphomandra betaceae* (Fruits) containing 35% flavanoid and 10% tannins
- 30% Aqueous extract of *Tagetes erecta* (Flower) containing 20% carotenoid
- 20% Gel of *Aloe vera* (Leaf) containing 0.3% polysaccharide and 98.5% water.
- 15% henna Extract
- 5% Red sandalwood Extract
- 30% sappan wood extract

DETAILS OF NATURAL PRODUCTS

5 Benefits of Aloe Vera for Hair

The benefits of Aloe Vera for hair can be traced to its 75 known nutrients, but it is hypothesized that Aloe Vera, or aloe barbadensis, contains over

100 traceable nutrients. It should come to know surprise that Organic Color Systems would take advantage of this awesome plant as an ingredient in the majority of products, including our ammonia-free professional color line.

Read the 8 Benefits of Aloe Vera for Hair here:

1. *Promotes hair growth:* According to University of Hawaii researchers, we can trace the use of Aloe Vera for hair loss back to the ancient Egyptians. In fact, Aloe Vera contains enzymes that directly promote healthy hair growth. These proteolitic enzymes are able to to eradicate dead skin cells on the scalp that could be clogging the the hair follicle, not allowing for the proper penetration of nutrients in the hair. Conditions like seborrhea, which occurs from an accumulation of sebum on the scalp, can contribute to partial baldness. Aloe Vera's keratolic action, breaks down the sebum and dead scalp cells, allowing for further hair growth. Also, Aloe Vera's alkalizing properties can help bring the scalp and hair's pH to a more desirable level, resulting in further hair growth promotion, while helping the hair retain water and moisture.
2. *Anti-pruritic:* Anti-pruritic properties are those that can alleviate itching and dryness. Pruritus ailments include vexing skin and scalp issues, like psoriasis and eczema. Psoriasis is an auto-immune disease characterized by the excessive production of skin cells. Recall, Aloe Vera's enzymatic properties, enabling Aloe to destroy excessive dead skin cells, while conditioning the skin and scalp. Since excess skin cell production is at the heart of Psoriasis' existence, you could see why Aloe is able help eliminate this issue. Aloe can also reduce the redness, scaling, itching and inflammation of scalp psoriasis, which directly benefits the hair, as well. In a study reported in Archives of Dermatology, more than 80 percent of the psoriasis patients treated with Aloe Vera showed improvement.
3. *Anti-inflammatory:* Historically, one of the primary uses of Aloe Vera has been to reduce redness and inflammation both internally and externally. In fact, Aloe Vera has long been used on burns and external wounds as an antiseptic to reduce swelling, and eliminate bacteria. This is a great attribute to have in our ammonia-free hair color and care products because it helps soothe those that have a sensitive scalp and are prone to irritation. The ingredients responsible for this calming property is Bradykinase, and analesgic anti-inflammatic enzyme, as well as salicylic acid, which is an aspirin-like compound with anti -inflammatory, analgesic, and anti-bacterial properties.
4. *Reduces dandruff:* Because of the aforementioned enzymatic breakdown of dead skin cells from Aloe Vera, this awesome plant has also been

used for the treatment of dandruff. There could be many underlying causes of dandruff (like the previously mentioned conditions), but some doctors attribute its existence to malassezia, a fat-eating fungus that can live on the scalp. Luckily, in addition to breaking down the dead skin cells, Aloe Vera also has anti-fungal properties, as well. This is because the fungus thrives in an acidic environment, and the alkalizing attributes of Aloe Vera counters this lucrative fungal environment, disallowing further growth and buildup.

Conditioning

In addition to soothing and eradicating any skin and scalp problems, the benefits of Aloe Vera for Hair as a a great conditioning agent is excitingly overwhelming. The gel-like substance of the aloe barbadensis leaf gives it a similar chemical composition of keratin, the naturally occurring protein in hair cells. This structural similarity allows for easier penetration along the entire length of the hair shaft. Now, you may be beginning to realize why Organic Color Systems utilizes this powerful plant in our ammonia-free hair color – greater penetration makes for richer hair color. We can credit these penetration properties to the lignins found in Aloe Vera, the major structural material of the the cellulose content. It has been proven that the skin can absorb the benefits of Aloe Vera up to 7 layers deep; as our scalps are more absorbent than our skin, can you imagine the conditioning benefits available to the scalp? The combination of Aloe Vera's 20 amino acids (which are the building blocks of hair and scalp) also adds both strength and luster to the hair.

Benefits of Aloe Vera for Hair Summarized:

- Relieves Scalp Itching
- Reduces Scalp Redness & Inflammation
- Adds Strength & Luster To Hair
- pH Balancing
- Promotes Hair Growth
- Heals Scalps Affected By Psoriasis & Seborrhea
- Easily Penetrates Hair & Scalp
- Anti- Fungal Properites Alleviates Dandruff
- Helps Hair Retain Water & Mositure

Tagetes Erecta

Yellow Dye Extraction from Tagetes erecta (Marigold) Petals.(Leutin)

Spectrophotometry

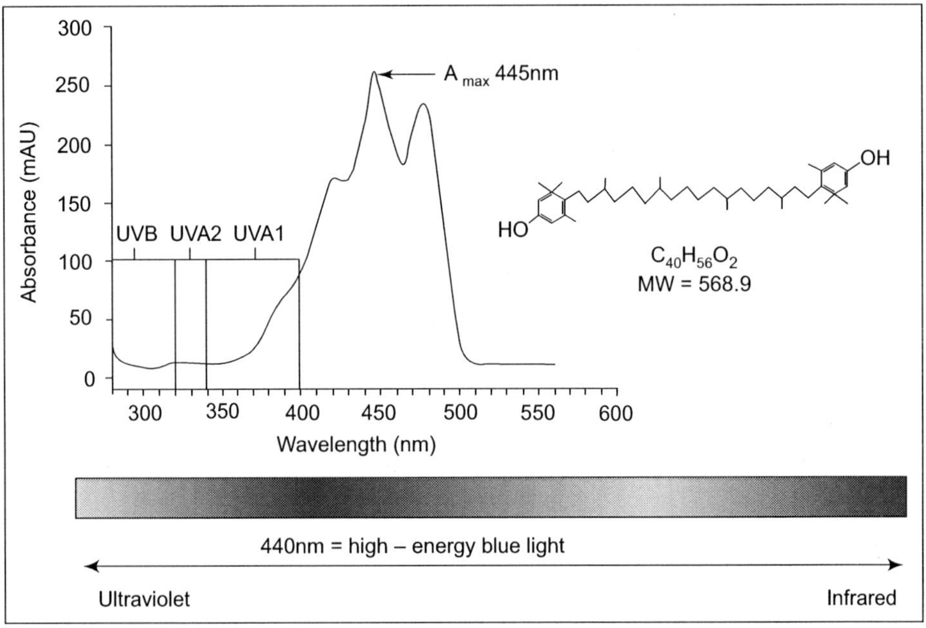

The photosynthetic pigments absorb much of the spectrum

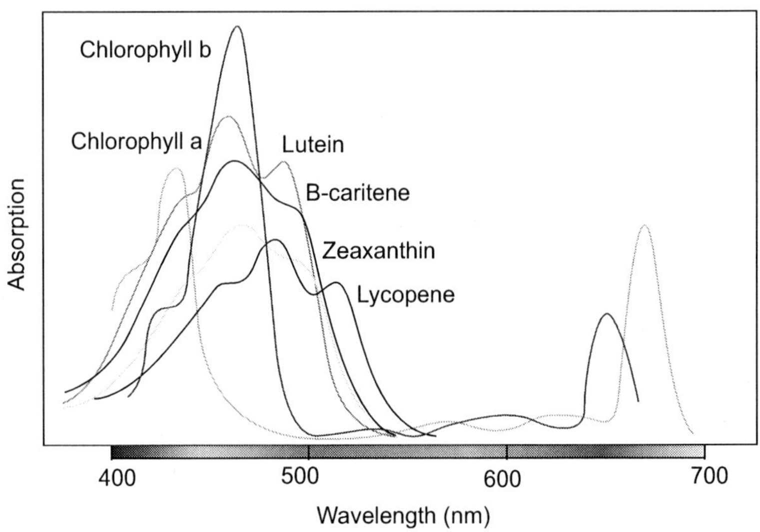

Cymphomandra betaceae

The fruits are high in pectin and therefore have good properties for preservatives.

SAPPANWOOD EXTRACT

Caesalpinia sappan is a small thorny tree about 6-9 metres in height. It has prickly branches and compound leaves. The heartwood which is used in traditional medicine as well, is light yellow when freshly cut, but it quickly changes to red.

Brazilin is a red pigment obtained from the wood of the brazilwood family (*Caesalpinia sp*), and is also known as **Natural red 24**. Among the natural colorants, brazilin is the only substance dating from the pre-Columbian era to survive the competition of synthetic dyestuffs. Brazilwood has been traditionally used as a food coloring, for example to color Easter eggs.

Sappanwood used to be one of the main sources of trade during the 17th century between Japan and its Southeast Asia neighbors (especially Siam) onboard Red Seal Ships, and its name probably originates from the Malay word "sapang" for Japan.

Sappanwood has been traditionally used in Ayurveda in the management of burning sensation in the mouth and in the topical treatment of wounds and ulcers.

The heartwood of Caesalpinia sappan contains a water-soluble compound brazilin. This transforms on oxidation to the red dyestuff, brazilein.

Brazilin itself is a leuco-compound, its solutions being achromatic in pure form. On oxidation, which proceeds somewhat slowly in absolute alcohol and more rapidly in aqueous solution, Brazilein, is formed. This change is also observed when pH changes from acidic to alkaline. Brazilein is, then, a chromophore or color-bearing compound, but it lacks strong auxochrome groups to make it a fast dye.

RED SANDALWOOD EXTRACT

The heartwood of red sandalwood tree or Red Sanders (Pterocarpus santalinus Linn.) also known as ruby wood, sanders red, saunderwood, santalwood, raktha chandana, is used as an ingredient in Ayurvedic medicines to support the management of inflammatory conditions and to improve skin health. When included in traditional cosmetic formulations with turmeric, it imparts a healthy glow to the skin. It has also been used as talcum powder traditionally. The powdered heartwood has a pleasant aroma and an attractive red color. Ayurvedic literature also describes the "cooling" properties of raktha chandana.

The principal red pigments in red sandal heartwood are santalin A and B, and these are soluble in organic solvents and alkalis, but not in water.

We can prepare different dyes of different colours from the above mentioned formulations.

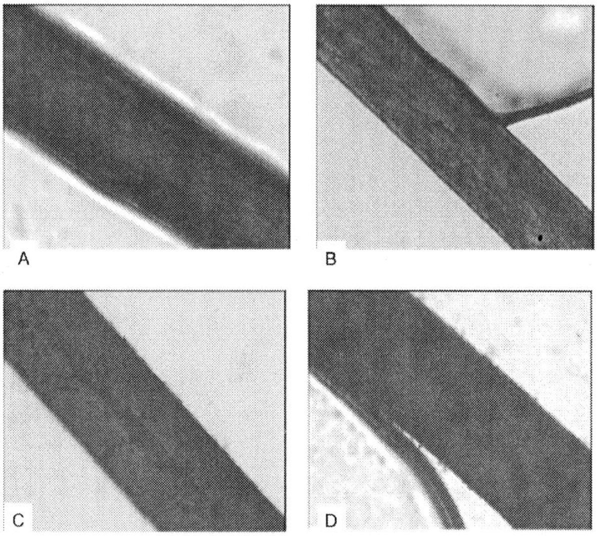

23.14: Coloring effect of herbal hair dye with natural mordant

(A) - Microscopic structure of human grey hair; (B) - Microscopic features of medulla region of human grey hair stained with herbal hair dye for 30 mnts; (C) - Microscopic features of cortex region of human grey hair stained with herbal hair dye after 30 mnts; (D) - Microscopic features of human grey hair treated with herbal hair dye after 3 treatments.

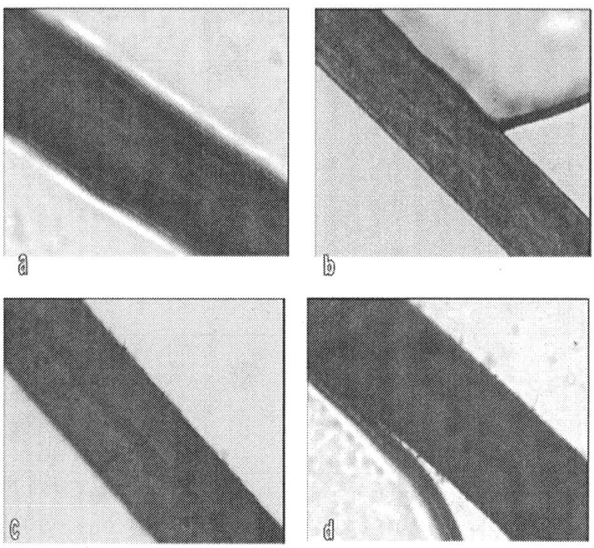

Fig. 23.15: Comparison of coloring effect of herbal hair dye with marketed brands on human hair (a) - Microscopic structure of human grey hair treated with synthetic hair dye for 15 mnts; (b) - Microscopic features of grey hair treated with synthetic hair dye showing damaged cortex after 2 treatments; (c) - Microscopic structure of human grey hair treated with semi synthetic hair dye for 15 mnts; (d) - Microscopic features of grey hair treated with semi synthetic hair dye showing damaged cortex after 2 treatments.

Dark Brown Henna

	Component	%
1	DI Water to	Add to 100 %
2	Natural Thickener- Guar Gum	1.0%
3	Natural solvent- Natural Propyl Alcohol	5.0%
4	Natural co-solvent- Propanediol	5.0%
5	Natural Primary surfactant - selected from one or more of Sodium Cocoyl Isethionate, Sodium Lauroamphoacetate, Sodium Methyl Cocoyl Taurate, Methylisothiazolione	15.0%
5a	Natural Secondary surfactant- Decyl Glucoside	10.0%
5b	Natural Tertiary surfactant - Cocamidopropyl Betaine	10.0%
6	Natural dye carrier- natural benzaldehyde	8.0%
7	Natural Citric Acid to pH 4.5 and lower	3.0%
8	Compounded henna complex at pH 4.5 and lower	20.0%
9	Natural conditioning agents- selected from one or more of Hydroxypropyl Guar & Chitosan Succinamide	3.0%
10.	Copper salt 2.0 %	

Composition for the Grey Hair is Prepared Having the Following Formulation

Ingredients	Weight percent
Indigo powder	65
Henna powder	31.6
Cationic guar gum	1
Citric acid	1.0
Aritha powder	1.0
Amla (Emblica officinalis)	0.1
Bhrigaraj(Eclipta prostrata/alba)	0.1
Brahmi {Centella asiatica)	0.1
Jaswant {Hibiscus rosasinensis)	0.1

To use the above formulations, preferably about 1 part, of one of the above compositions, are mixed with warm (60° C) water to a smooth consistency and applied to freshly shampooed hair. Keep it for 90 minutes to 120 minutes and then rinsed with plain water. Hair treated with above compositions of this invention will show lustrous, **brownish black hair.**

ORGANIC HAIR DYE FORMULATION

Extraction and Formulation of dye

Fresh leaves of aloevera were collected, washed thoroughly and the outer surface has been peeled off and inner mass was collected with the help of a scoop. Finally 50 gms of *Lawsonia inermis*, 20 gms of Hibiscus rosa –sinenis (leaves and flowers), 20 gms of Murraya Koenigii, 20 gms of Eclipta alba, 20 gms of Punica granatum, 30 gms of Emblica officinalis, 5 gms of Azadirachta indica, 5 gms of Ocimum Sanctum, 5 gms of Trigonella Foenum, 20 gms of Juglone Hussk powders were blended with 5 gms of aloevera gel along with 2 gms of Iron filings and soaking the mixture for 1 hour in water along with tea decoction to obtain a dye.

MEHNDI (HENNA) INGREDIENTS AND THEIR EFFECTS

WHAT the Basic Function is

Stain

The henna is what stains the skin. - dead, dry-ish skin stains better, and skin that exfoliates slowly keeps the design longer. The hennotannins bind with proteins.

Colorant release

Acids and perhaps other ingredients (or at least the effect of the ingredients, such as increased heat) can speed or slow the colorant release from the henna. The colorant (hennotannins that bind with proteins in the skin and then darken) are only released from the henna in the presence of an acid, such as lemon juice. The colorant needs to be released from the henna at a time when it can then go into the skin.

Oxidize

After the dye is in the skin, it slowly oxidizes. This darkens the color. If the dye oxidizes before it is in the skin, it won't stain well. (see Catherine Cartwright JOnes on July 31, 1999 at 00:41:52)

Exfoliate

The only way to get rid of the stain is to get rid of the skin cells containing the stain. Exfoliation removes the upper (dead) layer(s) of skin cells. Different skin types (in different areas as well as on different people) exfoliate naturally at different rates. Palms and soles exfoliate slowly, and so they maintain a mehndi design longest.

Moisturize

Adding fluid can pump up skin cells. This can sometimes slow exfoliation. It can also make the outermost (dead) skin layer somewhat more transparent, and thus make a mehndi design look better.

Texture

Various textures are desired for the different treatments, and especially for the henna paste. The texture should be varied to suit the particular use. For example, flexibility is useful for skin areas that are bent, stretched, or twisted frequently. Stringiness may be more important for fine designs on an area that will not be flexed while the paste is on. Knowledge and skill in adapting the textures to suit the particular application are important for a professional mehndi artist.

texture: smooth

Affects how you apply the treatment. A smooth paste is crucial for squeeze-type applicators with fine tips, and a smooth sealer is needed for fine designs. Smoothness is relatively unimportant for dip-style henna or nails. Only moderate smoothness is needed for stick-designs. (Alternatively: if your paste isn't as smooth as needed for a squeeze-design, you can usually still use it with a stick.)

texture: moisture / drying speed

Moisture helps get the colorant into the skin, but it also leaves the paste susceptible to adjustment and smearing. The speed of your work and the drying time end up closely related. This is one of the variables that must be adapted to a particular application. Moisture content and drying time are also important variables in a sealer.

texture: sticky

Paste and sealer must stay in contact with the skin to work. Stickiness helps adhere the treatment. It also can keep the treatment from cracking. (See also moisture.)

texture: flexible

Skin that bends, stretches, or twists needs a flexible treatment or immobility for the duration.

texture: stringy (tensile?)

Fine lines can be made by stretching a string of henna paste. Stringy or gummy paste, sometimes achieved with okra, can help keep the threads intact as the paste is stretched into fine lines. Moderate stringiness can also deter cracking in regular lines.

INGREDIENT LIST

Henna

Provides the hennotannins that act as a dye. The dye degrades with time, so freshness is important. For most uses, the henna needs to be finely ground into a powder and well-sifted (by the user, generally) in order to make a smooth paste. Both hue and saturation vary widely with the particular batch of henna powder. **HPDF** contributors have several recommended on-line sources. Beware old henna in the local store, however. Henna kits seem to be overpriced and the henna can be old, but some have reported good results. One HPDF contributor suggests a rough guideline of 1 oz. henna powder to 2 oz. liquid.

Lemon Juice

Provides moisture and acid. The acid releases the dye. This is apparently the most common liquid in North American pastes. (In Middle Eastern regions, the water may be acidic enough to promote dye release.) For most uses, juice should be strained to remove pulp. HPDF report no detectable difference between fresh and reconstituted lemon juice. Lemonade mixes (frozen or powdered) have also been used, with varying degrees of success (check other ingredients, especially sugar vs. corn syrup in the frozen mixes - sugar dries, corn syrup may not). Some of these have enhanced citric acid.

"rainwater dye release is ok. At suburban American room temperature henna will release a little dye with just water (7 brown dots in a 50X microscope field in 4 hours) but an acidic paste mix is far more efficient (30+ brown dots and a general color change in 4 hours)"

Vinegar

Moisture and acid; a less-fragrant substitute for lemon juice. (Does not appear to be very popular for mehndi, though often used for hair.)

Citric Acid

Acid for dye release, textur. One report of too much citric acid preventing stain and affecting paste texture.

Cloves

Darkens the henna stain; adds fragrance. Clove powder can be added to paste or sealer, if a fine texture is not required. Cloves (whole or powdered) can be boiled in liquid that is then used for paste or sealer. Clove oil can be added to a pre-treatment, paste, or sealer. It is found in New Skin (liquid bandage), some topical anesthetics (especially those used for toothache), some teas, and occasionally other commercial products. Note that clove oil (from oil or from the cloves) can produce an allergic reaction in some people, and undiluted clove oil can produce a rash.

"Cloves contain gallotannic acid, which is a companionable cousinto hennotannic acid. The addition of clove in one form or other makes the henna a tad blacker."

Water

Adds moisture. Hot water also adds heat to aid dye release. Tap water may contain all sorts of chemicals that can affect the henna, so filtered or distilled water is sometimes recommended. For a paste, the water is usually boiled with other ingredients, then strained, then mixed with the powder and further ingredients.

Promotes exfoliation. Having your hands (or skin) in water, particularly water containing chlorine or cleaners, tends to make the skin exfoliate faster and fade the design.

Tea

Adds tannins and increases acidity somewhat. Adds moisture, fragrance, and perhaps texture. Tea is also a traditional paste ingredient, probably because it's a handy hot liquid to mix into the henna powder. (The heat helps dye release.)

Coffee

Adds moisture, fragrance, and perhaps texture. May add some initial color, but does not darken the actual stain. Another traditionally hot liquid. Some HPDF contributors report alertness or sleeplessness due to the caffeine absorbed through the skin. (The caffeine effect could possible increase circulation and thus heat, but that's theoretical.)

Lime (limestone - calcium carbonate?)

Probably promotes oxidation.

Dried Limes or Lemons

Add acid (dye release), texture, fragrance, initial color. Dried limes produce a red color in the water when boiled.

Sugar

Most commonly mixed with lemon juice and used as a sealer. The sugar dries to make a coating that protects the paste below. Sugar also adds some stickiness to a paste. It can be cooked to change the texture or heated gently to dissolve more sugar into a given amount of liquid (affects drying time).

If outdoors, the sugar can attract insects. Wrap, or substitute New Skin or a peel-mask if this becomes a problem.

Honey

Preservative; also smooths, adds stickiness, and slows drying time. Good for texture adjustment. Honey can slow the dye release from the henna, so you may need to let a honey-paste age (3-5 days?) to get a normal stain;. Mixing in the honey after the paste has developed will probably not affect the color or timing.

Okra

Adds stickiness and stringiness to the paste, slows the drying and reduces cracking of the dried paste. Okra is boiled in water or water-based mixture, then strained.

Fenugreek (menthi seeds)

Fragrance; adds stickiness and stringiness to the paste. Fenugreek seeds or powder are boiled in water or water-based mixture, then strained.

Eucalyptus Oil

Fragrance; opens pores, can stimulate circulation (heat). Can be used as a pre-treatment, in the paste, or in the sealer. Mixed reports as to effect on color.

Some people have allergic reactions. As a pre-treatment, use sparingly and wait a few minutes before applying design; avoid having the oil sit on top of the skin (it can be a barrier).

Cooking Oil

Drying time, texture. (Smoothness?) As a pre-treatment, may help in paste removal, but it may also interfere with dye absorption. Also post-treatment to aid removal of paste & sealer, and to help make the skin water-resistant.

Some reports that adding peanut oil to the paste results in a darker stain than the same amount of vegetable oil in the paste. (1 Tbsp. oil per cup of paste.) Can make the skin look more transparent.

Petroleum Jelly

Not recommended for henna in general; petroleum jelly is reported to have adverse affects on a stain (possible fader). Check handcreams for ingredients if you're trying to make a design last extra-long. Petroleum jelly can be used for removing a liquid latex sealer, however, as petroleum products tend to destroy latex.

Peel-masks

Two kinds: regular and Alpha hydroxy.

Sealer. Transparent and flexible, so it can be good on clients. May be diluted (typically with other sealers and a bit of clove oil). Can wet and smear very fine lines. Can take a while to dry, especially in humid or cold air (hair dryer can help). Can re-absorb moisture and become sticky in humid air. Can be dusted with powder to prevent this It may reduce staining. Can help removal of paste.

Exfoliant (alpha-hydroxy). Also reported to dissolve New Skin. (Example: St. Ives Alpha Hydroxy exfoliating peel-off masque.)

Glue

Sealer. White glue is quite similar to a peel-mask. Can be thinned with lemon juice or water.

Tamarind

Texture, fragrance. No reported color effects. Fruit or paste - usually boiled with liquid for the paste.

Liquid Latex

Sealer and bandage. See, for example,. Does not affect color except to the extent it keeps the skin warm and henna moist. Some people have allergic reactions to latex. Also has depilatory effects (pulls out hair). Can blur the henna if applied directly, without a primary sealer. Highly flexible and tenacious. Adheres to self and peels, so inappropriate for some uses (may be powdered). Henna may stain through latex. Can aid paste removal when peeled off. See also Petroleum Jelly.

Ammonia

Oxidizes and exfoliates. On palms and soles, a brief (few minutes) post-treatment of dilute (10%) ammonia can darken the stain. On other skin, the exfoliation overwhelms the oxidation rate, and you lose skin rather than darkening the stain. Ammonia is the key ingredient in many animal urines, which have been used historically to darken the stain of henna. Ammonia is NOT good for your skin, so use with caution. Do NOT mix with chlorine (swimming pools) or bleach, as this creates poisonous chlorine gas. Ammonia is a base and will tend to counteract the effects of acids (ammonia inhibits release of colorant), so it's best avoided in paste and sealers. It's also quite pungent, so have good ventilation if you do use it. (The smell fades quickly as the ammonia evaporates.) On the other hand, if you're going to be scrubbing the floor anyway.

Camphor

Can darken stain; may also shorten the life of a stain (though stain may stay dark until it disappears). Pungent. Dangerous if concentrated or applied to delicate areas, so use with great care. Several forms; best success seems to be with camphor spirits (10% camphor in alcohol) or various rubbing lotions. HPDF are experimenting - pre-treatment, paste, sealer, and post-treatment; pre and post seem the most encouraging. May increase circulation and raise skin temperature (although reports are that it feels cool and tingly). Camphor is absorbed quickly and deeply into skin, and can carry other ingredients with it. Because of this, it can be rather nasty to play with - use only in diluted form. Found in many varieties (white camphor essential oil, camphor crystals) and as ingredients in other things, such as muscle rubs. Campho-phenique may also exfoliate (the phenol) deeply (the camphor), counteracting the darkening effect. Camphor can make a paste get lumpy (put the camphor in last if at all); can also speed the process so the paste maxes out faster (it seems to oxidize the paste and make it separate). Honey may slow the lumping..

Peroxide

Can lighten stain. Use hydrogen peroxide with caution. Generally considered gentler than bleach. (Soak a cotton ball in peroxide and apply to stain several times per day to lighten a stain.)

Bleach

Can lighten stain. Use a dilute solution, and use with caution; this is nasty to skin. Do NOT combine with ammonia; together they make poisonous chlorine gas. Bleach is an ingredient in many scouring powders, so wear gloves if scouring, to protect your hands & design. (Alternatively, if you're trying to get rid of a henna stain, it may be a good time to clean some grungy stuff and get two jobs done at once.)

Detergents

Can promote exfoliation. Minimize if you want a design to last; protect with oil if you must submerge skin in water with detergents.

Flammable Liquids

Things like gasoline, kerosene, and turpentine are used in many places to make a darker stain, but they are nasty to the skin and not recommended.

Dyes

Hair dyes, inks, and the like have been used in conjunction with henna. Some are quite nasty and these are not recommended. (May contain "ppd" - this has had some truly appalling effects on skin, leaving scars.) Do not combine henna even with safe dyes unless you've done a sample first, as the chemical reactions can give you some weird colors...like green.

Alpha Hydroxy

Also abbreviated (AH?). This exfoliates the skin. Comes in cleaning scrubs, peel-masks, and other forms. (Is it an ingredient in hair straightener?) Don't use too often at once; exfoliating the outer dead layer of skin is fine, but exfoliating too much is damaging. Can help remove opaque light-colored dead skin (especially around the feet) to make a later henna design more visible. Removes the skin that is stained, so it tends to lighten an existing henna design.

Glove in a Bottle

Skin protection. So-so as a masking fluid before a henna treatment - stain reported to be lighter, but present. As a post-treatment, softens skin but does not seem to slow exfoliation.

Metal and Metallic Compounds

NOT recommended, as they are potentially toxic. Some metal salts or oxides are used in various dyes, and apparently do make a stain darker, but are not worth the risk unless you really know what you're doing. Mixing an acidic paste in a brass, copper, or aluminum container - or letting the paste sit in one - can add metals unintentionally to your paste. (Glass, plastic, glazed ceramic, and stainless steel are usually safe.)

BLACK HEENA DYE

(1) First Component

Aluminum chloride hexahydrate	1
Isostearyl alcohol	0.5
Stearyl alcohol	2
Stearyl trimethyl ammonium chloride	1
Glycollic acid	1.5
Sodium lactate	0.7

Benzyl alcohol	2
Ethanol	2
Dipropylene glycol	2
Perfume	0.5
Ion-exchange water to	40.0
Second Component	
Carboxyvinylpolymer	3.0
Orange II (D & C Orange No.4)	0.4
New Coccin	0.1
Benzyl alcohol	8.0
Henna powder	15.0
Sodium hydroxide	0.03
Ion-exchange water	to 60.0

(2)

	Example 1	Example 2	Example 3	Example 4
The first liquid [Dyestuff intermediate]				
p-phenylene diamine	1.2	1.1	1.1	0.5
p-aminophenol	0.4	0.4	0.2	
[Coupling agent]				
m-phenylene diamine	0.3			
m-aminophenol		0.2	0.2	0.2
Resorcin		0.3	0.3	0.4
2,6-diaminopyridine	0.1			
o-aminophenol				0.25
[Chlorophyll, derivative]				
Sodium iron chlorophyllin	0.01	0.01	0.01	0.01
[Antiinflammatory agent]				
PHYTOBLEND TIPS	0.1	0.1	0.1	0.1
[Cream base agent]				
Stearyl alcohol	5.0	5.0	5.0	5.0
Cetyl alcohol	1.0	1.0	1.0	1.0
Myristic acid isopropyl	2.0	2.0	2.0	2.0
[Emulsifying agent]				
Polyoxyethylene cetyl ether	1.5	1.5	1.5	1.5
Stearyl trimethylammonium chloride [Alkaline agent]	3.0	3.0	3.0	3.0
Henna Dye	25.0	28.9	24.8	30.0

Perfumes	0.2	0.2	0.2	0.2
Purified water	Appropriate quantity			
Total	100.0	100.0	100.0	100.0
The second liquid	[Oxidant]			
Hydrogen peroxide [Stabilizer]	6.0	6.0	6.0	6.0
Phenacetin [pH adjuster]	A small amount			
Phosphoric acid	Until making the pH to 3.0			
Disodium pyrophosphate	dihydrogen			
Purified water	Appropriate quantity			
Total	100.0	100.0	100.0	100.0

(3)

The color tone of each hair bundle was evaluated by visual observation. When the hair bundle had any one of six preferred color tones, it was evaluated in accordance with the following standards. When the color tone of the hair bundle was not preferable, it was evaluated as "Bad". The color tone evaluated by visual observation was described in individual parentheses.

Good BK: Black

Good B: Brown

Good LB: Light brown

Good DB: Dark brown

Good RB: Reddish brown

Good AB: Ash brown

Method for Evaluating the Effect of Preventing Photofading:

A hair bundle, which had been exposed to sunlight, was evaluated in accordance with the following standards:

Good: Almost the same color as that before exposure to sunlight

Bad: Color faded rather than that before exposure to sunlight

		Example 1	Example 2	Example 3	Example 4	Example 5	Example 6
First agent	Tannic acid	3.0	0.2				
	Gallic acid			2.0			
	Propyl gallate				0.5		
	Pyrogallol					2.0	

	Hematein						3.0
	Tea extract						
	Cochineal						
	Hinokitiol						
	Sodium salicylate						
	Kaoliang						
	Turmeric						
	Oxybenzone-1			2.0			2.0
	Oxybenzone-3	2.0	2.0			2.0	
	Oxybenzone-4						
	Oxybenzone-6				2.0		
	Tetrahydroxy-benzophenone						
	Ethanol	5	5	5	5	5	5
	Henna Powder	30	30	30	30	30	30
	Sodium hydroxide	q.s.	q.s.	q.s.	q.s.	q.s.	q.s.
	Purified water	Balance	Balance	Balance	Balance	Balance	Balance
	pH	8	8	8	8	8	8
	Leaving time	5	5	5	5	5	5
Second agent	Ferrous sulfate	2.0	2.0	1.0	2.0		2.0
	Ferric chloride					2.0	
	Sodium hydroxide	q.s.	q.s.	q.s.	q.s.	q.s.	q.s.
	Hydrochloric acid	q.s.	q.s.	q.s.	q.s.	q.s.	q.s.
	Purified water	Balance	Balance	Balance	Balance	Balance	Balance
	pH	4	4	4	4	4	4
	Leaving time	10	10	10	10	10	10
Hair dyeing results	A	A	A	A	A	A	
Color tone	Good BK	Good B	Good BK	Good BK	Good BK	Good BK	
Photof-ading preven-tive effect	Good	Good	Good	Good	Good	Good	

		Example 7	Example 8	Example 9	Example 10	Example 11	Example 12
First agent	Tannic acid						
	Gallic acid						
	Propyl gallate						
	Pyrogallol						
	Hematein						
	Tea extract	3.0					
	Cochineal		3.0				
	Hinokitiol			0.5			
	Sodium salicylate				3.0		
	Kaoliang					3.0	
	Turmeric						2.0
	Oxybenzone-1						
	Oxybenzone-3			2.0	2.0	2.0	2.0
	Oxybenzone-4		2.0				
	Oxybenzone-6						
	Tetrahydroxy benzophenone	2.0					
	Ethanol	5	5	5	5	5	5
	Henna Powder	26	26	26	26	26	26
	Sodium hydroxide	q.s.	q.s.	q.s.	q.s.	q.s.	q.s.
	Purified water	Balance	Balance	Balance	Balance	Balance	Balance
	pH	8	8	8	8	8	8
	Leaving time	5	5	5	5	5	5
Second agent	Ferrous sulfate	2.0	1.0		2.0	2.0	2.0
	Ferric chloride			2.0			
	Sodium hydroxide	q.s.	q.s.	q.s.	q.s.	q.s.	q.s.
	Hydrochloric acid	q.s.	q.s.	q.s.	q.s.	q.s.	q.s.
	Purified water	Balance	Balance	Balance	Balance	Balance	Balance
	pH	4	4	4	4	4	4
	Leaving time	10	10	10	10	10	10
Hair dyeing results	B	A	A	B	A	B	
Color tone	Good BK	Good BK	Good RB	Good RB	Good RB	Good DB	
Photo-fading preventive effect	Good	Good	Good	Good	Good	Good	

Example Example Example Example Example Example

		Example 13	Example 14	Example 15	Example 16	Example 17	Example 18
First agent	Tannic acid				1.0	0.2	0.2
	Propyl gallate				0.2		
	Sodium salicylate				1.0		
	Kaoliang						2.0
	Scutellaria root				0.5		0.5
	extract						
	Quercetin	3.0					
	Turmeric		2.0			2.0	
	Ferulic acid			2.0			
	Oxybenzone-3	2.0	2.0	2.0	2.0	2.0	2.0
	Ethanol	5	5	5	5	5	5
	Henna powder	40	40	40	40	40	40
	Sodium hydroxide	q.s.	q.s.	q.s.	q.s.	q.s.	q.s.
	Purified water	Balance	Balance	Balance	Balance	Balance	Balance
	pH	8	8	8	8	8	8
	Leaving time	5	5	5	5	5	5
Second agent	Ferrous sulfate	2.0	2.0	2.0	2.0	2.0	2.0
	Sodium hydroxide	q.s.	q.s.	q.s.	q.s.	q.s.	q.s.
	Hydrochloric acid	q.s.	q.s.	q.s.	q.s.	q.s.	q.s.
	Purified water	Balance	Balance	Balance	Balance	Balance	Balance
	pH	4	4	4	4	4	4
	Leaving time	10	10	10	10	10	10
Hair dyeing results	A	A	A	A	A	A	
Color tone	Good DB	Good LB	Good LB	Good BK	Good LB	Good DB	
Photo-fading preventive effect	Good	Good	Good	Good	Good	Good	

		Example 19	Example 20	Example 21	Example 22	Example 23	Example 24
First agent	Tannic acid	0.2	0.2	0.2	0.2	0.2	0.2
	Propyl gallate						
	Sodium salicylate	1.0	1.0	1.0	1.0	1.0	1.0
	Kaoliang						
	Scutellaria root		0.5	0.5	0.5	0.5	0.5
	extract						
	Quercetin	0.5					
	Turmeric						
	Ferulic acid						
	Oxybenzone-3	2.0	2.0	2.0	2.0	2.0	2.0
	Ethanol	5	5	5	5	5	5
	Henna Powder	20	20	20	20	20	20
	Sodium hydroxide	q.s.	q.s.	q.s.	q.s.	q.s.	q.s.
	Purified water	Balance	Balance	Balance	Balance	Balance	Balance
	pH	8	8	8	9	8	8
	Leaving time	5	5	5	5	5	0
Second agent	Ferrous sulfate	2.0	2.0	2.0	2.0	2.0	2.0
	Sodium hydroxide	q.s.	q.s.	q.s.	q.s.	q.s.	q.s.
	Hydrochloric acid	q.s.	q.s.	q.s.	q.s.	q.s.	q.s.
	Purified water	Balance	Balance	Balance	Balance	Balance	Balance
	pH	4	4	5	4	4	4
	Leaving time	10	10	10	10	2	10
Hair dyeing results	A	A	A	A	A	B	
Color tone	Good DB	Good DB	Good DB	Good DB	Good DB	Good DB	
Photo-fading preventive effect	Good	Good	Good	Good	Good	Good	

		Example 25	Example 26	Compara-tive Example 8	Compara-tive Example 9	Compara-tive Example 10
First agent	Tannic acid	0.2	0.2	0.2	0.2	0.2
	Sodium salicylate	1.0	1.0	1.0	1.0	1.0
	Scutellaria root extract	0.5	0.5	0.5	0.5	0.5
	Oxybenzone-9	2.0				
	Dodecyloxy-benzone		2.0			
	Sodium 4-methoxycinnamate			2.0		
	Ethylhexyl methoxycinnamate				2.0	
	Ethylhexyl salicylate					2.0
	Methylene bisbenzotriazolyl tetramethyl butylphenol					
	Bumetrizole					
	Octocrylene					
	Homosalate					
	Ethanol	5	5	5	5	5
	Henna powder	20	20	20	20	20
	Sodium hydroxide	q.s.	q.s.	q.s.	q.s.	q.s.
	Purified water	Balance	Balance	Balance	Balance	Balance
	pH	8	8	8	8	8
	Leaving time	5	5	5	5	5
Second agent	Ferrous sulfate	2.0	2.0	2.0	2.0	2.0
	Sodium hydroxide	q.s.	q.s.	q.s.	q.s.	q.s.
	Hydrochloric acid	q.s.	q.s.	q.s.	q.s.	q.s.
	Purified water	Balance	Balance	Balance	Balance	Balance
	pH	4	4	4	4	4
	Leaving time	10	10	10	10	10
Hair dyeing results	C	C	C	C	C	
Color tone	Good AB	Good AB	Good AB	Good AB	Good AB	
Photo-fading preven-tive effect	Good	Good	Bad	Bad	Bad	

		Comparative Example 11	Comparative Example 12	Comparative Example 13	Comparative Example 14
First agent	Tannic acid	0.2	0.2	0.2	0.2
	Sodium salicylate	1.0	1.0	1.0	1.0
	Scutellaria root extract	0.5	0.5	0.5	0.5
	Oxybenzone-9				
	Dodecyloxy-benzone				
	Sodium 4-methoxy-cinnamate				
	Ethylhexyl methoxy-cinnamate				
	Ethylhexyl salicylate				
	Methylenebis-benzotriazolyl-tetramethyl-butylphenol	2.0			
	Bumetrizole		2.0		
	Octocrylene			2.0	
	Homosalate				2.0
	Ethanol	5	5	5	5
	Henna Powder	20	20	20	20
	Sodium hydroxide	q.s.	q.s.	q.s.	q.s.
	Purified water	Balance	Balance	Balance	Balance
	pH	8	8	8	8
	Leaving time	5	5	5	5
Second agent	Ferrous sulfate	2.0	2.0	2.0	2.0
	Sodium hydroxide	q.s.	q.s.	q.s.	q.s.
	Hydrochloric acid	q.s.	q.s.	q.s.	q.s.
	Purified water	Balance	Balance	Balance	Balance
	pH	4	4	4	4
	Leaving time	10	10	10	10
Hair dyeing results	C	C	C	C	
Color tone	Good AB	Good AB	Good AB	Good AB	
Photo-fading preventive effect	Bad	Bad	Bad	Bad	

* q.s.: quantum sufficiat (= appropriate amount)

(4)

	(% by weight)
Acid Orange 7	0.4
Acid Black 1	0.2
Henna powder	40.0
Ethanol	5.0
Benzyloxyethanol	3.0
^{3}-Hexanolactone	10.0
Partially crosslinked product of Methyl vinyl ether/ maleic anhydride Copolymer with 1,9-decadiene	3.0
Light isoparaffin	3.0
Polyethylene glycol (Mw: 2,000,000)	0.05
Polyoxyalkylene-modified dimethyl* Polysiloxane	2.0
Lactic acid (90%)	5.0
Sodium hydroxide	Adjusted to pH 3 (when diluted to 1/10)
Perfume base	3.0
Purified water	Balance
Total	100.0

*Silicone KF945A (product of Shin-Etsu Chemical Co., Ltd.)

BURGUNDY DYE FROM HENNA

	Example 1	Example 2	Example 3	Example 4	Example 5
Cocamidopropyl betaine	7.00				7.00
Cocamphocarboxy-glycinate		7.00		7.00	
Cocoamphodi-propionate			7.00		
Oleic acid	5.00	5.00		5.00	5.00
Henna Powder	20.0	20.0	20.0	20.0	20.0
Octylpolyglycoside	5.00			8.00	
Decylpolyglycoside		8.00			8.00
Dodecylpolyglycoside			5.00		
Ammonium hydroxide	5.00	5.00		5.00	
Monoethanolamine			3.00		
Aminoethylpropanol			3.00		

Sodium carbonate					2.50
Sodium bicarbonate					0.50
Sodium citrate					0.50
EDTA	0.10	0.10	0.10	0.10	0.10
Sodium sulfite	0.10	0.10	0.10	0.10	0.10
Fragrance	0.50	0.50	0.50	0.50	0.50
1-acetoxy-2-methyl-naphthalene	1.20			0.20	0.50
2-methyl-1-naphthol		0.20			
4-methoxy-2-methyl-1-naphthol			1.20		
4-amino-2-hydroxytoluene	0.60			0.10	0.10
2-methyl-5-hydroxyethyl-aminophenol		0.40			
2-methyl-5-ethoxyethyl-aminophenol			0.20		
p-aminophenol	1.00			0.30	0.40
3-methyl-p-aminophenol		0.30			
1-[(2-hydroxy-5-amino) phenyl]-1,2-			1.20		
ethanediol					
p-phenylene-diamine			0.10		0.50
N,N-bis(2-hydroxyethyl)-p-	0.50	0.02			
phenylene-diamine					
1-(2,5-diaminophenyl)-1,2-ethanediol				0.10	
Water	qs to 100	qs to 100	qs to 100	qs to 100	qs to 100
Developer Used	1	1	2	3	4
Cumulative HLB Index	2.36	2.36	2.36	2.41	2.49
Color results on gray hair:	Dk burgundy	Lt burgundy	Bright red	Copper red	Red brn

	Example 6	Example 7	Example 8	Example 9	Example 10
Cocamido-propyl betaine	7.00				7.00
Cocamphocar-boxyglycinate		7.00		7.00	
Cocoamphodi-propionate			7.00		
Henna powder	25.00	25.00	25.00	25.00	25.00
Lauric acid			5.00		
Octylpoly-glycoside	5.00			8.00	
Decylpoly-glysoside		8.00			8.00
Dodecylpoly-glycoside			5.00		
Ammonium hydroxide	5.00	5.00		5.00	
Monoethanolamine			3.00		
Aminoethylpropanol			3.00		
Sodium carbonate					2.50
Sodium bicarbonate					0.50
Sodium citrate					0.50
EDTA	0.10	0.10	0.10	0.10	0.10
Sodium sulfite	0.10	0.10	0.10	0.10	0.10
Fragrance	0.50	0.50	0.50	0.50	0.50
1-acetoxy-2-methyl-naphthalene				0.20	0.50
2-methyl-1-naphthol	0.60	0.20			
4-methoxy-2-methyl-1-naphthol			1.20		
m-phenylene-diamine	0.02			0.10	0.10
N,N-bis (2-hydroxyethyl)-m-phenyl-enediamine		0.40			
4-(N-ethyl-N-2-hydroxyethyl)-2-methyl-m-phenylene-diamine			0.20		
p-aminophenol				0.30	0.40
3-methyl-p-aminophenol	0.50	0.30			
1-[(2-hydroxy-5-amino) phenyl]-1,2-ethanediol			1.20		
p-phenylene-diamine	0.15		0.10		0.50
N,N-bis(2-hydroxyethyl)-p-phenylene-diamine		0.02			
1-(2,5-diaminophenyl)-1,2-ethanediol				0.1	

Water	qs to 100	qs to 100	qs to 100	qs to 100	qs to 100
Developer Used	2	3	4	5	5
Cumulative HLB Index	2.39	2.41	2.46	2.5	2.53
Color results on gray hair:	Dk burgundy	burgundy	Dk auburn	Auburn brn	Burgundy brn

	Example 11	**Example 12**	**Example 13**	**Example 14**	**Example 15**
Cocamidopropyl betaine	7.00				7.00
Cocamphocar-boxyglycinate		7.00		7.00	
Cocoamphodi-propionate			7.00		
Henna Powder	35.00	35.00	35.00	35.00	35.00
Lauric acid			5.00		
Octylpoly-glycoside	5.00			8.00	
Decylpoly-glysoside		8.00			8.00
Dodecylpoly-glycoside			5.00		
Ammonium hydroxide	5.00	5.00		5.00	
Monoethano-lamine			3.00		
Aminoethyl-propanol			3.00		
Sodium carbonate					2.50
Sodium bicarbonate					0.50
Sodium citrate					0.50
EDTA	0.10	0.10	0.10	0.10	0.10
Sodium sulfite	0.10	0.10	0.10	0.10	0.10
Fragrance	0.50	0.50	0.50	0.50	0.50
1-acetoxy-2-methyl-naphthalene	1.20			0.20	0.50
2-methyl-1-naphthol		0.20			
4-methoxy-2-methyl-1-naphthol			1.20		
Resorcinol	0.60			0.10	0.10
m-aminophenol		0.40			
3-amino-m-cresol			0.20		
p-aminophenol	1.00			0.30	0.40
3-methyl-p-aminophenol		0.30			
1-[(2-hydroxy-5-amino) phenyl]-1,2-ethanediol			1.20		
p-phenylene-diamine			0.10		0.50

N,N-bis(2-hydroxyethyl)-p-phenylenediamine	0.50	0.02			
1-(2,5-diamino-phenyl)-1,2-ethanediol				0.10	
Water	qs to 100	qs to 100	qs to 100	qs to 100	qs to 100
Developer Used	1	3	5	2	4
Cumulative HLB Index	2.36	2.41	2.5	2.37	2.49
Color results on gray hair:	Dk auburn	Brght Copper Brn	Auburn	Copper brn	Warm ash brn

	Example 16	Example 17	Example 18	Example 19	Example 20
Henna powder	26.00	26.00	27.00	26.00	25.00
Laureth-23			2.00	2.50	4.00
Soytrimonnium Chloride	1.00		2.00		2.00
Oleic acid	4.50	2.00	1.20	1.50	2.00
Decylpoly-glycoside	2.00	2.50		1.00	
Ammonium hydroxide (28%)	5.00		4.90	5.00	8.00
C18 Polycarbamyl Polyglycol					
Ester	1.20	1.50	1.00	1.30	1.10
Lauramide DEA			0.90	1.50	
Fragrance	0.20	0.50	0.24	0.10	0.30
Monoethanolamine		6.00			
p-Phenylenediamine	0.50	0.05			0.60
Resorcinol	0.45	0.40	0.80	1.10	0.35
N,N-bis(2-hydroxyethyl)-p-phenyl-enediamine	0.20	0.02			
1-(2,5-diaminophenyl)-1,2-ethanediol			1.40	1.30	
m-aminophenol		0.10	0.34	0.30	
m-phenylenediamine	0.20		0.10	0.20	
2-Methyl-1-Naphthol				0.50	0.70
3-Methyl-4-Aminophenol				0.80	0.90
Developer Used	7	7	7	7	6
Cumulative HLB Index	2.3	0.37	2.35	2.16	2.2
Color Result	Med Brown	Lt Blonde	Med Gold Brwn	Warm Brown	Rich Auburn

Table 23.5: Examples of Developers

	Example 1	Example 2	Example 3	Example 4	Example 5	Example 6	Example 7
Hydrogen peroxide	3.00	6.00	9.00	3.00	6.00	6.00	6.00
Acrylates Copolymer	1.50	1.50	2.50	1.00	3.50		
Acrylates/ steareth-20	1.50	1.50	1.50	5.00	3.50		
Methacrylate Copolymer							
EDTA	0.10	0.10	0.10	0.10	0.10		
Phosphoric acid	0.10	0.10	0.10	0.10	0.10	0.07	0.12
Nonoxynol-9						1.50	
Nonoxynol-4						1.00	
Oleth-4							2.20
Oleth-21							2.20
Water	93.80	90.80	86.80	90.80	86.80	91.43	89.48

BLONDE HENNA

Mixtures of Polymeric Dyes:

A dye emulsion, pH=10.5

Ingredient	w/w %
Henna powder	45
Cetearyl Alcohol	12.00
Ceteareth-20	4.50
Polysorbate 60	2.30
Glyceryl Stearate SE	2.00
Sorbitan Stearate	0.75
Oleth-5	1.25
Caprylic/Capric Triglyceride	0.50
Disodium EDTA	0.05
Monoethanolamine 99%	0.90
Ammonium Hydroxide 29%	6.60
Dihydroxypropyl PEG-5 Linoleammonium Chloride	0.50
Hydrolyzed Soy Protein 20%	0.50
Fragrance	0.50
Deionized Water 70° C.	ad 100.00

is mixed with 1.5 wt. % of a 9% hydrogen peroxide solution and the mixture is immediately applied to a tress of brown hair.

After 30 minutes the tress is rinsed, shampooed, rinsed and dried.

(2) A dye emulsion, pH=10.5

Ingredient	w/w %
Basic Blue 124	1
Cetearyl Alcohol	12.00
Henna Powder	34.50
Polysorbate 60	2.30
Glyceryl Stearate SE	2.00
Sorbitan Stearate	0.75
Oleth-5	1.25
Caprylic/Capric Triglyceride	0.50
Disodium EDTA	0.05
Monoethanolamine 99%	0.90
Ammonium Hydroxide 29%	6.60
Dihydroxypropyl PEG-5 Linoleammonium Chloride	0.50
Hydrolyzed Soy Protein 20%	0.50
Fragrance Drom 847 735 - Day at the Beach	0.50
Deionized Water 70° C.	ad 100.0

is mixed with 1.5 weight of 9% hydrogen peroxide solution and the mixture is immediately applied to a tress of **brown hair**. After 30 minutes the tress is rinsed, shampooed, rinsed and dried. The tress has been **dyed blue**.

Results:

Hair Type	Color	Intensity	Brilliance	Washing Fastness
Blond	Blue	good	good	3-4
Middle blond	Blue	good	good	3
Damaged	Blue	good	good	2-3

(3) A dye emulsion, containing 1% of the dye pH=9.8

Basic Blue 124	0.25
Basic Blue 151	0.25
Basic Red 51	0.25
Basic Red 76	0.25
Acid Red 52	0.01
Cetylstearylalcohol	11.00
Henna Dye	45.0

Oleic acid	2.5
Stearic acid monoethanolamide	2.5
Coco fatty acid monoethanolamide	2.5
Sodium laurylsulphate	1.7
1,2-Propanediol	1.0
Ammonium chloride	0.5
EDTA, Tetrasodium salt	0.2
Perfume	0.4
Cornproteinhydrolysate	0.2
Silica	0.1

is mixed with the same weight of 6% hydrogen peroxide solution and the mixture is immediately applied to a tress of **brown hair**. After 30 minutes the tress is rinsed, shampooed, rinsed and dried. The tress has been **dyed violet.**

(4) A dye emulsion containing

Cetearyl Alcohol	12.000
Ceteareth-25	5.000
Glyceryl Stearate SE	2.500
Glycol Distearate	0.500
Henna Powder	34.000
Cetearyl Ethylhexanoate	0.750
Deionized Water 70° C.	Ad 100
Disodium EDTA	0.050
Basic Blue 124	0.800
Basic Red 51	0.100
Monoethanolamine 99%	1 dro
Hydrolyzed Wheat Protein 20%	1.000
Monoethanolamine 99%	~0.900
Fragrance Drom 854 148 Linden Blossom	0.500
pH-Value: 6.02	

is applied for 30 minutes, at room temperature, to colored middle blond human hair, and rinsed. The result is a reddish blue dyeing with good fastnesses.

(5) 60 ml of part A, 60 ml of part B and 3 ml of part C are mixed in a mixing bowl or applicator bottle and the mixture is immediately applied to a tress of brown hair. After 30 minutes the tress is rinsed, shampooed, rinsed and dried. The tress has been dyed an intensive violet.

Shade: Pure Red

Ingredient	w/w %
Part A Deionized Water RT	20.00
Sodium Sulfite	0.60
Disodium EDTA	0.05
Cocamidopropyl Betaine 30%	4.00
Propylene Glycol	2.50
Monoethanolamine 99%	1.00
Toluene-2,5-Diamine Sulfate	0.25
p-Aminophenol	0.50
4-Amino-2-Hydroxytoluene	0.70
Henna powder	34.75
2-Amino-4-Hydroxyethyl AA Sulfate	0.10
Erythorbic Acid	0.40
Deionized Water RT	43.55
Hydroxyethylcellulose - Natrosol 250 HHR CG	0.75
Deionized Water RT	10.00
Isopropyl Alcohol	8.00
Oleth-10	1.00
Oleic Acid	1.10
Lactamide MEA	1.00
Fragrance Drom 837 375 Tropical Fever	0.50
Dihydroxypropyl PEG-5 Linoleammonium Chloride	0.50
Hydrolyzed Soy Protein	0.50
Monoethanolamine 99%	~2.50
Total:	100.00
Part B: Deionized Water RT	80.50
Developer Disodium Phosphate	0.15
6%	
Salcare SC80	5.00
Glycerin 99%	1.00
Sodium Laureth Sulfate 27%	1.00
Etidronic Acid 60%	~0.35
Hydrogen Peroxide 50%	12.00
Total:	100.00
Part C Deionized Water RT	99.00
Basic Blue 124	1.00
Total:	100.00

(6) A dye emulsion, containing 1% of Basic Blue 124 pH=10.5

Ingredient	w/w %
Cetearyl Alcohol	12.00
Henna Powder	40.50
Polysorbate 60	2.3
Glyceryl Stearate SE	2.00
Sorbitan Stearate	0.75
Oleth-5	1.25
Caprylic/Capric Triglyceride	0.50
Deionized Water 70° C.	66.65
Disodium EDTA	0.05
Monoethanolamine 99%	0.90
Ammonium Hydroxide 29%	6.60
Dihydroxypropyl PEG-5 Linoleammonium Chloride	0.50
Hydrolyzed Soy Protein 20%	0.50
Fragrance Drom 847 735 - Day at the Beach	0.50
Total	100.00

is mixed with 1.5 weight of 9% hydrogen peroxide solution and the mixture is immediately applied to a tress of brown hair. After 30 minutes the tress is rinsed, shampooed, rinsed and dried. The tress has been dyed an **intensive blue**.

(7) A dye emulsion, containing

0.1% Basic Blue 124 and

Ingredient	w/w %
Deionized Water RT	64.68
Acrylates/C10-30 Alkyl Acrylate Crosspolymer	0.55
Sodium Hydroxide 25%	0.03
DMDM Hydantoin	0.50
Sodium Cocoamphoacetate 32%	15.00
Ococamidopropyl Betaine 30%	3.00
Decyl Glucoside	3.00
Polyquaternium-7	0.50
PEG-15 Copolyamine	0.50
PEG-75 Lanolin	0.50
Deionized Water RT	10.00
Disodium EDTA	0.05

Basic Red 76	0.1
Basic Yellow 57	0.1
Henna Powder	35.00
PEG-40 Hydrogenated Castor Oil	0.95
Fragrance Drom 837 375 Tropical Fever	0.45
Citric Acid 25% Solution	~0.20
Total:	100.00

is applied for 30 min, at room temperature, to blond human hair, and rinsed.

The result is a very attractive vibrant violet dyeing with good fastnesses.

(8) A tress of gray hair is shampooed with a shampoo, containing

- 0.01% of Basic Blue 124 and

Ingredient	w/w %
Disodium PEG-5 Laurylcitrate Sulfosuccinate, Sodium	8.25%
Laureth Sulfate	
Sodium Cocoamphoacetate	20.9%
Methoxy PEG/PPG-7/3 Aminopropyl Dimethicone	0.5%
Hydroxypropyl Guar hydroxypropyltrimonium Chloride	0.3%
Henna powder	30.5%
Cocoate	
PEG-150 Distearate	0.5%
Citric Acid (30%)	2.2%
Perfume; Preservatives	q.s.
Water	Ad 100%

After 5 minutes the tress is rinsed and dried. The tress has been more **brilliant less yellowish.**

(9) A tress of gray hair is shampooed with a shampoo, containing

Ingredient	w/w %
Disodium PEG-5 Laurylcitrate Sulfosuccinate, Sodium	8.25%
Laureth Sulfate	
Sodium Cocoamphoacetate	20.9%
Methoxy PEG/PPG-7/3 Aminopropyl Dimethicone	0.5%
Hydroxypropyl Guar hydroxypropyltrimonium Chloride	0.3%
Henna Powder	40.0%
Cocoate	
PEG-150 Distearate	0.5%

Basic Blue 124	0.01
Basic Red 76	0.05
Citric Acid (30%)	2.2%
Perfume; Preservatives	q.s.
Water	Ad 100%

The tress has been more **brilliant violet.**

(10) A tress of gray hair is shampooed with a shampoo, containing

Ingredient	w/w %
Water	87.5
Hydroxyethylcellulose	2.5
Plantacare 50%	10.0
Sodium hydroxide 50%	0.17
Sodium hydroxide 0.1M	0.77
Henna Powder	15.0
Basic Blue 124	0.013
Basic Yellow 87	0.06
Citric Acid (50%)	0.35
Perfume; Preservatives	q.s.
pH Approx. 6.0	

The tress has been dyed middle brown with a medium gray coverage.

(11)

Ingredient	w/w %
Cetyl Alcohol	3.00%
Henna Powder	50.50%
Behentrimmonium Chloride	1.00%
Quaternium-80	0.50%
Citric Acid	Ad pH = 5
Dimethicone	0.9
Phenyltrimethicone, Silicone Quaternium-15,	2.5
Laureth-4 (Polysil 1849)	
Polysilicone-15	0.8
Basic Blue 124	0.1
Basic Blue 151	0.1
Basic Blue 99	1.0
Basic Brown 17	0.9

Basic Yellow 57	0.4
Basic Brown 16	0.9
Perfumes; Preservatives	q.s.
Water	Ad 100%

is applied to a tress of shampooed gray hair. After 5 min the tress is rinsed and dried. The tress has been **dyed dark brown.**

(12)

Ingredient	w/w %
Cetyl stearyl Alcohol	5.0
1,2-Propandiol	1.5
Behentrimmonium Chloride	2.0
Di-C12-C15-alkyldimoniumchlorid	1.0
Cocoamidopropylbetaine	1.0
Sodium cocoamphoacetate	0.5
Henna extract	45.0
Silicon oil	0.5
Basic Blue 124	0.1
Basic Red 76	0.1
Basic Blue 99	0.1
Basic Brown 17	0.1
Basic Yellow 57	0.1
Basic Brown 16	0.1
Perfumes; Preservatives	q.s.
Water	Ad 100%

is applied to a tress of shampooed middle blonde hair. After 5 min the tress is rinsed and dried. The tress has been dyed evenly brown.

(13)

Ingredient	w/w %
Hydroxyethylcellulose	1.00
Cetylstearylalcohol	1.25
1,2-Propandiol	3.00
Cetyltrimethylamonium Chloride	0.2
Dicetyldimethylamonium Chloride	0.30
Henna extract	45.0
Polyquaternium-10	
Laurylhydroxysultain	1.0

Camoille extract	0.5
Citric acid	0.5
Basic Blue 124	0.1
Basic Red 76	0.1
Perfumes; Preservatives	q.s.
Water	Ad 100%

is applied to a tress of shampooed blonde hair. After 5 min the tress is rinsed and dried. The tress has been dyed evenly violet.

(14)

Ingredient	w/w %
Cetyl stearyl Alcohol	5.0
Di-C12-C15-alkyldimoniumchlorid	2.0
1,2-Propandiol	1.5
Ceteareth-20	1.0
Sodium cocoamphoacetate	1.3
Henna Extract	45.0
Basic Red 76	0.1
Basic Blue 99	0.1
Basic Brown 17	0.1
Basic Yellow 57	0.1
Basic Brown 16	0.1
Methylparaben	0.2
Perfume	0.3
Water	Ad 100%

is applied to a tress of shampooed middle blonde hair. After 5 min the tress is rinsed and dried. The tress has been dyed evenly brown.

(15)

Ingredient	w/w %
Cetyl stearyl Alcohol	5.0
Di-C12-C15-alkyldimoniumchlorid	2.0
1,2-Propandiol	1.5
Henna extract	36.80
Sodium cocoamphoacetate	1.3
Basic Blue 124	0.15
Basic Red 76	0.01
Basic Brown 17	0.8

Basic Yellow 57	0.3
Basic Brown 16	0.8
Methylparaben	0.2
Perfume	0.3.
Water	Ad 100%

is applied to a tress of shampooed middle blonde hair. After 5 min the tress is rinsed and dried. The tress has been dyed evenly dark brown.

(16)

Ingredient	w/w %
Cocoamidopropylbetaine	1.0
Henna extract	35.0
Cetyl stearyl Alcohol	1.0
Dioleoylhydroxyethylmoniummethosulfate	2.0
Benzophenone-4	0.5
Perfume	0.2
Methylparaben	0.2
Pyrrolidoncarboxylic acid	0.1
Basic Blue 124	0.1
Basic Red 76	0.1
Basic Blue 99	0.1
Basic Brown 17	0.1
Basic Yellow 57	0.1
Basic Brown 16	0.1
Basic Red 51	0.1
Basic Yellow 87	0.1
Basic Orange 31	0.1
Citric acid	0.1
Water	Ad 100%

is applied to a tress of shampooed middle blonde hair. After 5 min the tress is rinsed and dried. The tress has been dyed evenly brown.

(17)

Ingredient	w/w %
Cetyl stearyl Alcohol	3.0
Hydroxyethylcellulose	1.00
Henna Extract	43.0
Cetrimonium chloride	2.0

Benzophenone-9	0.5
Panthenol	0.1
Hops extract	0.1
Basic Blue 124	0.1
Basic Yellow 57	0.1
Perfumes; Preservatives	q.s.
Water	Ad 100%

is applied to a tress of shampooed bleached hair. After 5 min the tress is rinsed and dried. The tress has been dyed evenly green.

(18)

Ingredient	w/w %
Ethanol	12.3
Monoethanolamine	0.2
Octyldodecanol	5.0
Ammonium laurylsulphate	2.0
Cocamidopropyl Betaine	12.0
Disodium EDTA	0.1
Henna extract	42.0
Basic Red 51	0.015
Basic Yellow 87	0.060
Basic Orange 31	0.001
Perfumes	0.5
Preservatives	q.s.
Water	Ad 100%
Propane/Butane	10

is applied to a tress of shampooed bleached hair. After 15 min the tress is rinsed and dried. The tress has been dyed brown.

CHESTNUT BROWN HENNA

	% by weight
Cetearyl alcohol	10.0
Cocamide MEA	4.0
Sodium lauryl sulphate	1.5
Propylene glycol	2.0
Allantoin	0.8
Henna extract	45.0

2,5-Diaminotoluolsulfat	0.55
4-Chlorresorcin	0.17
Resorcin	0.05
3-Aminophenol	0.03
Sodium sulfite	1.0
Monoethanolamine	8.0
Fragrance, preservative	q.s.
Water	to 100

(2)

	% by weight
Cetearyl alcohol	8.0
Cocamide MEA	2.0
Sodium lauryl sulphate	1.5
Propylene glycol	2.0
Henna extract*	45.0
2,5,6-Triamino-4-hydroxypyrimidinsulfat	0.01
2,5-Diaminotoluolsulfat	0.55
4-Chlorresorcin	0.17
Resorcin	0.05
3-Aminophenol	0.03
Sodium sulfite	1.0
Monoethanolamine	8.0
Fragrance, preservative	q.s.
Water	to 100

(3)

1. Dye Solutions

Inventive dye	Non-inventive dye		
	Raw material	solution F1	solution F2
Plantacare	® 818 UP	25.00	20.00
Dehyton	® K	—	26.00
Genagen	® KB	30.00	—
Henna Extract	30.00	30.00	
Tetrasodium EDTA	0.20	0.20	
p-Toluylenediamine sulfate	2.31	2.31	

2-Amino-4-(2-hydroxyethyl) aminoanisole sulfate	0.03	0.03	
Resorcinol	0.89	0.89	
m-Aminophenol	0.26	0.26	
Sodium sulfite	0.20	0.20	
Ascorbic acid	0.05	0.05	
Monoethanolamine	10.00	10.00	
Eau Vitale d'algue bleue	®	2.0	2.0
Perfume	qs	qs	
Water	ad 100	ad 100	

2. Developer Preparations

Raw material	E1	E1-DK	
Dipicolinic acid	0.10	0.10	
Disodium pyrophosphate	0.03	0.03	
Aculyn	®33A	2.50	2.50
Texapon	® NSO	2.00	2.00
Cremophor	®CO60		2.00
Eumulgin	®L		0.40
Sodium hydroxide (aqueous 45% conc.)	0.73		
Turpinal	®SL	1.50	1.50
Hydrogen peroxide (aqueous, 50% conc.)	15.20	15.20	
Water	ad 100	ad 100	

GOLDEN BROWN

The following hair dye composition was prepared.

Ingredient Percent by Weight

sodium cocomethyl tauride 12.50 lauricdiethanolamide 7.00 lauryl alcohol 0.95 hexylene glycol 3.00 reaction product of polyethylenimine (m.w. 1833) and 1-chloroanthraquinone(10% substitution) 1.39 Henna extract 45.0water q.s. to 100.00 pH 9.38

The dyeing properties of the above composition were evaluated by saturating a tress of bleached and waved human hair at a bath to hair ratio of 2:1 and allowing it to remain on the hair for approximately 15 minutes to simulate a color shampoo application. The hair was then water rinsed and air dried producing a pale red/golden brown coloration

DARK BROWN

Example 1: Synthesis of 4-{2-{(*E*)-[4-(diethylamino)phenyl]diazenyl}-5-[(1,3-dioxo-1,3-dihydro-2*H*-inden-2-ylidene)methyl]-1,3-thiazol-4-yl}-1,1-dimethylpiperazin-1-ium methylsulfate.

Step 1: Synthesis of 2-{[2-{(*E*)-[4-(diethylamino)phenyl]diazenyl}-4-(4-methyl-1-piperazinyl)-1,3-thiazol-5-yl]methylene}-1*H*-indene-1,3(2*H*)-dione.

1.00 g (2.20 mmol) 2-[(4-chloro-2-{(*E*)-[4-(diethylamino)phenyl]diazenyl}-1,3-thiazol-5-yl) methylene]-1*H*-indene-1,3(2*H*)-dione and 0.30 g (2.70 mmol) 1-methylpiperazine were dissolved in 40 ml tetrahydrofurane (THF) and heated under stirring for 5 hours when thin layer chromatography (TLC) analysis indicated complete consumption of the starting material. After cooling to room temperature the formed precipitate was filtered off, washed with THF and dried in vacuum at 40 °C to obtain a dark green powder.

Yield: 0.95 g (84%).

Step 2: Synthesis of 4-{2-{(*E*)-[4-(diethylamino)phenyl]diazenyl}-5-[(1,3-dioxo-1,3-dihydro-2*H*-inden-2-ylidene)methyl]-1,3-thiazol-4-yl}-1,1-dimethylpiperazin-1-ium methylsulfate.

0.93 g (1.80 mmol) 2-{[2-{(*E*)-[4-(diethylamino)phenyl]diazenyl}-4-(4-methyl-1-piperazinyl)-1,3-thiazol-5-yl]methylene}-1*H*-indene-1,3(2*H*)-dione was dissolved in 20 ml acetonitrile. After addition of 0.5 g (3.70 mmol) dimethylsulfate, the mixture was heated under reflux for 24 hours. After cooling to room temperature the formed precipitate was filtered off and dried in vacuum at 40 °C to obtain a dark green solid.

Yield: 0.85 g (74%).

Example 2: Synthesis of2-[{4-[(4-chloro-5-formyl-1,3-thiazol-2-yl)diazenyl] phenyl}(ethyl)amino]ethyl hydrogen sulfate.

Step 1: Synthesis of 4-chloro-2-((*E*)-{4-[ethyl(2-hydroxyethyl) amino[phenyl}-diazenyl)-1,3-thiazole-5-carbaldehyde.

1.3 g (18.56 mmol) sodium nitrite was added in small portions to 13.2 g conc. sulphuric acid and cooled to 0 °C and diluted with 4.8 ml propionic acid and 19.2 ml acetic acid. 3.0 g (18.45 mmol) 2-amino-4-chloro-1,3-thiazole-5-carbaldehyde were then added in small portions. The viscous reaction mixture was stirred for 2 hours at 0 °C. This mixture was then added slowly to a solution of 3.2 g (18.56 mmol) 2-[ethyl(phenyl)amino]ethanol in 180 ml water, containing 6 ml sulphuric acid. After stirring for another 2 hours at room temperature, the obtained precipitate was filtered off, washed with water and dried at 40 °C in vacuum.

Yield: 3.58 g (57%)

Step 2: Synthesis of 2-{4-[(4-chloro-5-formyl-1,3-thiazol-2-yl)diazenyl] phenyl}(ethyl)aminolethyl hydrogen sulfate.

0.8 g (2.36 mmol) 4-chloro-2-((*E*)-{4-[ethyl(2-hydroxyethyl)amino]phenyl}-diazenyl)-1,3-thiazole-5-carbaldehyde were dissolved in 35 ml THF and cooled to 0 °C. Then 0.28 g (2.36 mmol) chlorosulfonic acid were added slowly drop by drop with stirring. After the addition was completed, the reaction mixture was heated under reflux for 4 hours, allowed to cool to room temperature and stirred overnight. After further cooling in an ice bath the formed precipitate was filtered off, washed with a little cold THF and dried at 40 °C in vacuum.

Yield: 1.05 g (100%, containing traces of crystal water).

Example 3: Synthesis of 2-[{4-[(*E*)-{4-chloro-5-[(1,3-dioxo-1,3-dihydro-2*H*-inden-2-ylidene)methyl]-1,3-thiazo 1-2-yl}diazenyl]phenyl}(ethyl)amino] ethyl hydrogen sulfate.

Step 1: Synthesis of 2-{[4-chloro-2-((*E*)-14-[ethyl(2-hydroxyethyl)aminol-12henyl}diazenyl)-1,3-thiazol-5-yl]methylidene}-1*H*-indene-1,3(2*H*)-dione.

3.5 g (10.33 mmol) 4-chloro-2-((*E*)-{4-[ethyl(2-hydroxyethyl)amino]phenyl}-diazenyl)-1,3-thiazole-5-carbaldehyde and 2.33 g (15.50 mmol) 1*H*-indene-1,3(2*H*)-dione were dissolved in 90 ml ethanole and stirred under reflux. After 6 hours the mixture was allowed to cool to room temperature. The formed precipitate was filtered, washed with ethanol and dried in vacuum at 40 °C to obtain a dark powder.

Yield: 3.93 g (82%).

Step 2: Synthesis of 2-[{4-[(*E*)-{4-chloro-5-[(1,3-dioxo-1,3-dihydro-2*H*-inden-2-ylidene)methyl]-1,3-thiazol-2-yl}diazenyl]phenyl}(ethyl)amino]ethyl hydrogen sulfate.

0.5 g (1.07 mmol) 2-{[4-chloro-2-((*E*)-{4-[ethyl(2-hydroxyethyl)amino]-phenyl}-diazenyl)-1,3-thiazol-5-yl]methylidene}-1*H*-indene-1,3(2*H*)-dione were dissolved in 50 ml THF and cooled to 0 °C. Then 0.19 g (1.60 mmol) chlorosulfonic acid were added slowly drop by drop with stirring. After the addition was completed, the reaction mixture was heated under reflux for 4 hours, allowed to cool to room temperature and stirred overnight. After further cooling in an ice bath the formed precipitate was filtered off, washed with a little cold THF and dried at 40 °C in vacuum.

Yield: 0.53 g (90%).

Example 4: Synthesis of 2-[{4-[(*E*)-{5-[(1,3-dioxo-1,3-dihydro-2*H*-inden-2-ylidene)methyl]-4-(1-piperidinyl)-1,3-thiazol-2-yl} diazenyl]phenyl} (ethyl) amino]ethyl hydrogen sulfate.

Step 1: Synthesis of 2-{[2-((*E*)-{4-[ethyl(2-hydroxyethyl)aminol]phenyl}-diazenyl)-4-(1-piperidinyl)-1,3-thiazol-5-yl]methylene}-1*H*-indene-1,3(2*H*)-dione.

0.5 g (1.07 mmol) 2-{[4-chloro-2-((*E*)-{4-[ethyl(2-hydroxyethyl)amino] phenyl}-diazenyl)-1,3-thiazol-5-yl]methylene}-1*H*-indene-1,3(2*H*)-dione were dissolved in 20 ml THF. Then 0.2 g (2.14 mmol) piperidine were added dropwise and the mixture was stirred under reflux for 6 hours. After cooling to room temperature, stirring was continued overnight. The formed piperidine hydrochloric salt was separated by filtration and the solvent removed with a rotary evaporator. The resulting precipitate containing the crude product was recrystallized with toluene to obtain a dark powder.

Yield: 0.36 g (66%).

Step 2: Synthesis of 2-[{4-[(*E*)-{5-[(1,3-dioxo-1,3-dihydro-2*H*-inden-2-ylidene)methyl]-4-(1-piperidinyl)-1,3-thiazol-2-yl}-diazenyl]phenyl}(ethyl) amino]ethyl hydrogen sulfate.

0.32 g (0.62 mmol) 2-{[2-((*E*)-{4-[ethyl(2-hydroxyethyl)amino]phenyl}-diazenyl)-4-(1-piperidinyl)-1,3-thiazol-5-yl]methylene}-1*H*-indene-1,3(2*H*)-dione were dissolved in 33 ml THF and cooled to 0 °C. Then 0.11 g (0.93 mmol) chlorosulfonic acid were added slowly drop by drop with stirring. After the addition was completed, the reaction mixture was heated under reflux for 4 hours, allowed to cool to room temperature and stirred overnight. After further cooling in an ice bath the formed precipitate was filtered off, washed with a little cold THF and dried at 40 °C in vacuum.

Yield: 0.10 g (27%).

Example 5: Hair Colourant

2.5 mmol	dye according to formula (I)
Henna extract 5.0 g	50.0 ethanol
4.0 g	decylpolyglucose
0.2 g	ethylenediaminotetraacetic acid disodium salt hydrate
ad 100.0 g	water, demineralized

Examples 6 to 8:

2.5 mmol	dye according to formula (II)
Henna powder 50.00.2 g	1-hydroxyethane-1,1-diphosphone acid tetrasodium salt
1.3 g	citric acid
25.0 g	ethanol
10.0 g	1,2-propanediol
9.0 g	benzylalcohol
0.5 g	vinylpyrrolidone/vinylacetate copolymer
0.4 g	acrylic acid polymer crosslinked with a polyfunctional agent
ad 100.0 g	water, demineralized

The hair colouring for examples 5 to 8 is carried out by applying an amount of the colourant sufficient for the hair colouring to the hair and distributing it evenly using a brush. After a contact time of 30 minutes at 40 °C, the hair is rinsed with lukewarm water, washed with a shampoo, rinsed with lukewarm water and then dried.

In addition the dye of example 5 was also treated in the presence of hydrogen peroxide as an oxidizing agent at a basic and a neutral pH. For the second treatment 5 g of the above colour carrier mass according to example 5 were mixed with 5 g of a 6% strength hydrogen peroxide solution. For the third treatment, the pH was adjusted to a basic pH of 9 by using 25% strength ammonia. The colouring results are summarized in Table 23.1 below.

Table 23.6

Example No.	Compound of the formulas (I)/(II) as in example 5-8	Colour shade after colouring	Colour measurement values after colouring
5	4-{2-{(*E*)-[4-(diethylamino)-	iron grey (without	L: 34.37
	phenyl]diazenyl}-5-[(1,3-	hydrogen peroxide)	a: - 0.10
	dioxo-1,3-dihydro-2*H*-inden-2-ylidene)methyl]-1,3-		b: - 9.04
	thiazol-4-yl}-1,1-	iron grey (with	L: 38.23
	dimethylpiperazin-1-ium	hydrogen peroxide,	a: + 0.43
	methylsulfate	pH=7)	b: - 9.99
		pale grey (with	L: 50.89
		hydrogen peroxide,	a: + 4.83
		pH= 9)	b: + 2.49
6	2-[{4-[(*E*)-(4-chloro-5-	intense dark blue	L: 16.71
	formyl-1,3-thiazol-2-		a: + 7.41
	yl)diazenyl]phenyl} (ethyl)-amino] ethyl hydrogen sulfate		b: - 10.10
7	2-[{4-[(*E*)-{4-chloro-5-[(1,3-	steel blue	L: 30.07
	dioxo-1,3-dihydro-2*H*-inden-		a: +4.41
	2-ylidene)methyl]-1,3-thiazol-2-yl} diazenyl]phenyl} (ethyl)-amino] ethyl hydrogen sulfate		b: - 23.16
8	2-[{4-[(*E*)-{5-[(1,3-dioxo-1,3-	black	L: 18.50
	dihydro-2*H*-inden-2-		a: -0.03
	ylidene)methyl]-4-(1-		b: -0.78

piperidinyl)-1,3-thiazol-2-yl}diazenyl]phenyl}(ethyl)-amino]ethyl hydrogen sulfate

Unless otherwise indicated, all percentages in the present patent application are by weight.

LIGHT BROWN

Ingredient	w/w %
Cetearyl Alcohol	12.00
Ceteareth-20	4.50
Polysorbate 60	2.30
Glyceryl Stearate SE	2.00
Sorbitan Stearate	0.75
Henna extract	45.00
Caprylic/Capric Triglyceride	0.50
Disodium EDTA	0.05
Monoethanolamine 99%	0.90
Ammonium Hydroxide 29%	6.60
Dihydroxypropyl PEG-5 Linoleammonium Chloride	0.50
Hydrolyzed Soy Protein 20%	0.50
Fragrance Drom 847 735 - Day at the Beach	0.50
Deionized Water 70° C.	ad 100.00

is mixed with 1.5 wt. % of a 9% hydrogen peroxide solution and the mixture is immediately applied to a tress of **light brown hair.**

After 30 minutes the tress is rinsed, shampooed, rinsed and dried.

Best Formulation of Black Dye

Henna

Amla

Shikakai

Barium Peroxide

Magnesium Carbonate

Henna

Pure henna is a green plant *(Lawsonia inermis)* and the green leaves are dried, crushed and powdered. When used alone it will turn the hair an orange-red color. If it is properly used with pure indigo, the hair will dye to black.

Lawsone is a constituent of primary glycosides in henna leaves called hennosides A, B, and C and can be obtained from them after degradation and autoxidation. Lawsone, a quinone, dissolves rapidly in alkaline, aqueous solutions to produce an orange-red color. Dried powdered leaves of henna contain approximately 0.5 to 1.5 percent lawsone.

SHIKAKAI

Overview

Shikakai has been used for hair cleansing in India for centuries. The word 'shikakai' means "fruit for hair" and is a traditional variety of shampoo.

Shikakai acts as an natural astringent for hair enhancing as it consists binding properties. It clears dandruff and cleans the dirt accumulated on the scalp. Being a natural conditioner for hair, it strengthens hair roots and promotes luxuriant growth. The powder/the extract has certain vital properties that act as coolants for the scalp. This powder has to be mixed with water and used as a paste on the hair instead of shampoo.

Description

Shikakai is a prickly, scandent shrub, growing in tropical jungles shrub throughout India, particularly in Deccan. The scientific name/Latin name of shikakai is Acacia concinna. It belongs to the Leguminosae family.The leaves of this woody plant are bipinnate. It has yellow flowers with anxillary heads. The pods are brown, wrinkled and notched when dry. There are 6 to 10 seeds in a pod usually. These days it is commercially cultivated in India and Far East Asia.

Usage

- The powder or the extract from the bark, leaves or pods is used as a hair cleansing agent. It is very effective in removing oil and dirt from hair. The normal practice is to apply oil to hair and scalp and allow it soak for sometime. This will keep the body cool, reducing body heat and also prevent the scalp from getting dry. The powdered shikakai is used as a shampoo to wash off the oil.

- Since shikakai is naturally low in pH, therefore it is extremely mild, and does not strip hair of its natural oils. Usually no rinse or conditioner is used since shikakai also helps in the disentangling of the hair
- Actually the bark of shikakai is high on saponins - chemical compound; these act as foaming agents. Therefore shikakai is such a good cleaning agent and hence has been traditionally used as a detergent. Owing to the presence of this chemical compound shikakai is used in Bengal for poisoning fish and are documented to be potent marine toxins.

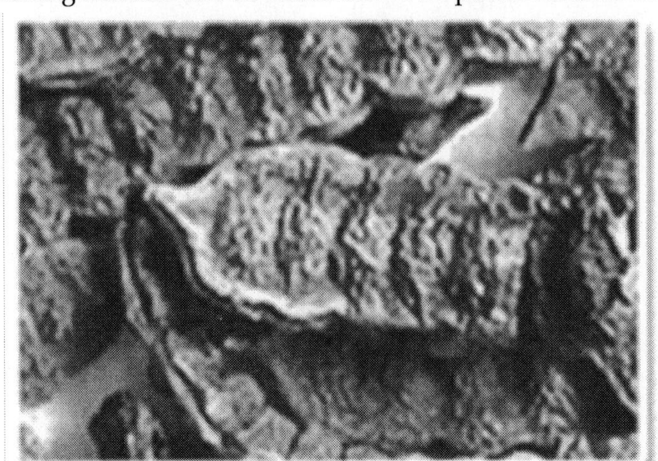

- The leaves because of the presence of oxalic, tartaric, citric, succinic and ascorbic acids, as well as two alkaloids, calyctomine and nicotine, taste acidic and are used in chutneys. Apart from this the leaves are also used as an infusion in anti-dandruff preparations.
- Extracts of the ground pods have been used for various skin diseases.
- An extract of the shikakai leaves is used to cure malarial fever.
- A decoction of the pods relieves biliousness and acts as a purgative.

Barium Peroxide

Barium peroxide is the inorganic compound with the formula BaO_2. This white solid (gray when impure) is one of the most common inorganic peroxides, and it was the first peroxide compound discovered. Being an oxidizer and giving a vivid green colour upon ignition; historically, it was also used as a precursor for hydrogen peroxide which is a strong bleaching agent.

Magnesium Carbonate

Metal Salt Dyes and Metal Compounds Metal salt dyes are usually composed of a solution of metal salt with thiosulfate. The metal salt dyes are called progressive dyes or color restorers, because each subsequent application increases the coating on the hair and it becomes progressively darker. These metallic dyes have a tendency to fade into peculiar colors. Those that contain lead turn purple. The dyes containing silver turn green, and those containing copper turn red. There are some disadvantages of metallic salt dyes. There are relatively few shades of metallic hair dyes available limited by the properties of metal salts. However, the degree of color can be regulated by the frequency of application. The more frequent the application, correspondingly the stronger the color. These dyes tend to produce quite dark and intense colors with frequent use. Metallic salt dyes can interfere with permanent waving they can and will cause a chemical reaction this can result in a heat reaction in some cases hair can dissolve or melt, so there are restrictions on using these dyes along with other forms of hair processing.

24

Chemical Investigation of *Lawsonia inermis* Leaves

INTRODUCTION

L awsonia inermis Linn (Henna) belongs to the family Lythreaceae and the sole member of its genus *Lawsonia.* It is glabrous branched shrub or small tree (2 to 6 m in height). The leaves are small, sub-sessile and greenish brown to dull green in color, and have either a glabrous, obtuse or acute apex with a tapering base. Flowers are small of redor rose color. Henna can only grow where minimum temperatures stay above 11 °C. It tolerates extreme heat and long droughts. *Lawsonia inermis Linn (L. inermis)* grows wild near desert oasis, and in semiarid regions. It thrives in alluvial soils, where there is annual precipitation of 0.2 to 0.4 m and a soil p^H of 4.3 to 8.0. *L. inermis Linn* is a perennial shrub native to North Africa, Asia and Australia and it is naturalized and cultivated in the tropics of America, Egypt, India and parts of the Middle East. It is commonly known as henna in Arabic and mehndi in Hindi. Also known as Ei-Henna, Egyptian priest, and mignonette tree. The species is sometimes classified as La Sonia alba Lam or *Lawsonia reba* reaching a height of up to 6 m and has fragrant white or rose-red flowers.

L. inermis Linn is one such plant known since with healing attributes and is now the subject of intense scientific study. The leaves are used in the treatments of wounds, ulcers, cough, bronchitis, lumbago, rheumatagia, inflammations, diarrhoea, dysentry, leucoderma, scabies, boils, anaemia, haemorrhages, fever, falling of hair and greyness hair.

L. inermis Linn is a worldwide known cosmetic agent used to stain hair, skin and nails. The plant leaf contains a red-orange color component, lawsone (2-hydroxy-1, 4-napthoquinone), which is also known as hennotannic acid. Soil and moisture affects henna's Lawsone levels. Dry, hot, iron bearing soils produce henna with high Lawsone levels. Moist fertile soils produce henna with lower level of Lawsone. Lawsone is the chief constituent responsible for the dying properties of the plant. Dried powdered leaves of henna contain about 0.5-1.5% lawsone, traditionally used to produce color fast orange, red and brown dyes. In Ethiopia, *L. inermi Linn* is traditionally used to develop a red or black coloring to hands, feet and hair in some occasions such as weddings and religious festivals. Although, numerous researchers have reported the antimicrobial activity and chemical composition of *L. inermis* grown worldwide, there was no previous report on chemical studies of *L. inermis Linn* species which grown in Ethiopia. The paucity of chemical data of Ethiopian *L. inermis Linn* promoted into an investigation. Therefore, the aim of this study was to investigate the chemical composition of *L. inermis Linn* leaves by using GC-MS and NMR spectroscopic methods.

EXPERIMENTAL

Plant Collection and Identification

Matured leaves of L. inermis Linn were collected from the trees growing around Asayta distinct, Afar region, North Eastern Ethiopia. The plant was identified by Mr. Abdurasek Abdulahi, department of plant science; college of Agriculture, Haramaya University and deposited in the Herbarium of the University for future reference with suitable herbarium specimen code.

Extraction of Essential Oil

The leaves were separated from the stalks thoroughly washed with tap water and rinsed with distilled water. The cleaned leaves were dried in a shady and aerated at room temperature until the weight was stable. The air dried leaves were powdered into small pieces using analytical mill. A 300 g of the leaves powder were hydrodistilled for 3 h using Clevenger's (Bibby Sterilin Ltd, Quickfit, England) to give a mixture of oil and aqueous[13]. The distillate was poured in to a separatory funnel contained 100 mL of chloroform (99.96%, Analytical reagent, Fisher Scientific UK Limited). The lower phase that contains the essential oil was separated from the upper one by using separatory funnel. Rotary evaporator was used to remove the solvent from the extract at 35 °C temperature and under reduced pressure. The oil collected was dried on anhydrous sodium sulphate, weighed to yield 0.3% (w/w) of yellowish volatile oil with characteristic smell and stored at low temperature (4 °C) until analysis.

GC and GC-MS Analysis of the Essential Oils

GC-MS analysis was performed using a Clarus 600 GC-MS fitted with a HP-5MS capillary column (30 m × 0.25 mm coated with 5% phenyl methylsiloxane, film thickness 0.25 μm). The GC oven temperature was programmed from 50 °C –250 °C at a rate of 5 °C/min. The injector and detector temperature was maintained at 250 °C. Helium was used as the carrier gas at a flow rate of 1 mL/min. The mass spectrometer was operated at electrum impact of 70 eV with ion source temperature of 230 °C. The constituents of the leaf were identified by comparing of their mass fragmentation (MS) patterns with those gathered in the library of NIST-MS and with those reported in the literature.

Extraction and Isolation of the Compound

A 400 g of the air-dried leaves were pulverized and extracted three times with *n*-hexane (ACS grade, Northampton, U.K) for 24 h. it was then filtered and concentrated to dryness under reduced pressure to give 12 g of the crude extract. The hexane extract (10 g) was applied on the top of the column chromatography (5 × 60 cm, Quickfit, England) by adsorbing on silica gel which was previously packed column with silica gel S (60 g, 63-200 μm, 70-230 mesh ASTM, Riedel-deHaen, Germany) in *n*-hexane and purified by increasing n-hexane /ethyl acetate (ACS grade, Northampton, U.K) solvent mixtures. Each fraction was then concentrated using a rotary evaporator under reduced pressure and temperature. The purity of different fractions was analyzed by TLC (pre-coated PLC plates, Al_2O_3 150 F-254, 20×20 size, layer thickness 1.5 mm, glass support, Merck, Darmstadt ,Germany) and spots were visualized by exposing under UV light (254 nm and 365) and spraying with H_2SO_4. Fraction 1 revealed the presence of two spots. They were not further investigated due to poor yield. Fraction 2 and 3 afforded compound LL*A1 (120 mg). The isolated compounds were then carefully dried in a freeze-drier and weighed.

Analysis of the Isolated Compound

NMR spectra were recorded on a Bruker Advance instrument (400 MHz and 100 MHz) and with TMS as an internal standard (chemical shifts in ä, ppm). The isolated compound was dissolved in $CDCl_3$ and analyzed with One-dimensional NMR (proton ^1H, carbon ^{13}C) and two-dimensional NMR measurements (including COSY, HSQC, and HMBC) were performed in order to identify the compounds. At least 10 mg of the pure compound was required for structural elucidation.

RESULTS AND DISCUSSION

Essential Oil Composition

The GC-MS analysis revealed that the presence of at least twenty eight of components in L. inermis Linn leaves. Nine compounds were indentified; representing 80.6% of the total oil (Table 24.1). The major constituents are listed in order of their elution from a HP-5MS capillary column as shown in Figure 24.1 and Table 24.1. The constituents of the oil were eugenol (17.6%), hexadecanoic acid (15.1%), Phytol (10.2%), α-terpineol (8.4%) and Etherphenylvinyl (6.7%). Of these major constituents, eugenol, hexadecanoic acid, phytol and α-terpineol are relatively common for essential oils of higher plants. In the earlier report, from the essential of *L. inermis* Linn leaves, α-terpineol and Phytol were reported as the major constituents. It is necessary to point out that the chemical compounds of any plant essential oil can vary greatly depending upon geographical region, the age of the plant, local climate, seasonal variations, experimental conditions and genetic difference are responsible for the changes in the types of chemical compounds.

Table 24.1: Chemical Composition of the Essential Oil of Leaves of *L. inermis Linn*

Retention time (min)	Compound*	Composition (%)
7.56	Linalool[M]	4.23
10.48	a-terpineol[M]	8.36
11.42	Etherphenylvinyl[A]	6.72
15.32	1,3-indandione[A]	6.60
15.91	Eugenol[A]	17.61
21.04	Cis-hexahydro-8a-methyl1, 8-[2H,8H]-naphthalenedioneĸ	5.60
29.23	Oxirane-tetradecyl[E]	6.20
32.53	Hexadecanoic acid[F]	6.20
32.53	Hexadecanoic acid[F]	15.07
35.99	Phytol[D]	10.17

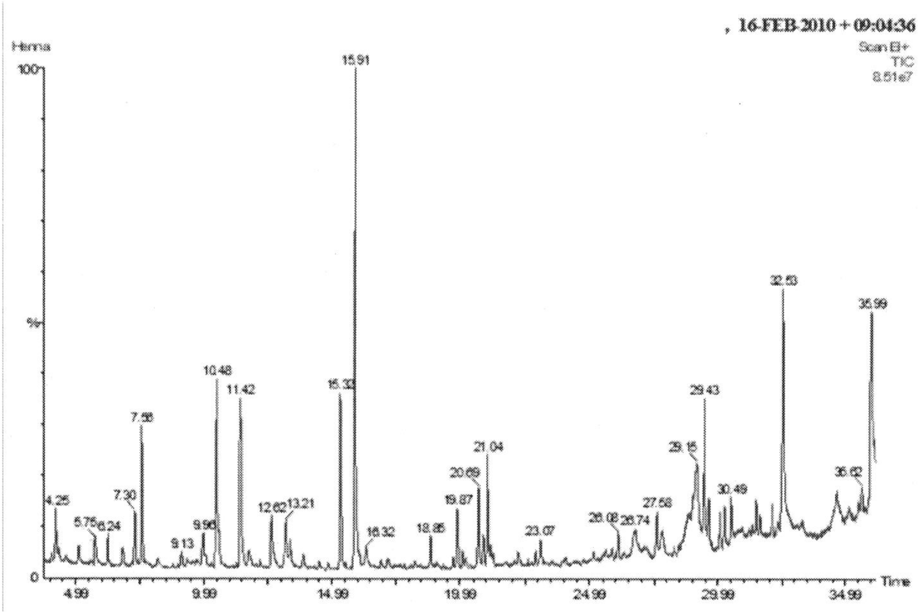

Fig. 24.1: GC of the leaf essential of *L. inermis Linn*

Structure Elucidation

The leaves of *L. inermis Linn* were extracted with n- hexane at room temperature followed separation by column chromatography using n-hexane-ethyl acetate solvent system which led to isolation and structure elucidation of one compound labeled as LL*A1. TLC analysis of n-hexane extract using hexane/ ethyl acetate (7:3) solvent system revealed the presence of four major spots. The compound (LL*A1) was fully characterized using NMR techniques. The

^{1}H-NMR spectrum depicts two clearly separated regions, one in the olefin region from δ 5.1 to 5.2 and the other in the aliphatic region from δ 1.6 to 2.2.

There are three protons in the region from δ 5.1 to 5.2. The ^{1}H -NMR spectrum showed the presence of a trisubstituted olefinic proton of H-2, H-8 and H-10 at δ 5.1 (dd), δ 5.1(dd) and δ 5.2 (d) and four tertiary methyl groups at δ 1.60 (Me-12), δ 1.73 (Me- 13), δ 1.60 (Me-14) and δ 1.60 (Me-15), respectively. A sharp singlet at δ 1.60 is integrated for nine protons that are for three methyl groups in the same chemical shift. Furthere more, a multiplet peak from δ 1.96-2.14 were integrated for nine protons. The ^{13}C-NMR spectrum of compound LL*A1 also strengthens the fact that there are two different chemical shift regions, one from δ 124.3 to 134.9 which is for the olefinic carbons region and the other from δ 16.0 to 39.8 which is for the aliphatic group. The^{13}C-NMR spectrum of compound LL*A1 is therefore in line with ^{1}H- NMR spectrum. The region from δ 16.0 to 39.8 has nine carbon atoms. The longest peak with two carbon atoms at δ 39.8 is for two carbon atoms that overlapped. The region from δ 124.3 to 134.9 is that of olefinic carbons of compound LL*A1. In the ^{13}C-NMR spectrum, there are six carbons in the olefinic region. Therefore, compound LL*A1 has a total of fifteen carbon atoms. Using information from the ^{1}H -NMR spectrum and ^{13}C-NMR spectrum made us deduce that the molecular formula of compound LL*A1 is $C_{15}H_{24}$. These data implies that compound LL*A1 was presumed to be a sesquiterpene. The DEPT spectrum showed twelve peaks corresponding to twelve carbon atoms. The compound has four methyl groups at δ 17.7, 25.8, 16.1, and 16.0. The difference in the number of carbon atoms of the ^{13}C-NMR spectrum and the DEPT spectrum is three, compound LL*A1 has three quaternary carbon atoms at δ 134.9, 134.7, and 130.9. There are five methylene carbons at δ 39.8, 39.8, 28.3, 26.8, and 26.7. The Longest peak at δ 39.8 tells us there is overlapping of two methylene carbons in the same chemical shift. There are three methine groups at δ 124.5, 124.4, and 124.3.

The protons located at the adjacent carbons were assigned by performing a standard COSY experiment. The COSY interactions of H-1 with H-2 and H-6, H-2 with H-3, H-5 with H-6, H-8 with H-9 and H-9, H-9 with H-10 led to formulate the side chain as depicted in the structure. The ^{1}H-^{1}HCOSY spectrum showed that the H-8 coupled to the H-10. Moreover, the methine proton at δ 5.1 (d) was coupled to the methy group (H_3-12). Additionally, in the ^{1}H-^{1}H COSY spectrum exhibited that the methyl singlet (δ 1.60, H_3-13) was coupled to another methylene multiplet centered (δ 1.96-2.14, H2-9). The Hetronuclear Single Quantum Correlation (HSQC) experiment correlates the chemical shift of proton (s) with the chemical shift of directly bonded carbon atom (s). The HSQC spectra of LL*A1 indicated that two olefinic protons at δ 5.1 were directly bonded to the carbon signals at δ 124.5 (C-8) and 124.4 (C-10), respectively. Additionally, the HSQC spectra LL*A1 showed that one olefinic proton at δ 5.2 was directly attached to carbon at δ 124.3 (C-2). Methyl groups were also identified by the correlation of the proton signals at δ 1.60, δ 1.73, δ 1.60 and δ 1.60 directly bonded carbon signals at δ 17.7 (C-12), δ 25.8 (C-13), δ 16.1 (C-14), and δ 16.0 (C-15), in the ^{13}C-NMR spectrum, respectively. Besides, nine protons with multiplet peak from δ 1.96-2.14 were attached to carbon signals at δ 39.8, 39.8, 28.3, 26.8, and 26.7.

Table 24.2: ^{1}H (400 HMz, $CDCl_3/CCl_3$), 13C (100 MHz, $CDCl_3/CCl_4$) and HMBC Spectral Data of Compound LL*A1

Position	δC	δH	HMBC (1H ® 13C)
1	39.8	1.96-2.14 (m, 1H)	C-4
2	124.5	5.2 (d, 1H)	C-1, C-15
3	134.9	—	—
4	39.8	1.96-2.14 (m, 2H)	C-6
5	26.8	1.96-2.14 (m, 2H)	—
6	28.3	1.96-2.14 (m, 2H)	C-5
7	134.7	—	—
8	124.4	5.1 (dd, 1H)	C-1
9	26.7	1.96-2.14 (m, 2H)	C-9, C-10, C-11, C-14
10	124.3	5.1 (dd, 1H)	C-12
11	130.9	—	—
12	25.8	1.73 (s, 3H)	C-10, C-11, C-13
13	17.7	1.60 (s, 3H)	C-9, C-10, C-11, C-12
14	16.1	1.60 (s, 3H)	C-1, C-3, C-8
15	16.0	1.60 (s, 3H)	C-2, C-3, C-4

Hetronuclear multiple bond correlation (HMBC) experiment gives information about coupling of hydrogen and carbons that are two or three bond away. The HMBC spectrum of LL*A1 correlation between carbons and protons is presented in Table 24.2.

In the HMBC spectrum, it was observed that two of the allylic methyl groups at δ 1.73 (H_3-12) and δ 1.60 (H_3-13) exhibited long range couplings with each other and also with the olefinic methine doublet of doublet at δ 5.1 (H-10). In addition, each of these methyl signals was coupled to the olefinic quaternary carbon at δ 130.9 (C-11) in the HMBC spectrum. This clearly indicated that these two methyl groups must be geminal and connected to the olefinic quaternary carbon that itself was connected to the olefinic methine carbon. The methyl group at δ 1.60 (H_3-15) exhibited long range coupling with the olefinic methine carbon at δ 124.5 (C-2) and olefinic quaternary carbon at δ 134.9 (C-3). Furthermore, this methyl signal was coupled to the methylene carbon at δ 39.8 (C-4). Another methyl signal at δ 1.60 (H_3-14) was coupled to one olefinic carbon at δ 124.4 (C-8), as well as to the olefinic quaternary carbon at δ 134.7 (C-7). In the HMBC spectrum, this methyl group also coupled to the aliphatic methine carbon at δ 39.8 (C-1). Additional coupling correlations were observed between the methylene multiplet (δ 1.96-2.14, H_2-4) with the methylene carbon at δ 28.3 (C-6) (Figure 24.2). The assignment of all the protons and carbons by 1D and 2D NMR spectra confirmed that compound LL*A1 was bisabolene (Figure 24.3).

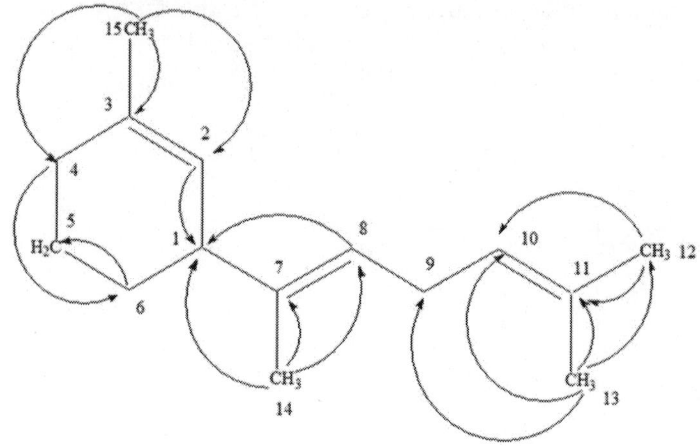

Fig. 24.2: Important HMBC correlation ($^1H \rightarrow {}^{13}C$) of compound LL* A1.

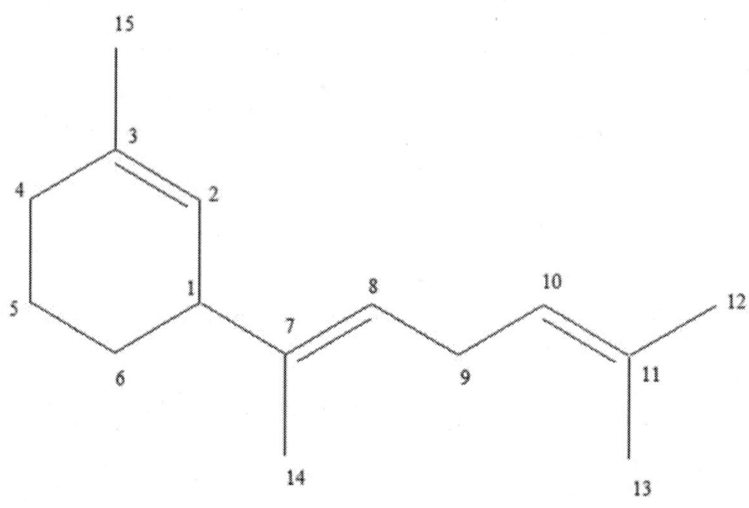

Fig. 24.3: Chemical structures of identified bisabolene

References

1. Evan, C.W., 1992. Trease and Evans Pharmacology, (13 ed.). Bailliere Tindall, London, pp. 758-762.
2. Nohynek, G.J., R. Fautz, F. Benech-Kieffer and H. Toutain, 2004. Toxicity and Human Health Risk of Hair Dyes. Food Chem Toxicol., 42: 517-43.
3. Khattak, S.G., S.N. Gilani and M. Ikram, 1985. Medicinal Plants. J. Ethno. Pharmacl., 14: 45-51.
4. Ali, B.H., A.K. Bashir and M.O.M. Tanira, 1995. Anti-inflammatory, Antipyretic and Analgesic Effects Extracts. J. Egypt Soc. Parasitol., 32: 725-36.

Index